Asperger's, Autism, & Non-verbal Learning Disorders

Screening, Assessing & Diagnosing

John M. Ortiz, Ph.D.

The Asperger's Syndrome Institute
2008©

The right of John M. Ortiz, Ph.D. to be identified as author of this work has been asserted by him in accordance
with the Library of Congress Copyright office.

First published in the United States in 2008 by
The Asperger's Syndrome Institute
P.O. Box 113
Dillsburg, PA. 17019

DrO@asperger-institute.com
www.asperger-institute.com

Copyright © 2008 by John M. Ortiz, Ph.D.

Edited by Laura Hudson

First Edition

Library of Congress Catalog Card Number: 2007943637

Distributed by The Asperger's Syndrome Institute

ISBN 978-0-9773071-2-8

Printed and bound in the United States

This book is dedicated to Dr. Bain Wainwright, who, on October, 1961,
based on a battery of tests written in English
—a language I did not speak at the time—
assigned me the label of "Mental Retardation," and to
Dorothea Clark, Ph.D., who, on March, 1967,
based on a battery of tests written in English
—a language I had by then mastered—
and a full-scale IQ of 148,
assigned me the label of "Gifted."

Nothing is always

Table of Contents

Asperger's, Autism
& Non-verbal Learning Disorders

Screening, Assessing & Diagnosing

John M. Ortiz, Ph.D.

"Testing students with ASD requires special expertise, training, and experience to minimize the effects of autistic behavior on test validity. The school psychologist must constantly assess the degree to which tests being used reflect symptoms of autism or the specific targeted abilities (e.g., intelligence, achievement, psychological processes). ...[E]xaminers will often need to make testing accommodations....[I]t is important to acknowledge that this population is very heterogeneous....[T]here is not any one set of accommodations that will work for every student....[I]t is important to consider each student as an individual and to select specific accommodations to meet specific needs." (Brock, 2004, p. 28)

The Asperger's Syndrome Institute
© 2008

Introduction

Research Gems: What is Assessment?

"Assessment is an evaluation of a person using multiple means of gathering information upon which a clinical opinion will be based. Assessment may include testing. Testing means the standardized administration of a psychological instrument, such as an IQ test, in exactly the same way each time. Testing produces results reported as numbers. Assessment is more than testing though. It also includes observations, answers given to questions pertaining to life experiences, material obtained from other sources such as report cards, an extensive history of early development, and knowledge of family, medical, school, and social history." (Lovecky, 2004, pp. 412—414)

Let's get this out in the open right off the bat. The screening, assessment and diagnosis of the three conditions this book will address is no easy task, so, if to date you have found yourself as confused as a first time tourist trying to find an address in a foreign country with the aid of an outdated GPS system you are not alone. The vast complexity of symptoms and comorbidities (accompanying or secondary conditions) that define Asperger's syndrome (AS), high-functioning autism (HFA), and nonverbal learning disorders/disabilities (NLD) make early identification to formal referral an extremely complicated endeavor. The challenges faced by parents and caregivers, educators, and other non-clinicians—as well as many inexperienced professionals—confronted with a child exhibiting behavioral, cognitive, and emotional distortions unlike anything they have ever encountered before can be quite daunting. Since some of the earliest concerns presented by children with the above conditions involve a mixture of speech and language, sensory, motor-related, behavioral, and/or emotional problems, initial referrals are typically directed to speech language pathologists, occupational therapists, counselors, or psychologists whose focus will be on the immediate presenting concerns. Unless the professional in question is experienced with AS, HFA, and/or NLD, however, it is quite possible that the efforts to address the more obvious, direct cause of referral (speech or pragmatic language delays, sensory challenges, motor deficits) may impede the recognition of AS, HFA, or NLD as the larger diagnostic picture. For this reason, many children presenting with these conditions must often scale their way through a labyrinth of intermittently misleading and/or tangential diagnostic impressions—such as expressive language disorder, sensory integration dysfunction, central auditory processing disorder, conduct disorder, ADHD, dyspraxia, OCD, etc.—before an experienced diagnostician eventually recognizes the diagnostic tapestry as illustrative of a spectrum or non-verbal disorder.

Research Gems: Unique Profiles

"When interpreting the results of these scales it is important to keep in mind that the profiles of students with ASD are unique." (Brock, 2004, p. 32)

Further complicating the diagnostic picture, children undergoing the laborious, stressful process of seemingly endless evaluations and treatment regimens conducted by a long line of strange faces in alien environments can quickly become emotionally and mentally exhausted. Eventually, they become tired, anxious, defensive, and frustrated by a confusing system that does not understand them. Acting out behaviors resulting from the above frustrations lead to the manifestation of additional, and at times more severe, symptoms such as nervous twitches, depression, and acting out behaviors that lead to (mis)diagnostic labels such as "tic disorder, clinical depression, bipolar disorder, and oppositional defiant disorder," some of which may in fact be part of the actual diagnostic picture, or just reactions to the exasperating process.

Research Gems: "Complexity of Autism Comorbidities"

"The co-occurrence of autism with so many other truly separate psychiatric disorders, which is the definition of comorbidity, is most unlikely. Advances in autism genetics, neuroimaging, pathology, and epidemiology will help determine why children with autism have features of so many other psychiatric syndromes." (Leyfer, et al., 2006, p. 858).

In addition, the child now diagnosed with any number of disorders that fall under the standard of psychopharmacological interventions—such as ADHD, depression, bipolar disorder, and OCD—is now placed under medications that often serve to further obscure the actual diagnostic picture of AS, HFA, or NLD by triggering a host of new symptoms, which lead to even further misdiagnostic impressions steering confused clinicians even further away from the core diagnostic issues.

Because of the above issues the necessity for increasing the awareness of community-wide systems of early identification, coupled with readily accessible screening and referral networks, is paramount when dealing with populations presenting with AS, HFA, and NLD. More so than with most other diagnostic disorders, the essential nature of early identification of these conditions is paramount. The earlier the proper diagnostic picture is identified, and a network of resources is set in place, the greater the benefits will be to the child. When addressing the needs of children presenting with these conditions, each day of intervention will make a world of difference that will yield exponential results. The potential of every day that is lost will never be regained.

Research Gems: "The Challenge of Characterizing Autism"

"Characterizing all elements that are important about autism is exponentially more complex and involves many spheres and levels—behavior and behavioral interventions, environmental influences and their impact, cognitive impairments and skills and their relationship to each other and to the heterogeneity of behavior, and the multiple dimensions of neural representation of cognition, the complexity of the proposed polygenetic disorder and developmental neurobiologic mechanisms, the heterogeneous pharmacologic responses and their genetics and numerous other aspects. It is worth pausing for a moment to appreciate the task ahead." (Minshew, 2005, p. 877)

Formal Assessment

The majority of individuals with AS, HFA, and NLD are not at their best under conditions typically associated with "formal assessment" protocols. Nonetheless, the world of resources and health system networks that can be potentially secured for their benefit will usually not be accessible without some form of formal evaluation records accompanied from clinical documentation from a licensed psychologist.

> "Diagnosis on its own is of limited value, but it is the gateway to a great deal of information, specialist groups and resources, including financial support. It is often not recognized that a diagnosis is simply a working hypothesis: it is a clinical judgment that has to strike a balance between being too broad and being too narrow; and it is a process that can evolve with time and changing circumstances. It is essential, therefore, that it is categorical and that everyone involved appreciates its purpose, as its cut-off points will depend on whether it is
>
> - for research – excluding any doubtful cases
> - clinical – a best guess to guide further treatment
> - administrative – giving access to services or resources"
> (Berney, 2004, p. 348)

Whenever possible, direct, personal observation in one or more live settings—the home, school, community, work place—contributes integral information toward a comprehensive clinical evaluation of persons with AS, HFA, and NLD. In most cases, the objective type of details that can be collected during such observations by a trained professional will help to offset most biased or erroneous, albeit well-meaning, accounts contributed by untrained non-professionals, or those who may be too close to the person being evaluated. The fact that behaviors of persons with AS, HFA, and NLD can vary greatly across settings and situations makes the importance of collecting detailed observations in various settings where the client can be allowed to function at his or her own comfort in familiar settings almost indispensable.

> "Some studies suggest that parents of children with ASD tend to report the absence of typically developing behaviors but not the presence of subtle atypical behaviors." (Wiggins et al., 2007, p. 35)

Fortunately, the recent emergence of improved diagnostic observation tools that have emerged over the past few years has dramatically improved our abilities to standardize such objective observations, as well as contributing to more valuable, consistent, and time-effective diagnostic interpretations.

Psycho-Educational Assessment

In order to obtain and maximize the availability of special education eligibility and school-based resources, a formal, psycho-educational assessment is a vital component of a comprehensive evaluation protocol.

A sensory-friendly environment where the evaluation can take place is fundamental to the success of the testing experience. Regardless of the amount of time, effort, and—whenever necessary—expense that is usually associated with the planning and provision of a "haven of psychological comfort and safety," carefully planned sensory-friendly accommodations will yield enormous short- and long-term benefits both in terms of assessment and subsequent therapeutic interventions.

Research Gems:

Autism = Genetic Susceptibility + Environmental Triggers

"We need to shift our thinking to a new paradigm of autism. It's an illness that has a genetic susceptibility factor exacerbated by an environmental trigger or a series of environmental triggers….Autism is a complex metabolic disorder involving multiple organ systems, primarily the toxicological, immunological, gastrointestinal, and neurological systems….Autistic children are predisposed to environmental toxicity because of underlying metabolic abnormalities." (Jepson, 2005, p. 9)

The assessment instruments recommended and otherwise listed throughout this book can be obtained directly through the publishers listed under Appendix F

Chapter 1

The Essential Integral Network

The myriad levels of complexity that underlie the interweaving tapestries which define Asperger's, autism, and non-verbal learning disorders demand the efforts of a collective network of both professionals and laypersons before the multidimensional needs of a comprehensive assessment can be realized. The grassroots movement that began the avalanche of increased public awareness to these very challenging, and widely misunderstood, conditions originated at home. After years of frustration wrestling with erroneous clinical labels, concerned parents and caregivers came to terms with the fact that deceptive clinical labels such as "ADHD," "OCD," "conduct disorder," and "oppositional defiant disorder"—among others—neither applied to or helped to describe the concerns expressed by children and adults presenting with these easily misunderstood conditions. Resourceful and often desperate parents and caregivers instead turned to relentless personal research, the accessibility of the Internet, and consultations with "on the edge" practitioners, slowly unearthing the inner cores of obscure research findings and anecdotal information. Eventually, these grassroots efforts fueled a growing awareness of these conditions what began to extend from the privacy of their homes to the labyrinths of educational settings. There, caring teachers and school administrators, sharing similar concerns regarding their students' "eccentricities" took up the awareness baton, helping to bridge the tumultuous waters between the "lay" and "professional" communities.

"A diagnosis should only be given if it has a useful function"
(Berney, 2004, p. 348)

In 1984, both the DSM-IV and the ICD-9 at long last added the disorder that was to bear the name of its original champion, Hans Asperger, to their ranks, including "Asperger's Disorder" as one of the five Pervasive Developmental or autistic spectrum disorders. The formal acknowledgement of this label led to the formalization of a diagnostic entity that had eluded legions of clinicians and health practitioners, many of whom had developed specialty careers revolving around autism disorders. As public demand and clinical awareness led to increased research in these areas, a surging interest in these conditions began to emerge exponentially, taking what had just a few years prior been a small ripple and creating waves of interest. Through those collective efforts, a resurgence of both understanding and motivation have contributed to the foundation of virtual global communities dedicated to deciphering the puzzling tapestries that define these conditions.

A valid, clinical-based "comprehensive assessment," however, will often mean that many experienced, thorough, and conscientious clinicians may have to go further, and dig deeper, than they had ever anticipated or found necessary up to this point in their careers. Regardless of the quantum strides that we have made over the past few years in our quest to decipher the intricacies and unconventional patterns that tend to describe these populations, effective tools that can help us measure their challenges and promises remain elusive. Over the past few years, even though a number of rating scales, screening instruments, and assessment tools aimed at these conditions have emerged, our collective accomplishments remain in their infancy.

Research Gems: Making Predictions from Normative Assessments

"Many professionals perceive the results from normative assessments to be limited in predictive value in offering concrete suggestions on ways to support the child or providing insight into how behaviours will manifest in different environments….The limited availability of information is the result of issues with the child including:

- Difficulties following adult directives due to linguistic limitations and problems with joint attention
- Lack of responsiveness to an unfamiliar adult (the examiner) and environment
- Challenges in modifying typical routines to participate in assessments
- Restricted patterns of expressive communication
- Heterogeneity of characteristics and abilities among children with autism." (Vacca, 2007, p. 51)

A team effort, then, is the best current recourse.

Comprehensive assessment team members
Compiling a comprehensive network of team members for the purpose of assessing a child with AS, HFA, or NLD may stretch standard efforts far beyond the boundaries that most of us had ever considered, much less explored. Without the team, however, individual, non-synchronized attempts at gathering and assembling invaluable tidbits of information to create a substantial, coherent picture may remain unrealized. Without a collective effort involving both laypersons and professionals, the end result will almost invariably result in a puzzle with missing pieces, with the essence of the true image remaining perplexing and misunderstood.

Since it is impossible to know exactly which team member may be able to contribute that elusive missing piece, or pieces, that may give us the needed edge, it is best to take nothing for granted and leave no source unexplored. With these populations, we often find it is not going the extra mile that's important, but rather, remaining acutely aware of every seemingly inconsequential inch.

Suggested team members
Considering the tapestry of interweaving threads that serpentine within and throughout every layer of these richly embroidered conditions it has been my experience that every bit of information that can be compiled from laypersons, paraprofessionals, and professionals who have been involved with the child in question is consistently worth the time and effort expended. In fact, as it is true in most cases, attempts at shortcuts or "saving time" is not only apt to result in failed assessments or incorrect diagnostic impressions but to backfire, sending us right back to step one where we are forced to discard our half-based attempts at understanding. The results of such half-baked efforts simply lead to greater amounts of stress and expenses for the already overstressed, financially over-extended family members, not to mention the injustice of the disservice done to both the child and family.

"At times the diagnostic label reflects the clinician's
specialty rather than the syndrome"
(Berney, 2004, p. 346)

With a collective, comprehensive effort at gathering potentially invaluable data, the following personnel should be considered:

- Parents and caregivers
- Involved relatives
- Babysitters and other extended caregivers
- Teachers, educational paraprofessionals, and classroom support staff
- Coaches, special ed instructors, tutors, and any creative art personnel who has worked with the child in connection with, or outside, the school
- School psychologist, counselor, and social worker
- School nursing staff and school medical records
- School custodians
- Community mental health records
- Family physician and medical records
- Community-based mental health records (hospitalizations, mental health treatment facilities, counseling and social work information)
- Any and all previous treatment and assessment records (diagnostic labels, rule-outs, and diagnostic impressions should be considered very carefully and not accepted outright without examining in the light of all other existing findings and reports)

Figure 1
Typical Referral Network Hierarchy

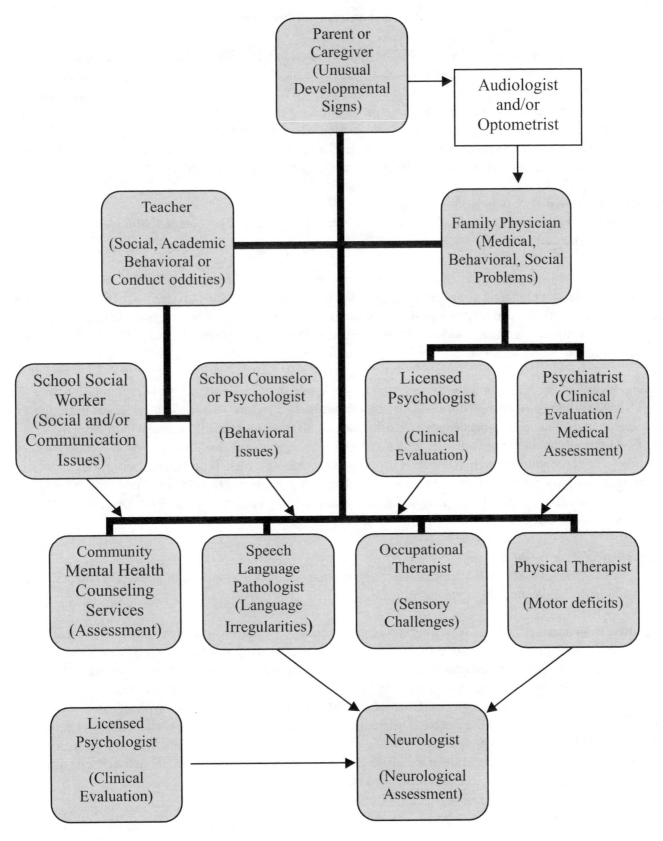

Below is a short summary of the purpose of various types of assessment by different professionals and the nature of information that will typically be obtained by each discipline.

General Assessment Protocol

"Evaluation of AS/HFA by a psychologist, in collaboration with professionals from other disciplines (generally speech/language, occupational therapy, and medicine) provides a foundation for educational and therapeutic interventions for individuals with AS/HFA and their families. Establishing the diagnosis, identifying strengths and needs, and interpreting these to families, teachers, and other service providers are key elements of the assessment process. Evaluations should include information from parents and teachers/caregivers, observation and interaction with the client, and formal testing with specific instruments selected based on the questions and goals of the assessment." (Mesibov, Shea & Adams, 2002, p. 45)

Medical Assessment

The purpose of the medical assessment, performed by a family physician or psychiatrist, is to identify any potential, underlying medical conditions.

Medical assessments usually involve exploration of an extensive medical history, physical examination, laboratory studies, auditory and visual examinations, and neurological assessment if deemed necessary. Seizures, gastrointestinal problems, and other medical problems typically associated with autism spectrum disorders and AS are noted. Current or previous medications, both prescription and natural remedies, should be explored and a thorough medical picture established.

A comprehensive physical examination is essential to obtain a professional's attention to developmental milestones as well as identifying any existing disorders that are often mistaken for, are secondary to, or appear in conjunction with autism including developmental language disorders, intellectual impairment, selective mutism, early childhood schizophrenia, Rett Syndrome, William's Syndrome, Angelman's Syndrome, Landau-Klefner syndrome and others. Other conditions, such as attention deficit hyperactivity disorder, Tourette's, Tic disorder, epilepsy, tuberous sclerosis or fragile-X and various neurological impairments should be ruled out. Assessing language, vision, hearing and motor coordination, as well as presenting sensory challenges, are also imperative as these are regularly co-occurring (comorbid) with AS, HFA and NLD.

Psychological Assessment

Clinical and school psychologists attempt to identify potential behavioral, emotional, intellectual, and other mental health and/or developmental impairments.

Cognitive, behavioral, emotional, academic, and adaptive testing are typical components of psychological evaluations. Verbal, performance and full-scale IQs, nonverbal skills, daily functioning (ADL) abilities, communication, self-help, and social and motor skills are evaluated. Potential comorbidities, or secondary conditions, such as obsessive compulsive disorder, bi-polar disorder, ADHD, Tourette's or Tic disorder, nonverbal learning disability, sensory integration dysfunction, and other psychological diagnoses typically associated with autism spectrum disorder and AS are noted. Differentiation should be made between characteristics of autism spectrum disorders or AS and unrelated conditions with which the child may have been labeled with such as oppositional-defiant disorder, intermittent explosive disorder, conduct disorder, schizophrenia, schizoid disorder, post-traumatic stress disorder, selective mutism, and others.

Mental Status Assessment

The objective of the mental status exam is to identify behavioral and cognitive-behavioral presentation during an interview. Particularly with these populations, this procedure should be conducted in both structured and non-structured settings (such as at home and school). Observation of the child's mode of interaction, relationships, and behaviors with both familiar and non-familiar people is an essential part of the mental status exam. Any peculiar habits, rituals, compulsions, perseverations, unusual behaviors, special topics, restricted range of interest, and communication skills should be noted.

Family Assessment

As would be expected, accurate input shared by parents, caregivers, relatives, and any other persons able to identify family dynamics and existing support systems is invaluable. Immediate family members, including siblings and other relatives in the home and any others who function as caretakers should be interviewed. Psychological diagnoses of family members and relatives should be noted, particularly those of natural parents and siblings. The possibility of autistic phenotypes markers among family members should also be explored.

Research Gems: Familial Autistic Phenotypes

"Compared to parents of children with Down syndrome, parents of children with autism demonstrated higher rates of aloof, rigid and anxious personality traits, fewer close friendships, communication deficits, and impairments in performance IQ and executive function. Other studies have identified elevated rates of specific cognitive and language impairments in family members, including impairments in executive function, reading ability, and pragmatic language." (Dawson, et al., 2007, 524)

Community Assessment

In an effort to understand the interests, existence—or lack—of support systems, adaptive capabilities, level of environmental awareness, and social capabilities, community-based evaluations are extremely helpful in identifying the viability of educational, mental health, social, community, medical, and other supportive clinical and therapeutic services that will need to be explored.

Speech-Language Pathologists: ASHA Principles

♦ SLPs play an important role in promoting social communication skills that further the independence and self-advocacy of individuals with ASD.

♦ SLPs play a critical role in the screening and diagnosis of individuals with ASD, as early intervention is a critical variable associated with positive long-term outcomes.

♦ SLPs should prioritize assessment and intervention approaches that are related to improvements in social communicative competence, that is, the ability to form relationships, function effectively, and actively participate in natural routines and settings.

♦ SLPs should form partnerships with families of individuals with ASD in assessment and intervention.

(Reference: Ad Hoc Committee on Autism Spectrum Disorders American Speech-Language-Hearing Association, 2006, pp. 13-16)
http://www.asha.org/members/deskref-journal/deskref/default)

Speech and Language Assessment

Speech-language pathologists (SLPs) are an essential component of an integral, comprehensive assessment effort. As professionals who are very often at the first line of intervention with these populations, SLPs are trained to identify speech, expressive and receptive language, and communication capabilities including language processing and pragmatics. Comprehensive communication assessments, typically needed by persons presenting with AS, HFA, and NLD should be performed by a certified speech-language pathologist.

In general, SLPs will explore the degree of impediment presented by the child's speech and language peculiarities. The degree of delayed speech and language development, superficially perfect (pedantic) expressive language, signs of odd prosody, peculiar voice characteristics, rhyming, unusual patterns of stuttering (cluttering) will be noted. Signs of impaired comprehension including misinterpretation of literally and implied meanings; problems with slang, metaphor, analogies; and difficulties reading nonverbal types of communication will be investigated. Examples include limited use of facial and body gestures, clumsy or awkward body language, and limited or inappropriate facial expressions (reading or demonstrating).

Research Gems: Occupational Therapy Assessment

"An occupational therapy assessment can help reveal many of the factors that can interfere with an individual's ability to function in different settings and perform various activities of daily living. The assessment includes evaluation of an individual's underlying abilities including balance and postural reactions, muscle tone and strength, fine/gross/oral motor planning, visual perception and visual motor integration, attending behaviours, and sensory integration. The individual's ability to perform self-care, community living, pre-academic, play, social, pre-vocational, and vocational skills are explored. A review of the physical environment, family situation, and community supports is an important part of the assessment process." (Stoddart, 2005, pp. 203-204.)

Occupational and Physical Therapy Assessment

Another essential professional component of the comprehensive team effort is the information that can be obtained and provided by occupational and physical therapists. Again, often at the preliminary line of defense in terms of initial referrals, these professionals aim at identifying sensory integration challenges as well as fine and gross motor skills and deficits. Evaluations may include any peculiar or "stiff" gaze or apparent problems with eye contact. Difficulties adjusting to or regulating physical proximity and problems with balance or coordination will be examined. It should be noted, however, that motor-related difficulties may not be part of the picture in all cases. Remember, *nothing is always*.

Social Interaction Assessment

Particular emphasis should be placed on a child's social interaction and interpersonal behaviors.

Does the child have friends? Initiate communication and social interactions? Play with same age, older, or younger peers? Use eye contact? Use body language, facial expressions, and nonverbal communications? Play and/or communicate with siblings? Interact with extended family members, relatives, familial friends, and neighbors? Areas of social impairment should note signs of egocentricity, inability, or lack of desire to interact with peers, poor appreciation or awareness of social cues, atypical or inappropriate social and emotional responses.

Research Gems: HFA's *Islets of Abilities*

"Capacities that exceed the average level of an individual with autism, or *islets of abilities*, are of an increased theoretical importance for understanding the cognitive underpinnings of this disorder. *Islets of abilities* that are among the general population of individuals with autism or Asperger syndrome should be distinguished from special abilities that are evident only in a small number of 'savant' individuals with autism." (Gagnon et al., 2004, p. 679)

Limited interests and preoccupations

Persons with AS, HFA, and, at times, also those with NLD, will often present with very intense special themes or topics with which they will be excessively involved. Special talents, or "splinter skills," are also common. As such, questions exploring whether the child demonstrates a restricted range of interests, and, if so, are these more rote than purposeful, should be pursued. Does the person present with exclusive interests? Is there a repetitive adherence to routines that interferes with daily functioning? Are routines or rituals imposed on self, or others? Are there other identifiable preoccupations, such as with collecting objects or information? In terms of preparing for the initial visit, conducting a formal assessment, formulating goals for school, home, clinical, and community-based interventions and strategies, knowledge of these issues will yield invaluable results.

Research Gems: Focusing on Talents and Interests

"When children are viewed and treated with respect to their talents and interests as opposed to their deficits, efforts to include children with disabilities are more likely to be successful. Embracing children's interests, no matter how narrow or stereotypical, establishes a secure foundation from which the child can assert independence and creativity." (Vacca, 2007, p. 52)

In essence, one should explore any notable:

- Special splinter skills (math, music, calculation, art, reading, memorization, decoding)
- Unusual skills or behaviors
- Problems with generalizations, transitions, or changes
- Sterotypic motor movements
- Level of play that is imaginative
- Sensory-motor challenges
- Functional-symbolic issues
- Simple or constructive impairments
- Complex and interactive deficits
- Dramatic or socially odd predispositions

Once all preliminary information is gathered from relevant sources, the formal, initial clinical assessment can be scheduled. Prior to the evaluation session, however, it is strongly recommended that clinicians follow these three simple rules:

1. Secure a flexible, sensory-friendly environment (see chapter 2: "Sensory Challenges")
2. Have the child visit the evaluation setting
3. Use the acquired information to individualize the assessment room

---

Research Gems: Need for Sophisticated Assessment

"The restricted patterns of communicating, relating, and behaving seen often in children with autism necessitate a sophisticated approach to assessment. There is an increasing need in the field to use alternative assessment approaches in order to allow professionals to interact and communicate with the child on multiple levels. Assessment approaches that provide the child with choices yield data that go beyond confirmation of a diagnosis to include information about suitable educational and therapeutic interventions and programming outcomes as well as ideas to support functioning in the natural environment." (Vacca, 2007, p. 51)

The Initial Visit

Preparing for the Initial Evaluation or Assessment Visit

Most persons throughout the autism, Asperger's, and NLD spectrums find a deep sense of comfort and relief in structure, consistency, and knowing what expectations lie ahead. As such, it is imperative that concrete, accurate information regarding an upcoming evaluation or assessment visit be shared with them via their preferred learning style (see chapter 11, "Learning Styles"). Visually oriented persons, for example, should be provided a visually accurate schedule indicating the exact time and place of the visit by marking it on a clearly visible, easily accessible calendar and/or daily planner. In addition to the visual cues noted above, those with auditory orientations should be verbally reminded often about the upcoming visit and asked to verbally repeat back the information shared. Persons with a kinesthetic (hands-on) orientation can be asked to personally write down the schedule information on their own in a preferred place, such as a calendar, PalmPilot, or daily planner. "Practice runs" should be exercised as often as necessary so that when the time comes the child knows exactly what the routine will be, which clothes will be worn, which family vehicle will be taken, who will serve as the escort, and any other details that may prove advantageous to reducing any anxiety, apprehension, or concerns about the visit.

Additional measures that will serve to orient and relax the child in both preparing for, and attending to, the initial and follow-up sessions should be exercised. For example, children who are preoccupied with direction should be given a map and encouraged to "map out the best route" to the setting. Those who are mathematically inclined can be asked to calculate how long the ride will take. Weather fanatics can be asked to keep an eye on meteorological patterns and apprise the family, or escort, of current patterns that may necessitate precautions such as wearing a hat to ward off the sun, bring an umbrella in case of rain, or wear extra layers to protect from dropping temperatures. Asking the child to think about, and prepare, a "survival travel kit" to bring along to the first session is also helpful. Items in these kits, which can include a favorite book, toy, music, or sensory manipulative (see later in this chapter) should be kept to a maximum of 3-4 articles. DVDs, videos, and time-consuming games should be discouraged as they will be difficult for the child to pull away from them when the time for the evaluation arrives. A summary—written for visual learners, spoken for auditory thinkers—of the structure that will be followed and information regarding what will take place during the evaluation should be prepared for, and if possible, with the child. Kinesthetic learners will particularly benefit from actively preparing such a document themselves based on acquired information from brochures and/or discussion with family members.

Research Gems: Proactive Prevention

"If you deal with 'challenging behaviours' in autism, do not focus too much on the behaviours themselves, they are just like the tip of the iceberg; do understand the underlying causes of the behaviours and try to develop an approach not based on symptoms but on prevention….Try to understand autism 'from within'….We need to learn to put ourselves in the brains of autistic people and then we will understand better through their eyes the obstacles in their attempts to survive among us….For a better cohabitation with people with autism we will indeed need to learn to look at life through 'the Asperger lens'." (Bogdashina, 2003, p. 15)

Visiting the Assessment Setting: Creating a Routine Route

"Many students with ASD have great difficulty adjusting to environmental changes….Before assessing the student with autism it will be important to familiarize him or her with the examiner, the testing room, and the testing experience….Once the student has become familiar and comfortable with the testing environment, the next important consideration is to make sure he or she knows exactly when the testing session(s) will take place….Another way to minimize disruption to the student's daily routine is to break testing sessions into smaller, more discrete segments." (Brock, 2004, p. 28)

Inviting the future evaluee to visit the assessment setting a few days prior to the physical evaluation also yields a number of positive results. Particularly with children, the person (escort) who is going to bring the child to the initial evaluation for a scheduled appointment should be strongly encouraged to bring the child for a "get acquainted visit" that will serve to minimize, if not eliminate, a number of potentially stressful variables, but also often yield additional valuable information that can be accessed during the assessment. If possible, the child's escort should anticipate as many variables as possible during this "practice" visit that will be likely replicated on the actual assessment date. Beginning the journey at the same time, and following the same route from door to door as on the scheduled assessment date, are examples of this. By doing this, the child will know, as much as possible, what will most likely be expected, and what route will be traversed, on the evaluation date. Seeing the parking lot, evaluation building, waiting room, and other physical components that will be encountered on the scheduled assessment date will usually help to minimize and alleviate potential fears and concerns of the unknown.

Once the children arrive at the assessment center on the practice run they should be encouraged to visit the center and, whenever possible, take a short tour of the building, introducing themselves to the individuals with whom they will most likely interact during the actual day of the evaluation. Meeting the receptionist, secretary, and, whenever possible the actual clinician who will be conducting the evaluation, prior to the actual assessment date can work wonders by helping to add some friendly faces to a potentially anxiety-provoking venture. During this visit the child's escort can also help to provide the above personnel with any last minute information that may prove useful during the day of assessment. Although at times unusual, these tidbits of preventive information can prove extremely beneficial. Some examples are below.

Does your child
- have any particular preferred colors or any which cannot be tolerated?
  (extreme aversion to certain colors may result in aborted evaluation attempts while the presence of others which the child has an affinity toward may enhance one's chances of establishing an early, positive working alliance)
- have any particular aversion to, or preference for, certain scents? Sounds? Textures? If so, try and make accommodations to fulfill their respective sensory needs in these areas.
- have any particular environmental or ecological seating preferences? (some children may prefer to face in a certain geographical direction)
- have any particular preferences, or needs, for furnishings that can be provided to help facilitate the assessment? (vibration pads, weighed vests or blankets, swing or hammock, rocker, hard/soft chair, recliner, etc.)
- prefer window, or window-less settings?
- have any particular special topics that one may bring up initially to help facilitate discussion? (At times, if possible, it is helpful to frame assessment questions from the perspective of a child's special topic, rewording questions within the context of their special interest themes, or engage the child by referencing favorite characters.)

- have any particular days of the week, or times of day, when functioning is at optimal levels? Some children perform best early in the morning, others later on in the day. Checking these priorities before scheduling can make significant differences in their levels of sensory receptivity and modulating their sensory over- or underloading.

With this experience under her or his belt, the child will have a concrete, accurate visual image of the exact route that will be followed on the day of the actual assessment. The purpose, as always, is to exercise preventive measures and help to minimize the potential for stress and anxiety by providing a sense of familiarity, comfort, and consistency. Rewards that the child may earn as part of following through with the evaluation can also be discussed at that time.

In addition to the above, as briefly mentioned earlier, the child should be well and comprehensively appraised of all expectations that may accompany the actual assessment and these should be written down, in a formal manner, and presented as formally as possible in order to emphasize the momentous importance of this visit. As such, the date and time should be marked on the child's visit calendar, daily planner, or other scheduling form that is regularly used and this should be visible to the child from the time that it is prepared. If possible, allowing the child to take photographs of both the outside and inside of the testing facility, as well as of the office manager who will greet him and psychologist who will conduct the evaluation, preferably posing alongside the child, is also encouraged. Asking the child if there is anything else that may help her or him to feel comfortable on the day of evaluation, such as any favorite colors the evaluator could wear, is also helpful. Encouraging the child to bring along "one favorite toy, book, or other trinket," as well as preferred "comfort snacks" is also advantageous. Encouraging the child to also bring "something special that can be shared with the office manager and psychologist" also tends to pay dividends, helping the child to recognize that their needs are to be respected as integral to the evaluation process.

Using the information provided to maximize the evaluation setting.

In addition to integrating information presented personally by the child yielded from the above visit, all information obtained from relevant sources via face to face interviews, telephone or e-mail contacts, and through existing records and current screening forms should be reviewed prior to the initial session to help facilitate the assessment session. By taking into account the child's failures and successes during previous similar experiences, particularly if any of these have involved previous attempts at evaluation, one can help to maximize these initial encounters in order to obtain valid, reliable, and timely information to help obtain a clear diagnosis and contribute to comprehensive Individualized Education Plans (IEPs).

Assessing the School-age AS, HFA, or NLD child or adolescent

The following questions should be answered before the most effective,
multi-modal treatment plan can be assembled:

1. Does the child meet the DSM-IV, TR criteria for AS?

2. If not, does the child better fit the criteria for an AS-related condition? (NLD, HFA, SID)

3. Are there any evident secondary diagnostic impressions? (ADHD, ODD, Bi-Polar Disorder)

4. To what extent are this child's/teen's behaviors impairing educational, social, and/or interpersonal functioning?

Figure 2
The Assessment Network

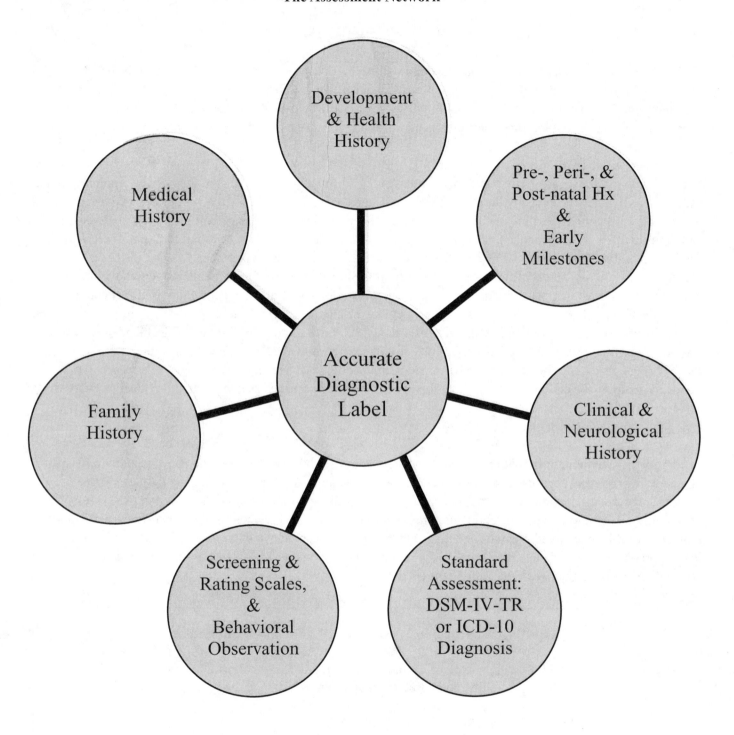

Figure 3
A 6-step Early Assessment Plan

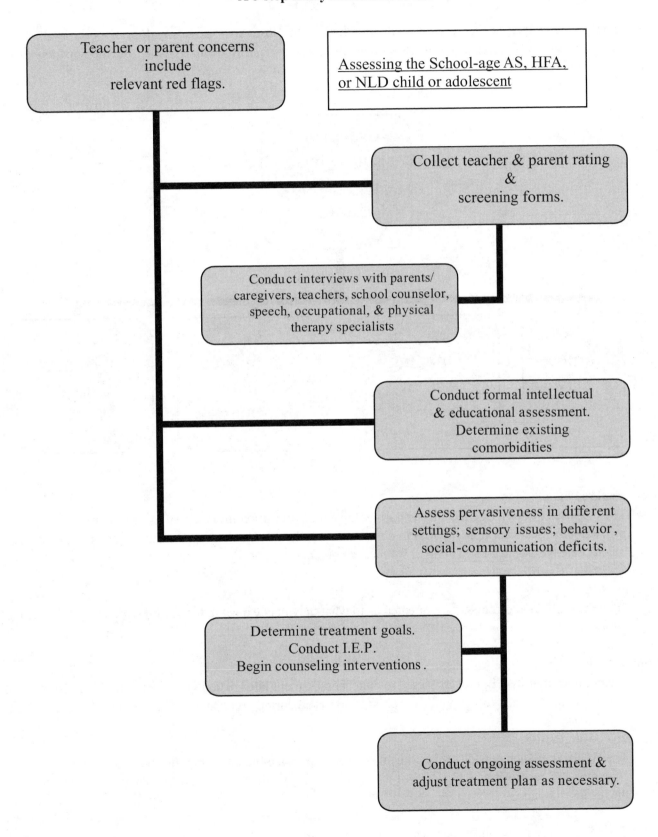

Teacher or parent concerns include relevant red flags.

Assessing the School-age AS, HFA, or NLD child or adolescent

Collect teacher & parent rating & screening forms.

Conduct interviews with parents/ caregivers, teachers, school counselor, speech, occupational, & physical therapy specialists

Conduct formal intellectual & educational assessment. Determine existing comorbidities

Assess pervasiveness in different settings; sensory issues; behavior, social-communication deficits.

Determine treatment goals. Conduct I.E.P. Begin counseling interventions.

Conduct ongoing assessment & adjust treatment plan as necessary.

Figure 4
Vacca's Four-Phase Assessment Model

Recognizing the challenges that come from conducting formal diagnostic assessments with persons across the autistic spectrum, Vacca (2007, p. 57) suggests a Four-Phase Assessment Model that enables the therapist to pull together a network of resources in an effort to facilitate the process and maximize results.

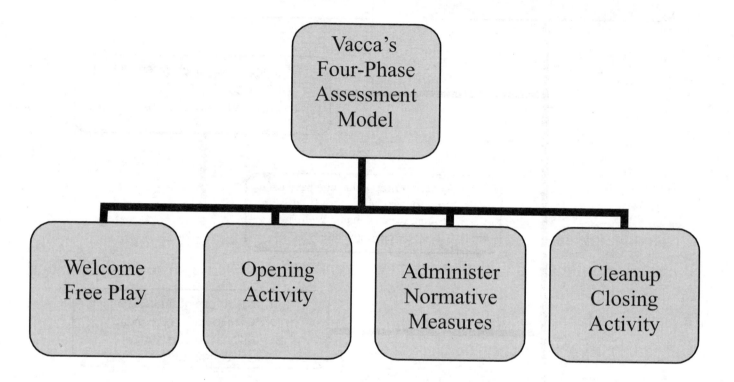

1. Welcome/Free Play

    The purposes of this phase include supporting the child's transition into the testing environment, providing the evaluator opportunities to observe the child, and enabling rapport-building activities that can incorporate the evaluator and child as well as caregiver.

2. Opening Activity

    Here the child (and caregiver) are oriented as to what they may expect in terms of the routines of the testing period.

3. Administration of Normative Measures

    A natural, routine-type approach is used to collect assessment information via formal item administration following an authentic format while the child is observed during problem-solving activities.

4. Cleanup/Closing Activity

    The child's transition outside of the clinical environment is facilitated during this phase at which point the evaluator and caregiver are able to assist the child in finishing the tasks at hand, cleaning up, and exiting the testing situation.

(See the Four-Step Assessment and Diagnosis Diagram, Appendix A.)

Chapter 2

Sensory Challenges

<u>Research Gems: Sensory Diets</u>

"A sensory diet is a strategy that consists of a carefully planned practical program of specific sensory activities that is scheduled according to each child's individual needs. Like a diet designed to meet an individual's nutritional needs, a sensory diet consists of specific elements designed to meet the child's sensory integration needs. The sensory diet is based on the notion that controlled sensory input can affect one's functional abilities. A sensory diet can help maintain an age appropriate level of attention for optimal function to reduce sensory defensiveness." (DiMatties, 2004, p. 3)

Prior to embarking on a formal clinical interview it is imperative that clinicians be aware of the indispensability of providing a sensory friendly environment, or environments, where the various parts of the evaluation will take place.

Sensory Processing Challenges: Providing a Sensory-Friendly Environment

Imagine trying to sit through an assessment while the evaluator is smoking a cigarette and blowing smoke or sprinkling cold water in your face. Try to envision yourself focusing on the completion of an evaluative task while a constant stream of water drips on your head and rolls down your back. Picture yourself being timed on an assignment by a clock that rings so loud in your oversensitive ears that it sounds like a gong being repeatedly struck. Since we are at it, envisage trying to concentrate on an evaluator's instructions that are being spoken as he scrapes his fingers…yes, across the dreaded chalkboard…or while you are made to chew on aluminum…or sit on sharp pebbles. Try and visualize yourself having to complete a puzzle, or complete a maze, while you spin around on a merry-go-round, or go up and down on a teeter-totter. For persons who struggle with sensory issues the similarities to the challenges presented above can be very real.

Sensory dysfunction or disorder (SD) is also termed sensory integration dysfunction or disorder, sensory defensiveness, or sensory sensitivity. Wilbarger & Wilbarger (1993) defined it as a combination of symptoms resulting from aversive responses to nonharmful sensory stimuli. I would modify that definition to clarify that the sensory stimuli that are nonharmful to most people may sometimes actually be harmful to the SD person. For example, if a sound or touch is painful, then it is perceived as harmful." (McMullen, 2001, 469)

Almost universally, persons with AS, HFA, and NLD present with various levels of Sensory Processing Challenges. Invariably presented throughout the literature as Sensory Integration Dysfunction, Dysfunction of

Sensory Integration, or Regulation, or by other similar terms this condition refers to a neurological disability where one's brain, and sensory system, is unable to accurately and effectively process information coming in through the various senses. Resulting in myriad degrees of intensity and combination, children and adults with Sensory Processing Challenges will present with oversensitivity to some sensations and/or under-sensitivity to others. Although the five primary senses typically come to mind when this condition is first presented, clinicians, teachers, parents, caregivers, and others who serve the needs of persons with AS, HFA, and NLD must keep in mind that these integration problems can also effect the vestibular (body in space orientation) and propioceptive (what position our body is in from moment to moment) senses. Often misinterpreted as hyperactivity, conduct disorder, oppositional defiance, stubbornness, obsessive-compulsive behaviors, spoiled-child irritability, disruptive behaviors, or other "wanting to be in control," persons challenged by these conditions are merely reacting to and attempting to compensate for the overwhelming sensory triggers that are constantly bombarding their nervous systems. As such, the importance of acknowledging these sensory challenges and taking measures to provide sensory friendly environments in general, and meeting the sensory needs of each client in particular, cannot be overemphasized.

Research Gems: "A Short in the Circuitry"

Three possible results of "shorts in the circuitry" are:

1. *Hypersensitivity* (hyper-responsiveness, hyper-reactivity, over-responsiveness, and oversensitivity) to sensory intake. The brains and nervous systems of hypersensitive children register sensations too intensely. They are over-aroused by sensations and may react in irritating, annoying, or even threatening manners.

2. *Hyposensitivity* (hypo-responsiveness, hypo-reactivity, under-responsiveness, and under-sensitivity) to sensory intake. The brains of hyposensitive children register sensations less intensely than normal as the child is not receiving enough sensory information.

3. *Combined hyper- and hypo-sensitivity*. Children with this mixed circuitry may be oversensitive to some stimuli and under-sensitive to others. In this condition the brain is unable to properly modulate sensations and the nerve circuitry functions as if it is jammed. "The child may seek intense sensory experiences—such as spinning on playground equipment—but be unable to tolerate them. Or, he may seek intense experiences some days but avoid them on other days. His over- or under-reaction may depend on the time of day, the place, and the stimulus." (Kranowitz, 1998, pp. 57-59)

The Sensory-Friendly Environment

"The visually defensive individual is overly sensitive to light, especially bright, flashing, or blinking lights. Fluorescent lights, which are common in schools and workplaces, can be bothersome because they tend to flicker. The SD (sensory dysfunction) person notices the flickering long before most others do." (McMullen, 2001, p. 469)

As experienced parents, teachers, and clinicians know, children within the spectrum of AS, autism, and NLD will always present with diverse levels of sensory challenges. In effect, their combination of hyper- and hypo-sensitivities to any number of potential sensory triggers needs to be noted, and taken into account, *prior* to the initial testing session. Without the advantage of a personalized, sensory-friendly environment, most attempts at a standard clinical evaluation will often fail, fall short of its goals, or be aborted at times even before it begins.

Clinical assessments are almost universally stressful and anxiety-producing endeavors even among test-savvy individuals. The apprehensions that surround these extended visits with a stranger (the evaluator) who is going to use a number of unspecified tools (the assessment protocol) to find out "all of one's personal secrets," as well as "identify and unearth all of one's strengths and deficits" are difficult enough without the added challenge of invasive and pervasive sensory issues. Even across "neurotypical" testing situations, disruptive contextual effects such as disorderly office clutter, neighboring clatter (voices intruding from an adjoining room, hearing an office manager speaking over the telephone, individuals walking past the testing room at random), uncomfortable furniture, unsettling (too bright, too dim, or fluorescent in particular) lighting, distracting décor, exotic or off-putting smells (cigarettes, perfume, cologne, scented candles, incense, snacks), can serve to derail otherwise successful assessments. When one adds the challenge of prevailing sensory issues, however, the hurdles that must be surpassed to avoid potentially disastrous results can seem daunting.

> "Some students with ASD have unusual visual and auditory sensitivities…before assessing the student it will be important to inquire about such sensitivities and to make appropriate environmental adjustments." (Brock, 2004, pp. 28-29)

Efforts to avoid potential sensory-based disruptions, then, should be strongly adapted before the initial visit. With this in mind, clinicians are advised to collect information from sources close to the client that may help to identify sensory-related challenges that need to be considered, in order for a sensory-friendly setting to be modified in preparation for the evaluation session. Does the child or adult who is about to be evaluated have a particular aversive sensitivity to certain lighting? Does this client prefer dim or bright lights? Fluorescent lights are typically disruptive and should be avoided in clinical (as well as school, home, and other settings) whenever possible. As such, natural or full spectrum lighting should replace any existing fluorescent lighting before the visits commence. Is the child or adult uncomfortable with any particular odors? Does he or she prefer certain types of furniture? For instance, is a small cubicle more comforting than a large, spacious room or the latter the better option? Whenever possible, the best option should be exercised even if one's "favorite" or "regular" testing room does not provide the best choice for the clinician.

Research Gems: Sensory Interrelationships

"Significantly strong inverse relationships were found between the specific adaptive behaviors of functional academics, leisure, social skills, and symptoms of depression. Functional academics were also significantly inversely related to anxiety. Specifically, sensory hyper- and hypo-sensitivity were significantly inversely related to community use and social skills. The data supports positive relationships between anxiety and sensory defensiveness in all age ranges and a relationship between depression and hyposensitivity in older children." (Pfeiffer et al., 2005, p. 335)

We must remember, it is the *client's* needs that should come first and foremost. Would standing, walking around, rocking on a rocker, sitting in a "bean-bag" or a "video (banana)" chair, a swing, or even on the floor feel safer for the client in question? Does the client typically react better to cluttered (busy) settings with lots of pictures and colors, or to stark surroundings, void of lots of stimulation? Are there any colors that the child or adult dislikes or cannot tolerate? In my experience, simply having particular colors prominent—particularly red, orange, or yellow, and most particularly if these are specially bright—can serve to abort a testing or counseling session. Are there times of the day when the potential evaluee feels most comfortable or performs best?

> "It will not be surprising to find students with ASD unmotivated to perform in testing sessions....It will be important to consider how to reward test performance and increase test-taking motivation....Specific strategies include the use of frequent reinforcement breaks and behavioral shaping....The specific rewards selected may make use of some of the unusual and intense interest students with ASD have." (Brock, 2004, p. 29)

How many breaks, and for how long, will help to maximize the efficacy of the evaluation? What does the client prefer to do during these breaks? Be alone? Play a video game? Read a familiar book? Walk around in "figure eights" in a solitary room? Write down thoughts or "internal noises" on a white board or memo pad? Play with a favorite toy? Talk to his or herself for a few minutes in private? Although during the course of a standard evaluation breaks must be obviously kept to reasonable limits, and times allotted be sensibly regulated, the needs posed by each individual will vary from person to person. As much as possible, respecting and honoring these needs will pay enormous dividends while allowing each client to not only complete many otherwise failed assessments, but remain mentally and emotionally refreshed on the way to maximizing personal efforts.

In effect, the provision of a personalized sensory-friendly environment should take into account every feasible advantage that can be accessed to facilitate the child's, or adult's, testing session.

Research Gems: Importance of Sensory Modulation

"Stronger inverse relationships were apparent between specific adaptive behaviors including: (a) symptoms of depression and functional academics, leisure, social skills; (b) anxiety and functional academics; and (c) both sensory hyper- and hyposensitivity and community use and social skills. In this study, as the symptoms of affective disorders increased in children and adolescents with Asperger's disorder, the functional performance in the adaptive behaviors of functional academics and social skills appeared to decrease. Performance in the adaptive behaviors of community use and social skills appeared to decrease as symptoms of dysfunction in sensory modulation increase." (Pfeiffer et al., 2005, p. 335)

<u>Providing a Sensory-Friendly Clinical Environment: Suggestions</u>

General Guidelines: In terms of "general guidelines," focusing on the following components is strongly recommended:

◆   <u>Structure</u>

Because of problems with executive functions and hypo- hypersensitivity challenges, children and adults with AS, HFA, and NLD will almost universally struggle in environments that lack organization and well-executed ecological arrangements. As such, the need for providing, and maintaining, a structured setting is paramount. Because the evaluation should focus on providing the best possible environment to facilitate the relationship and maximize the testing results, input from the person being evaluated, and/or caregivers, should be acknowledged and considered respectfully. An appointment board positioned out in the lobby, as well as in the assessment, that visually displays the child's name at the scheduled time will help to further orient the child that this time has been set for him or her alone.

◆   <u>Consistency</u>

Along with structure a sense of regularity, constancy and uniformity will help children, as well as adults, with AS, HFA, and NLD to feel secure and stable. In effect, the same advice given above applies here.

◆   <u>Comfort</u>

Again, as the old adage states, "the customer is always right." Arranging the assessment session in a manner that will help to maximize the client's comfort will not only help to optimize results, but to make the entire process flow more smoothly by minimizing both internal and external stressors and anxiety. Any measures that can be taken to help soothe, reassure, and provide a sense of well-being, security, and contentment will benefit both the client and evaluator.

◆   <u>The Five Senses</u> (visual, olfactory, auditory, gustatory or taste, and tactile or kinesthetic)

Provisions that acknowledge the immediate sensory needs of the person being assessed will consistently result in accomplishing utmost possible results and yield clearer objectives that can later be implemented, in various settings, to accommodate each client's personal needs. Preparations that take into account the prerequisite and transitional needs of each individual with regard to minimizing disturbances that may affect their mental and emotional receptivity will help to augment comfort and results.

◆   <u>"Time-off" Room</u>

In general, the term "time-out" tends to have "negative" (unpleasant, punitive, implying problems) connotations. Although "time-outs" are often used as opportunities for children to recharge, regroup, or re-establish their sense of balance, the term is just as often used for disciplinary purposes, imbuing it with corrective or penalizing implications.

In contrast, the term "time-off" carries with it consistently positive undertones. "Time-off" is something taken to renew or revitalize oneself. Unlike the phrase "time-out," which can carry positive as well as negative implications, "time-offs" imply taking a break, going on vacation, or taking time for a restful retreat from life's overwhelming demands. A "time-off," then, serves as a departure from surrounding stressors or temporary overwhelming demands, providing a refuge where one can reorganize one's thoughts and regain one's emotional balance. In essence, "time-offs" bestow the opportunity for one to re-entrain and regain one's sense of harmony. As a result, the use of term "time-off," vs. "time-out," is strongly recommended. The provision of a sensory-friendly haven where a child, or adult, can find a temporary sanctuary in order to re-establish a sense of rhythmic synchronicity between oneself, others, and the environment is paramount across home, school, therapeutic, assessment, and other settings that cater to persons with sensory integration challenges.

Recommended "Time-Off" Room Objects

Swing	Massage chair
Hammock	Interactive games
Well-padded floor mats	Room to spin/dance/hop
Bouncing balls	Music components
Small trampoline (supervised)	Computer with Internet
Ceiling sling	Basic video games
Beanbag chairs	Physio Rolls*
Snuggle blankets	Sensory Peanut Balls*
Weighted vests	Rockers
Toxic-free paints & crayons	Paper pads & crayons
White board & markers	Cushions & wedges
Sensory manipulatives	Deep pressure tops/vests
Play weights	Motion toys (twirlies)
Water fountain	Aroma therapy diffusers
Entrainment music compilation	Soothing music compilation
Stimulating music compilation	Progressive relaxation CDs
Moodlights	Visual & auditory timers
Vibro-animals & toys*	Jittercritters*
Chewy tubes*	Soft Chewlery*
Legos	Pop Up Bubble Animals*
Blow games*	Puppets
Air action blow gun*	Building blocks
Puzzles	Books
Coloring books & crayons	Communication cards
Bop bags	Medicine balls
Play tunnels	Resistance tunnels*
Stretch blankets/Body sox*	Jump-O-Lene*
Rody rockers*	Moon shoes*
Yoga/Stretch mats	Bean bag animals
Strobe lights	Lava lamps
Shakers & other percussion instruments	Electronic keyboard
Etch-A-Sketch	Where's Waldo? books
Calvin & Hobbes books	Alphabet sets
Dominoes	Magnetic color letters
Kaleidocolor sets*	Parquetry blocks & cards*
Wiggly Gigglys*	Nubbly Wobblys*
Balloons	Amazing String Thing*
Grab balls*	Juggling balls
Talking pens	Calculator
Train set	Toy dinosaurs

Morph & Squeeze Fidgets*

Tangles

Image Captors*

Transparent Yuk-E-Balls*

Water Wigglers*

Squishy key chains*

Ther-a-Saurs*

Emotions chart

* Available through Integrations catalog, 800-850-8602, and Web site: www.integrationscatalog.com.

Research Gems: Sensory Issues

"The results of these studies show that sensory abnormalities are a pronounced problem in individuals with autism. At least 90% of the individuals in both Study 1 and in Study 2 had sensory abnormalities, a striking finding given that sensory problems are not an essential diagnostic criterion for autism....Our results also show that individuals with autism tend to have sensory abnormalities, not only in one sensory domain but in two or three. Study 2 supported these results, showing that sensory abnormalities persist across age and IQ in people with autism." (Leekam et al., 2007, p. 906)

Restrooms

Because a significant number of persons with autism spectrum conditions tend to find water soothing or fascinating, at times restrooms tend to provide safe, socially acceptable havens where they can relax long enough to renew their emotional batteries. As such, therapists and teachers need to be aware of the possibility that children with these conditions may request "bathroom breaks," and spend more times in these settings at a greater rate than their neuron-typical peers. The provision of a safe, sensory-friendly restroom, then, should be part of the overall "sensory-friendly plan."

With this in mind, the following suggestions are recommended:

- adjust the water temperature so that it is not too hot
- install movement sensitive faucets that regulate water flow
- if possible, secure the toilet cistern so that the internal mechanisms are inaccessible by either installing them behind the wall or by installing a safety lock
- keep all cleaning solutions and other chemicals in a locked closet in an area outside of the restroom
- if possible, install unbreakable mirrors on the restroom walls
- install safety lock guards on all electrical outlets
- install fire alarm
- lighting should consist of built-in wall and ceiling lamps rather than exposed lighting fixtures
- if possible, provide cloth, as well as paper towels, and a dryer fan
- liquid soap and anti-germicidal agent dispensers should be internally installed to the wall and secured by safety locks
- install a ceiling fan that helps to maintain the air clean and fresh
- do not install or make available air-freshener or scented sprays
- Fold-Up Potty seat adapters
- Soothing music compilation to help child relax

"The most often reported visual sensitivities are sensitivity to bright light, fluorescent light, colours and certain patterns (especially stripes)....Fluorescent light has been reported by many autistic individuals to be very difficult to tolerate, because they can see a 60-cycle flicker. Problems with flickering can range from excessive eyestrain to seeing a room pulsate on and off. Some people report that they feel sleepy when the fluorescent lights are on." (Bogdashina, 2003, p. 63)

The Reception Area

Reception areas provide an introduction and as such serve as a microcosm of what likely awaits first-time visitors inside. Because of this harbinger of those invaluable mental and emotionally laden first impressions, a clinic's reception area needs to be given a sizable amount of care and consideration.

- The room should be free of fluorescent lights. Various characteristics of these lights can have serve to over-stimulate the keen senses of persons with sensory integration challenges through the flickering or humming that they emit. In effect, using natural or full-spectrum lamps are strongly recommended

- Soft, unobtrusive music playing in the background can be helpful by serving to create a calming, yet gently stimulating environment to instill a sense of inner comfort and complementary structure. As research has consistently shown, using largo movements from string concertos by baroque composers tends to be the most universally effective choice to fulfill this purpose (Ortiz, 1991). While helping to block out, or mask, potentially disturbing external sounds, this type of music is also effective in helping to quiet internal preoccupations and reducing stress and anxiety. A "white-noise," or water-sounds machine (one that simulates various digitized water sounds such as running streams, rain, ocean waves) are also good choices.

- Diverse furnishings should be made available. A combination of soft and firm chairs, sofas, lounges, and rocking chairs should be available so that options are maximized. A variety of soft, cushiony pillows, therapeutic balls, and soft but firm floor mats also tend to fulfill common preferences. Bean bags, inflatable balance balls, and "Reading-Banana-Video" rocking chairs are highly recommended.

- Provide a mix of sensory stimulating and sensory soothing games, toys, and sensory manipulatives (see chapter 2: Sensory Challenges). The goal is to establish a balance between keeping the child relax while preventing boredom, and stimulated enough to maintain a sense of motivation and alertness that will not interfere when the time for transitioning into the therapeutic setting arrives.

- An air cleaner and ionizer are recommended to help minimize indoor allergens and pollutants.

- Ornamentation should be kept to a minimum, eliminating potential breakables and sharp objects. Computers or television sets should not be available in the reception area, as that will likely make it very difficult for the children to break away and transition to therapy.

- Low arousal, such as off-white, cream, or beige, wall colorings are recommended. Ornamental wallpaper, paneling, and intricate design patterns should be kept to a minimum in lieu of a "minimalistic" décor.

- Escorts—parents, caregivers, therapists, relatives—accompanying the child should be encouraged to bring along two or three of the child's preferred toys or items such as books, music, games, and toys. Aside from providing a sense of security, comfort, and transitional entertainment to help segue way into the therapy or assessment visit, these items typically also serve as social catalysts that help the therapist to bond with the child through impromptu "show and tell" sessions of mutual interest.

- A clock, synchronized with others throughout the therapeutic setting, should be visible so that the child can see exactly how long remains between the start and end of the scheduled session. It is very important that therapists maintain very precise adherence to the scheduled appointments both in starting and ending times.

Research Gems: Clean, Healthy Air

Dr. Sharon Heller, author of the book *Too Loud, Too Bright, Too Fast, Too Tight* recommends cleaning indoor air and neutralizing noxious chemicals by adorning the office with houseplants. She recommends the following plants for reducing the effects of various pollutants (2003, p. 227):

Areca Palm	Boston Fern	Spider Plant
Azalea	Dieffenbachia	Philodendron
Golden Photos	Chrysanthemum	Bamboo Plant
Corn Plant	English Ivy	Mother-in-law tongue
Gerbera Daisy	Peace Lily	Marginata Dracaena
Warneckeii Dracaena		

Sensory Manipulatives

Sensory manipulatives are safe, non-toxic tools that a child (or adult) can use to help soothe her or himself, reduce stress, or increase the ability to focus while engaging in other activities that would be occurring during an assessment. Although referred to by almost endless popular and trademark names, they are essentially tools that a person who is either under- or over-stimulated can chew on, squeeze, twist, or spin that will help to stabilize one's sensory needs.

Some of these sensory manipulatives include the following items (for children who prefer certain animals many of these come in the shape of different animals or toys such as trains, cars, dinosaurs, etc.).

Jigglers	Blowers	Widgets	Bug-outs
Vibrators	Spinners	Wigglers	Stress/Koosh Balls
Massagers	Spikey Animals	Fidgets	Squigglies
Ticklers	Strokers	Slinkies	Poppers
Chewies	Stretchies	Huggies	Fuzzies
Grabbers	Squishies	Tanglers	Yuckies

Personal plush animals, clay, putty, beads or jewelry, fabrics, Legos®, favorite (quiet) toys, dolls, and any other object that may assist the child with calming down and focusing on the tasks at hand should be permitted. It should be added that many children presenting with AS, HFA, and even NLD will often bring in calming objects that may appear inappropriate or odd to the inexperienced professional. Although the list is exhaustive in my practice I have seen both children and adults function much more calmly and effectively when allowed to hold, or manipulate things such as bottle caps, stones, coins, a police badge, door handles, audio CDs, models of animals or planets, a stapler, a spoon, a 1947 radio transistor, alphabet letters, something blue (or orange, or green, etc.), a thermometer, a railroad spike, a World War II medal, feathers, Native American artifacts, a Civil War bullet, a 45 RPM record, calendars, a portrait of Abe Lincoln, clocks and watches, toy dinosaurs, a guitar, drumsticks, guitar picks, a 1962 Harmon Killebrew baseball card, and myriad other objects.

The list is exhaustive. For the uninitiated think of these items functioning as a lucky coin, rabbit's foot, lucky four-leaf clover, security blanket, lucky cap/hat/socks/shirt, or anything else that a mildly superstitious person may call upon during times of stress.

The Evaluation/Assessment Room

The setting where the formal assessment will take place should follow the same guidelines and provisions as have been indicated above. Once these ecological modifications are set in place the following suggestions are made to further help to minimize sensory-based challenges and maximize the assessment process.

- If the child appears overstimulated or anxious, encourage her/him to spend a few minutes engaging in some active movement exercises. Introducing any number of brain gym, or mid-line crossing activities, preferably accompanied by music will help the child with dispelling excess energies and entrain to the evaluation process.

- Invite the child to either bring in a preferred toy or object that may assist in instilling a sense of safety or relaxation. Another option is to offer the child the choice between a set number (three is suggested) of sensory manipulatives (a chewy, squishy, or spinner) to manipulate during the testing process.

- Remaining alert to each child's sensory triggers and signs of fatigue, stress, or discomfort allow the child to take short (one to three minute) breaks throughout the assessment session. Although allowing the child to engage in his/her own preferred type of self-management activity during these periods of self-refreshment are best—when appropriate—this is a time during which the "time-off" room can serve as a splendid resource.

- Rather than requiring the child to sit and undertake the assessment tasks in a standardized manner, exercise a "flexible structure" approach. As such, whenever possible, allow the child to stand, press against the wall, sit on a therapy ball or massage chair, lay on the floor, play with manipulatives or pull on an elastic band, hold on to a vibrating object, avoid eye contact, stare at a lava lamp or a wall, stand or sit and rock, hum while processing, etc., when answering questions.

- If the child has a favorite chair, pillow, inflatable cushion at home that she/he wishes to bring along, this should be encouraged.

- Many children with AS, HFA, and NLD have problems with handwriting which may create frustration, physical exhaustion, or consume energy that could otherwise be directed at focusing and remaining on task. For these children, and there are many, the availability of a keyboard or, when possible, answering questions verbally is strongly recommended.

- Allow the child to wear a weighed vest, chew gum or suck on sugarless candies, remove shoes and/or socks, or wear dark or tinted glasses if this helps her/him to focus and relax during the assessment.

- If the child insists on using a "tiny," monotone, or inflected voice to answer the questions, or responding as a favorite historical character or superhero, and this makes the evaluation possible, or more effective, there is no reason to insist that he/she use "her/his own voice."

- When "standard reason" begins to get in the way, clinicians need to remind themselves that (a) children with these conditions do not think "in the box," or "outside of the box," but, rather, from a "no-box" perspective, meaning that expectations, traditional approaches, and common deviations from those often do not work. (b) The 2/3 maturity rule, which suggests that, in general, the maturity of children with these conditions tend to be, on average, about 2/3 of their actual age is tremendously helpful when we begin to forget "why" a child may be acting "immature," or "not his/her age." In terms of *maturity level*, a fifteen-year-old is actually "about ten (2/3 X 15 = 10)," an eighteen-year-old "about 12," a nine-year-old "about 6," etc.

- Providing a well-padded carpet, or carpet square, where children may rub their bare feet or massage their soles or toes for tactile input during the assessment is often helpful.

- Showing and discussing the test items that will be administered, and lining them up in order within the child's view is often helpful. In this manner the child will know exactly what comes next, how many subtests or activities remain, and how many have been accomplished.

- Providing a small reinforcement after either each subtest, or a set number of tests (three is recommended) helps the child to stay on task and maintain motivation.

- Having the child's name written on a clearly visible schedule or appointment board in the assessment room so that the child can see exactly what time the evaluation is set to start, and end, is very helpful in helping to modify the child's structure and reduce preoccupations with time issues. Indicating scheduled break times, and their duration, on the calendar is also recommended. These should be in addition to "time-offs" needed by the child throughout the evaluation process.

- For children who have problems staying on task, sometimes playing soft, entrainment music (a compilation tape of largo movements from string concertos composed by baroque composers is recommended) in the background or using a steady rhythm metronome will help the child to establish a steady, comfortable working pace. The music should be played in the background, barely audible at about 45 decibels as measured in the center of the room.

- Above all, the focus should be on identifying and—as far as possible—providing the components that will help to create the most comfortable, stress-free, structured, and amicable environment possible to facilitate the client's involvement and maximize results.

Assessment Instruments Designed to Evaluate Sensory Related Challenges

---

Research Gems: Need for Sensory Assessment

"More detailed assessment of sensory problems may enable clinicians to identify and assist with the distress that many people with autism experience. The distress caused by particular sensory inputs can cause severely disturbed and aggressive behaviour in low functioning people with autism who cannot explain their distress. Identifying the specific sensory input causing the problem is essential in order to organize the environment and daily routine that will minimize the chances of such distress. A programme of desensitization may be helpful." (Leekam et al., 2007, p. 907)

Sensory Profile

Intended ages:
- Infant/Toddler: Birth to 26 months
- Sensory Profile: 3–10 year of age
- Adolescent/Adult: 11 years and above

Testing time:
- Infant/Toddler: 15 minutes
- Sensory Profile: 10-15 minutes
- Adolescent/Adult: 20-30 minutes

Administration: Individual

Intended to be administered by: Parents, caregivers, teachers, and professionals

Purpose: To help identify sensory-related challenges of neurotypical children as well as those with ADHD or ASDs. Helpful in assisting persons with sensory challenges to better recognize the cause of their sensory processing issues in the areas of taste/smell, movement, visual, touch, activity level, and auditory processing, and develop strategies for meeting their sensory-related issues.

Consists of:
Seven Model Categories
- Sensitivity to Stimuli
- Poor Registration
- Sensation Avoiding
- Sensation Seeking-   -
- Sensory Processing
- Modulation Processing
- Behavior and Emotional Responses

Seven Sections
- Tactile Sensitivity
- Taste/Smell Sensitivity
- Movement Sensitivity
- Under-responsive/Seeks Sensation
- Auditory Filtering
- Low Energy/Weak
- Visual/Auditory Sensitivity

Nine Factors
- Sensory Seeking
- Emotionally Reactive
- Low Endurance/Tone
- Oral Sensory Sensitivity
- Inattention/Distractibility
- Poor Registration
- Sensory Sensitivity
- Sedentary
- Fine Motor/Perceptual

Other information: A measure of a person's responses to sensory events in daily life. The frequency of the person's responses to 125 items related to certain sensory processing, modulation, and behavioral/emotional events is used to help identify the person's sensory processing patterns and examine how these might be contributing to, or creating, barriers to daily functioning (W. Dunn, 1999).

Research Gems: Autism as a Sensory Dysfunction Disorder

"Some researchers describe autism as a disorder of the senses rather than a social dysfunction, where each sense operates in isolation and the brain is unable to organize the stimuli in any meaningful way….Autism is sometimes defined as sensory dysfunction, a sensory integrative disorder in which the brain is not able to attach meaning to sensations and organize them into percepts and finally into concepts, etc. Unusual sensory experience is claimed by some authors to be a primary characteristic feature able to account for the basic symptoms of autism." (Bogdashina, 2003, p. 25)

Adolescent/Adult Sensory Profile

Intended ages: Adolescents through adults
Testing time: 5-10 minutes
Administration: Individual

Intended to be administered by: Self

Purpose: To assist clients in understand and improving their own sensory experiences and help to identify and maximize sensory regulation adaptations and strategies.

Consists of: A self-report inventory designed to provide information about behavior in six sensory processing categories noted by Winnie Dunn:
- Taste/Smell
- Movement
- Visual
- Touch
- Activity Level
- Auditory Processing

Other information: Results can be used to assist in identifying the cause of sensory processing issues and develop strategies to control them.

Available from: PsycCorp.com (800-211-8378), or Dr. Winnie Dunn, http://www.kotaweb.org/WinnieDunn.html.

Sensory Supplies

Abilitations	www.abilitations.com
Special Needs Toys	www.specialneedstoys.com
Therapro	www.theraproducts.com
OT Ideas, Inc.	www.otideas.com
Pocket Full of Therapy	www.pfot.com
The Therapy Shoppe	www.therapyshoppe.com
William's Store	www.williamsstore.com
PDP Products	www.pdppro.com
Sensory Comfort	www.sensorycomfort.com
Southpaw Enterprises	www.southpawenterprises.com
Special Kids Zone	www.specialkidszone.com

Processing Deficits Chart

PROCESSING DEFICIT	DESCRIPTION Problems with:
Auditory Sequencing	Recalling sounds, letters, or number sequences; lists; directions; and word order in spoken phrases ("evelator" vs. "elevator")
Auditory Memory	Storing and recalling spoken information; following verbal instructions.
Phonological Awareness	Recognizing or isolating individual word sounds, recognizing word similarities; rhyming, reading, writing, & understanding spoken language
Auditory Discrimination	Recognizing phoneme differences; understanding spoken communications, distinguishing between similar words and sounds, "hears without listening"
Auditory Figure Ground	Hearing & distinguishing sounds over background noises, voices, auditory clutter
Auditory Memory	Arranging individual phonemes into words (can recognize separate letters: "d, a, r, and t" but cannot see these compose the word "dart"
Receptive Language	Appearing to listen
Visual Sequencing	Reading, using answer sheets, reversing or misreading numbers or letters
Visual Memory	Recalling visual information, reading comprehension, math
Dysgraphia	Forming letters correctly, reading own writing
Visual Motor Integration	Mechanical writing, copying from external sources, organization; using visual cues to guide one's gross and fine motor movements; orienting to space
Visual Closure	Recognizing and identifying symbols, images, and objects when details are missing (a face without a mouth or nose)
Visual Figure Ground	Seeing images against competing backgrounds; recognizing known faces in a crowd; differentiating words on a page

Visual Agnosia	Recognizing words, pictures, numbers, letters, symbols or patterns due to an inability to integrate visual components into a coherent whole or problems with visual memory
Visual Discrimination	Differentiating between similar objects; identifying objects based on form, color, position, size, shape, and pattern; working with graphs, charts, pictures, and symbols.
Visual-spatial Perception	Distinguishing left/right, up/down, front/back, personal/physical boundaries; form constancy; position in space; spatial and directional awareness
Visual Processing	Accurately perceiving objects in space with relation to other objects, distinguishing between similar letters (i/l, b/d, p/q, m/n) and seeing words and numbers as separate units
Spatial Orientation	Being on time, keeping track of belongings, oral reading, organization, time management
Expressive Language	Expressing self, coming across as authentic
Whole/Part relationships	Perceiving or synthesizing relationships between objects or symbols as a whole and its partial component details
Propioceptive Dysfunction	Body awareness, motor control and planning; posture
Tactile Perception	Perceiving texture, shape, size, temperature, or density of physical objects
Body Awareness	Orienting limbs; getting dressed; activities that involve physical movements
Dyspraxia (praxis) (motor planning)	Sequencing motor movements (using scissors, riding a bicycle); running and jumping; climbing; eye-hand coordination
Vestibular Dysfunction	Movement and balance; muscle tone; bilateral coordination; visual-spatial processing; motor planning; auditory processing
Body Percept	Interrelationships of the awareness between body parts and their movement

References: National Center for Learning Disabilities, 1999, pp. 1-7; Kranowitz, 1998; LDOnline, 1999.

Chapter 3

The Assessment Toolbox:
Screening for Asperger's Syndrome, Autism, and Nonverbal Learning Disorders/Disabilities

---

Research Gems: "Advantages of Early Screening"

"A screening instrument for ASD suitable for infants would facilitate the identification of children at high risk and speed up the subsequent referral to specialized centers for further diagnostic evaluation....Establishing the diagnosis can help parents understand the handicaps of their child, take away feelings of anguish, and help them to find ways to support their autistic child in its development....Parents might want to know the diagnosis because of the genetic risks when considering having another child....Some evidence exists for the benefits of early intervention terms of IQ gains, language gains, improved social behavior, and reduction in symptom severity." (Dietz et al., 2006, p. 714)

General Screening Measures Designed for Autism, AS, and NLD Conditions

Although our understanding of autism spectrum and related conditions is still in its infancy, the combined efforts of researchers, clinicians, and psychometricians over the past decade or two have resulted in a growing number of viable resources that have become both increasingly practical and reliable in terms of their validity and reliability ratings.

The purpose of this section is to introduce some of the currently available screening tools to the growing number of diagnosticians, clinicians, and therapists who are searching for effective resources that may help to identify persons across the autism, Asperger's, and NLD spectrums early during the referral process.

The tools described throughout this section may be obtained through the catalogs and companies listed below, over the Internet, or directly from the sources noted within each particular instrument. Additional publishers of assessment instruments are listed in the resource section at the end of this book.

Psychological Assessment Resources
16204 North Florida Avenue
Lutz, FL 33549
Telephone: 800-331-8378
Fax: 800-727-9329
www.parinc.com

Western Psychological Services
12031 Wilshire Boulevard
Los Angeles, CA 90025-1251
Telephone: 800-648-8857
Fax: 310-478-7838
E-mail: cutsvc@wpspublish.com
www.wpspublish.com

Pearson Assessments
Ordering Department, 5th floor
P.O. Box 1416
Minneapolis, MN 55440
Telephone: 800-627-7271
Fax: 800-632-9011
www.pearsonassessments.com

(Additional companies are listed in the Appendix)

There are various types of screening measures. Primary, or universal, screening tools are typically used to help identify those persons who will likely be referred for more extensive, standardized assessment to help identify their diagnostic impression. Secondary screening tools, on the other hand, are those that may be used as early diagnostic tests for persons presenting with known developmental problems (Williams & Brayne, Autism, 2006, p. 12). Nonspecific screening measures are those that are designed primarily to identify children at risk for a wide range of developmental problems. These are at times used to screen for cognitive and/or language delays that can, in turn, help to identify children with autism. While one type of nonspecific measures screens for deficits in a normal of developmental areas, a second type is aimed directly at identifying social-emotional and/or communication problems making them both quite helpful in helping to screen for potential autism spectrum disorders. In general, the measures look at areas of cognitive, social, self-help, and behavior skill areas.

More specific to screening for autism-related conditions, there are two levels of autism-specific screening measures. While level *one* is designed to specifically target *symptoms* of autism, level *two* measures are designed to *differentiate young children at risk* for autism versus those at risk for other developmental disabilities.

Research Gems: Screening Tools

"Screening as a public health service is a means of actively identifying cases where there may or may not be a previous concern about development. It has been shown that the mean age of diagnosis for typical autism is 5.5 years, and as late as 11 years for Asperger syndrome, in spite of much earlier parental worries. Screening might be able to bring the age of diagnosis earlier, and also function to reassure the worried well. Earlier diagnosis may be desirable for a number of reasons: to allow time for genetic counselling; to initiate parental support; and to allow for earlier intervention. (Williams et al., 2005, p. 45)

Some recommended Level Two Autism-Specific Screening Measures are include:

The Scale of Red Flags (SORF)
Designed for scoring the Behavior Sample (above) and function as a "level 2" screener. Effective in differentiating children with and without autism who present with language delays.

The Pervasive Developmental Disorders Screening Test-Stage 2 (PDDST-Stage 2) (Siegel, 1998; Siegel & Hayer, 1999).
The PDDST-Stage 2 is a parent report measure essentially designed to function as a screening tool for the PDDST-Stage 1. Designed for children aged six years and under, this
tool helps developmental specialists to separate children who need more extensive autism-specific related evaluations from those who would benefit from non-autism specific developmental assessments.

The Screening Tool for Autism in Two-Year-Olds (STAT) (Stone et al., 2000; Stone & Ousley, 1997)
Designed to differentiate children, aged between 24 and 36 months, who are at risk for autism from those needing more extensive, general developmental evaluations. Designed to be directly administered by a trained examiner and used in multiple child-care settings, the STAT consists of 12 interactive items that assess various behavioral domains including play, requesting, directing attention, communication, and imitation skills. Effective in discriminating between children with ASD and those with other developmental disorders but weaker efficacy at distinguishing children with autism from those with pervasive developmental disorders not otherwise specified.

Contact:
    Wendy L. Stone
    Vanderbilt Child Development Center
    426 Medical Center South
    2100 Pierce Avenue
    Nashville, TN 37232
    E-mail: Wendy.stone@vanderbilt.edu

RECOMMENDED
Pervasive Developmental Disorders Screening Test – II (PDDST-II)

Intended ages: 18 months–48 months
Testing time: 10–20 minutes
Administration: Individual

Intended to be administered by: Parents and caregivers, and early childhood professionals.

Purpose: To assist with screening autism, in infants as early as 18 months. Also effective in assessing pervasive developmental delay and Asperger's syndrome.

Consists of: A parent-report screening measure designed to be completed in less than 20 minutes to assist in early identification and intervention for children with autism spectrum disorders.

Other information: The test includes three stages developed for use in a number of clinical settings:
- Stage 1: Primary Care Screener
- Stage 2: The Developmental Clinic Screener
- Stage 3: The Autism Clinic Severity Screener

Temperament and Atypical Behavior Scale (TABS)

Intended ages: 11–71 months
Testing time: Screener: 5 minutes, Assessment tool: 15 minutes
Administration: Individual

Intended to be administered by: Trained professionals

Purpose: To assess the critical temperament and self-regulation problems that tend to signify a child's risk for developmental delay during early stages of development.

Consists of: A 15-item, single-sheet screening form, and a more detailed, 55-item checklist administered when the screener indicates an area of potential concern. The TABS provide an indication of atypical behavior in four categories:

- detached
- hypersensitive-active
- underreactive
- dysregulated

Other information: A norm-referenced assessment that helps to "red flag" concern areas for children who are at risk, who are experiencing developmental delays or disabilities, and who can potentially qualify for timely early intervention and behavioral support services.
Resources available: Brookes publishing. E-mail: custserv@brookespublishing.com, Phone: (800) 638-3775, Web site: http://www.brookespublishing.com/tools/tabs/index.htm.

The Early Screening for Autistic Traits (ESAT)

Intended ages: 14–15 months
Testing time: 5–10 minutes
Administration: Individual

Intended to be administered by: Trained professionals

Purpose: An early screening tool for young (14-15 month) children suspected of having autistic traits.

Consists of: Fourteen items found to have maximal sensitivity and specificity for autism spectrum disorders.

<u>Other information</u>: This tool emphasizes play over joint attention, with children receiving high scores typically indicating the possibility of developmental problems. To be used with caution when differentiating between autism spectrum and other developmental disorders particularly with children younger than age 24 months. A pre-screening, 4-item version has also been developed by Dietz et al. (2006) and Swinkels et al. (2006).

<u>Research Gems: "The ESAT"</u>

"Our results suggest that, in addition to items on social impairments, items relating to lack of variability in play behavior and interest might also be of use for the very early detection of autism. The parents in our second study hardly ever spontaneously mentioned abnormalities in play development when asked about their first concern. This might explain the relative unpopularity of play-related items in screening instruments. However, when specific questions were asked, most of the same parents reported that they had noticed a lack of variability in play or interest as early as 14 months." (Swinkels et al., 2006, p. 731)

Greenspan Social-Emotional Growth Chart: A Screening Questionnaire for Infants and Young Children

<u>Intended ages</u>: 0–42 months
<u>Testing time</u>: 10 minutes
<u>Administration</u>: Individual

<u>Intended to be administered by</u>: Parents, educators, and caregivers

<u>Purpose</u>: To help screen social-emotional milestones in young children ages 0–42 months of age and yield understanding of how each child uses all capacities to meet needs, deal with feelings, think, and communicate.

<u>Consists of</u>: Thirty-five developmentally ordered items that relate accordingly to the ages at which each item is typically mastered. Items are rated using a simple, 5-point scale and reported as cut scores. The items are designed to assist in:

- Determining the mastery of early capacities of social-emotional growth
- Monitoring health social and emotional functioning
- Establishing goals for early intervention planning

- Monitoring progress in early intervention programs
- Detecting deficits or problems with developmental social-emotional capacities.

<u>Other information</u>: Intended as a preliminary, screening step for the purpose of child-care, early-identification, and pediatric screenings.

Temperament and Atypical Behavior Scale (TABS)

Intended ages: 11–71 months
Testing time: 30 minutes
Administration: Individual

Intended to be administered by: Parents and professionals

Purpose: A norm-referenced screening and assessment tool designed to identify temperament and self-regulation behavioral problems that may indicate a child's risk for atypical development. To help parents/caregivers and professionals to identify at risk, delayed, or disabled infants and young children and create a plan to help them to qualify for essential early intervention and behavioral support services.

Consists of: TABS Screener, TABS Assessment Tool, TABS Manual

Other information: The 15-item, TABS Screener form can be completed by parents in five minutes. Children with scores indicating potential problems are then assessed with the more extensive TABS Assessment Tool. This more detailed, 55-item checklist can be completed by parents in about 15 minutes, yielding results that give a detailed evaluation of atypical behavior in four categories:

- detached
- hypersensitive-active
- under-reactive
- dys-regulated.

Resources available: Brookes Publishing. Web site: www.brookespublishing.com/tools.

Autism Spectrum Screening Questionnaire (ASSQ)

Intended ages: 6-17 year olds
Testing time: 10 minutes
Administration: Individual

Intended to be administered by: Parents/caregivers, teachers, therapists

Purpose: To identify if the child tends to stand out as different from his or her same-age peers. Symptoms are endorsed as not present ("0"), somewhat present ("1"), or definitely present ("2"), with a total raw score that can range from "0-54." Designed as a screening instrument to identify children who require more extensive evaluations in order to formally diagnose AS or HFA.

Consists of: Twenty-seven behavioral descriptions rated on a 3-point scale.

Other information: Helps to differentiate between Autism spectrum disorders, attention/behavior disorders, learning disabilities, and correlates moderately with Connors/Rutter's scales.

Sensory Screening Checklist

The following is a *suggested checklist* on topic areas that could be considered when preparing information to share between parent/caregiver and professional, among professionals, and across settings coordinating multi-modal services or preparing a formal assessment of AS, NLD, and HFA children.

Sensory Patterns: General

My child, or client, tends to:	YES	NO
Dislike being touched, stroked, or caressed lightly		
Avoid certain clothes or textures		
Have an aversion to certain scents or odors		
Be annoyed by certain sounds		
Become easily startled by mild or moderate noise		
Become annoyed with music		
Become easily startled by loud voices		
Come across as if having vision problems		
Have difficulties judging physical distance		
Shy away from physical activities		
Have difficulties with fine-motor coordination		
Have difficulties with gross-motor coordination		
Be unable to use eating utensils when compared to peers		
Struggle with mechanical toys when compared to peers		
Struggle with blocks, Legos®, puzzles or other assembly		
Have difficulties dressing, tying shoes, buttoning		
Come across as anxious, squirmy, or uneasy		

	YES	NO
Avoid playground games involving spinning		
Have problems establishing hand preference (left vs. right)		
Be behind in general communication skills		
Be behind in overall pragmatic language skills		
Have problems with concentrating or focusing		
Have difficulties falling or staying asleep		
Be unusually clumsy or physically uncoordinated		
Run in an awkward manner		
Rarely be invited to peer games, groups, or activities		
Act immature for his/her age		
Come across stubborn and uncooperative		
Have poor tolerance for frustration		
Have problems making friends		

Sensory Patterns: Visual

My child, or client, tends to:	YES	NO
Have difficulty copying from boards or books		
Struggle differentiating betweens shapes, colors, symbols		
Have an aversion to certain lights (bright, fluorescent)		
Cover or rub eyes, squint, or show discomfort when reading		
Look "through" or "around" people when communicating		
Avoid direct eye contact		
Exhibit "laser-like" eye contact (looking directly into eyes)		

Reverse phonemes, numbers, letters, words		
Rely on peripheral (sideways) rather than direct eye contact		
Struggle with written instructions		
Lack adequate visual-spatial		
Have difficulties judging objects in the distance		
Misjudge physical boundaries (bumps into objects)		
Lose his/her place when reading		
Have problems tracing or cutting outlines on paper		
Struggle with playing "catch and throw"		
Become exasperated in busy visual environments		
Learn by listening, or doing, rather than by watching		
Be oversensitive to visual stimuli in general		
Be under-sensitive to visual stimuli in general		
Obsess about certain images, sights, lights, or visual patterns		
Orient to the world by way of visual imagery		
Memorize and categorize images and/or visual patterns		

Sensory Patterns: Auditory

My child, or client, tends to:	YES	NO
Have difficulties retaining or following spoken instructions		
Easily forget things that are said to her/him		
Hear only fragments of conversations		
Speak in "little" voices		

Speak in a monotone or "robotic" voice		
Speak very loudly		
Ask that things be repeated time and time again		
"Listen but not hear"		
Make unusual, repetitive sounds		
Have difficulties hearing against background noise		
Focus on one voice when in group situations		
Become exasperated in busy auditory environments		
Learn by watching, or doing, rather than by listening		
Cover his/her ears in the presence of mild noise or music		
Confuse similarly sounding words ("free vs. three")		
Speak or repeat things to her-/himself		
Be oversensitive to auditory stimuli in general		
Be under-sensitive to auditory stimuli in general		
Obsess about certain sounds or musical tones and melodies		
Orient to the world by way of auditory sensations		
Memorize and categorize sounds, music, and/or songs		
Seek, or make, strange noises		

Sensory Patterns: Tactile

My child, or client, tends to:	YES	NO
Avoid physical contact		
Crave touch, strong hugs, or deep pressure		
Yearn active—or aggressive—physical contact		
Have a low tolerance to mild pain (scrapes, bumps)		
Have a high tolerance to moderate pain		
Shy away from messy play (clay, paint, dirt, sand, dust)		
Avoid getting his/her hands dirty		
Need warnings before being touched or hugged		
Become easily startled when touched from behind		
Insist on wearing the same textures or fabrics		
Prefer to sit on certain types of furniture		
Come across as a hypochondriac		
Avoid wearing any tight clothes		
Have an aversion to tags on clothing		
Be very picky about shoes and/or socks (prefers loose sandals)		
Prefer short sleeves and shorts		
Prefer long sleeves and long slacks		
Prefer old, worn-out clothes than anything new		
Have an aversion to wearing hats or caps		
Insist on wearing gloves, scarves, or coats in warm weather		
Avoid wearing gloves, scarves, or coats in cold weather		

Refuse to walk on certain surfaces (water, sand, grass, tiles)		
Have inordinate reactions to either cold or hot food/drink		
Dislike washing hair or clipping nails		
Touch things repeatedly or in patterns		
Be described as "all thumbs," or "having two left feet"		
Struggle with zipping, buttoning, and tying shoes		
Rub, touch, or bite self		
Yearn for vibration, spinning, hopping, or repetitive movements		
Be unable to recognize objects by how they feel		
Concentrate best when moving around		
Find it difficult to sit still		
Be oversensitive to tactile stimuli in general		
Be under-sensitive to tactile stimuli in general		
Obsess about certain textures, fabrics, and physical surfaces		
Orient to the world by way of tangible, physical components		
Learn by watching, or listening, rather than by doing		
Memorize and categorize concrete, physical components		
Have discomfort during grooming		

Sensory Patterns: Olfactory

My child, or client, tends to:	YES	NO
Complain about mild, generally inoffensive odors		
Pick up on very mild scents		

Habitually smell objects (smells everything)		
Habitually smell his hands and/or fingers		
Has very little tolerance for how some people smell		
Complain about the smell of various foods		
Have little to no tolerance to mild cologne or perfume		
Be easily annoyed by scented candles or incense		
Have little to no tolerance to being in musty environments		
Struggle in discriminating between different odors		
Have an extraordinary ability to distinguish similar odors		
Be oversensitive to odors in general (smoke, chemicals)		
Be under-sensitive to odors in general		
Obsess about certain odors		
Memorize and categorize odors and scents		
Orient to the world by way of the olfactory sense		
Become ill when in the presence of certain odors		

Sensory Patterns: Gustatory

My child, or client, tends to:	YES	NO
Prefer certain tastes (bitter, sweet, sour)		
Crave certain condiments (salt, sugar, pepper, spices)		
Avoid eating or trying out new foods		
Prefer very bland foods		
Prefer to eat the same foods over and over again		

Dislike foods with certain textures		
Be a very picky eater		
Always need/seek oral stimulation		
Chew a lot of gum or suck on hard candies		
Chew on his fingernails, fingertips, knuckles, or palms		
Find pleasure in "chewy"-type sensory objects		
Eat very slowly		
Chew every bite a certain number of times		
Spend a lot of time brushing his/her teeth		
Avoid brushing his/her teeth		
Enjoy making strange noises and sounds with his mouth		
Enjoy humming		
Talk to him-/herself a lot		
Enjoy making rhymes out of ordinary words		
Enjoy repeating things that are asked of her/him even when she/he seems to have understood them		
Enjoy imitating sounds of machines, animals, cartoons, etc.		
Make gurgling and/or perculating sounds		

Sensory Patterns: Vestibular & Propioceptive

My child, or client, tends to:	YES	NO
Lack a sense of bilateral coordination		
Be athletically challenged		
Move in a stiff, rigid, or robotic manner		
Move in a sagging, slack, or limp manner		
Have very little tolerance for physical exertion		
Have enormous tolerance for physical exercise and never tires		
Have extremely poor eye-hand coordination		
Have a weak or floppy handshake		
Have very poor balance		
Enjoy rocking back and forth or hopping repeatedly		
Be hypersensitive to movement		
Always be on the move		
Avoid physical, dynamic activities		
Crave physical, dynamic activities		
Appear to struggle to hold her/his head up while reading		
Climb stairs in an awkward, uncoordinated manner		
Easily trip over objects		
Be clumsy and accident prone		
Have difficulty establishing lateral (right vs. left) dominance		
Have very poor handwriting skills		
Be apprehensive about riding "people movers" or escalators		

Be unable to physically "juggle" two things at once		
Struggle with reading proficiency		
Have difficulties tracking moving objects (a ball being thrown)		
Switching attention or focus across moving objects		
Have problems with spatial awareness		
Often misjudge body or physical proximity		
Over- or under-estimate distances, heights, and/or speeds		
Have problems with motor planning activities		
Lack "physical security" or feel physically unstable		
Avoid playground activities involving swings, spinning, slides, merry-go-rounds, teeter-toters, climbing, monkey bars, etc.		
Be afraid of heights or moving fast (bicycles, cars, sleighs)		
Lack tolerance for being physically inverted (upside down)		
Have difficulties with brain-gym (crossing midline) activities		
Lack tolerance for being picked up or swung about		
Be attracted to fast, dare-devil type activities, rides, & games		
Have an extraordinary ability to spin without dizziness		
Crave trampolines, seesaws, carnival rides, and acrobatics		
Find comfort in spinning around in chairs, tumbling, pivoting, hopping, jumping off diving boards, crashing against waves		
Enjoy wildly swinging or spinning his/her head around, twirling in circles, and crashing against objects		
Have a poor sense of confidence and/or self-esteem		
Become easily stressed particularly in physically demanding situations or when complex movements are required		

Have difficulties relating to same-age peers		
Alienate or isolate him-/herself and be described as a "loner"		
Easily abandon mechanical-type pursuits		
Become quickly discouraged when new activities require multitasking, organization, sequencing, or shifting attention		
Struggle with generalizing learned skills, transitioning across settings or tasks, and/or adapting to change		
Be always "on the go"		
Not tolerate changes in plans and expectations		
Not stay between the lines when coloring		
Like to lean against people, furniture, or walls		
Enjoy hand-flapping		
Crave stomping his/her feet, climbing, or hopping		
Engage in toe walking		
Wiggle constantly when sitting		

Research Gems: Synesthesia

"Many people with autism do not remember verbally but while remembering they actually see, hear, feel, smell or taste the items (in their mind). The thought about something produces real experiences they had when encountering this thing or event for the first time. They store their visual, auditory, olfactory, gustatory and tactile memories, which are very real. For instance, the thought of textures they hate might cause goose bumps and chills and a general sense of unease would follow." (Bogdashina, 2003, p. 105)

"Synasthesia in autism is another 'remnant' that fails to become inhibited." (Bogdashina, 2003, p. 123)

Sensory Patterns: Synesthesia

(Note: the following are *examples*—synesthetic experiences can have endless varieties and personal associations)

SYNESTHETIC SENSATION EXAMPLES	YES	NO
My child, or client, tends to:		
Refer to sounds in terms of color ("her voice is orange")		
Describe scents in terms of color ("this perfume smells blue")		
Depict touch sensations as color ("your sweater feels purple")		
Express sounds in tactile terms ("your voice feels wooden")		
Explain sights in tactile terms ("the sunset felt too tight")		
Speak of textures as a shape ("this fabric feels too circular")		
Allude to taste as a shape ("this pudding tastes triangular")		
Relate to numbers as colors ("seven is indigo, eight is green")		
Describe words as postures ("that word is just too droopy")		
Depict letters as colors ("p is turquoise, q is tangerine")		
Refer to letters as shapes ("w is circular, b is square)		
Refer to people in terms of colors ("he's such a maroon guy!")		
Complain about things/numbers/letters being "the wrong color"		
Complain about food *tasting* "too hard, rough, soft"		
Delight in taste sensations as shapes ("I love triangular flavor!")		
Complain about images *smelling* "too aqua, a little chartreuse"		
Delight in images as scents ("I love how beige smells!")		
Complain about sounds *looking* "too square, not round enough"		
React to sounds/taste/sights with involuntary movements		
Complain about touches' "taste" or "smell"		

Complain about the "look" of certain odors/tastes/sounds		
Express frustration over how someone staring "sounds"		
Express delight over how a certain shape "smells"		
Describe pain sensations as colors, shapes, sounds, or odors		

BEHAVIORAL/PERSONAL CHARACTERISTICS

Do poorly in mathematics		
Have a poor sense of direction		
Have problems telling left from right		
Have an aversion to changing daily routines		
Insist on doing tasks in the same order repeatedly		
Have an exceptional memory for details and facts		
Feel overwhelmed in busy settings or crowded settings		
Feel anxious when things are not organized or in order		
Avoid noisy or colorful settings or places		
Do well on tasks or tests that require memorization		
Do well on tests that require pattern recognition		
Excel at noticing fine detail		

Sources: Ayres, 2005; Baron-Cohen et al., 1993; Biel & Peske, 2005; Bogdashina, 2003; Bragdon & Gamon, 2000; Cesaroni & Garber, 1991; Citowic, 1989, 1995; Heller, 2003; Knanowitz, 1998; Lemley, 1999; Luria, 1987; O'Neill, 1999; Robertson & Sagiv, 2005; Williams, 1996, 1999.

"Probably, the reported low incidence of synaesthesia in autism can be accounted for by the fact that it is not easily detected in the autistic population." (Bogdashina, 2003, p. 124)

Research Gems: Types of Synesthesia

Colored graphemes
Colored musical sounds
Colored musical notes
Colored tastes
Colored pain
Colored touch
Colored orgasms
Smell-synesthetic taste
Smell-synesthetic touch
Sound-synesthetic taste
Sound-synesthetic touch
Taste-synesthetic temperature
Temperature-synesthetic sound
Touch-synesthetic sound
Touch-synesthetic temperature
Vision-synesthetic sound
Vision-synesthetic temperature
Personality-synesthetic smell

Colored time units
Colored general sounds
Colored phonemes
Colored odors
Colored personalities
Colored temperatures
Smell-synesthetic sound
Smell-synesthetic temperature
Sound-synesthetic smell
Sound-synesthetic temperature
Taste-synesthetic sound
Taste-synesthetic touch
Touch-synesthetic smell
Touch-synesthetic taste
Vision-synesthetic smell
Vision-synesthetic taste
Vision-synesthetic touch

(Robertson & Sabiv, 2005, p. 15)

Research Gems: Diagnosing Synesthesia

Richard E. Cytowic, a renowned scientist well known in the field of synesthesia, proposes the following five diagnostic criteria for differentiating actual synesthesia from common, ordinary sensory blendings or associations.

<u>Involuntary</u>:

Cross-sensory experiences are beyond the synesthete's control.

<u>Projected</u>:

The triggered sense is perceived outside the mind, externally rather than "in the mind's eye (or "ear," etc.)

<u>Durable and Unique</u>:

The sensory associations of true synesthetes to specific triggers. For example, if a given word or tone brings to mind the color "turquoise" at any given time, this synesthetic association will remain consistent throughout the person's life.

<u>Memorable</u>:

Triggered sensory experiences are vividly remembered, even if the triggers are forgotten.

<u>Emotional</u>:

Synesthetes have a persistent, emotional certainty of their cross-sensory perceptions.

(Bragdon & Gamon, 2000, p. 112)

Chapter 4

Autism

"Given the complexities of autism, an assessment that incorporates familiar play activities and interest of the child is strongly recommended....Developmental theory posits that participation in high-interest activities that are relevant to one's experiences is a fundamental right and skill of all individuals regardless of ability or need. This provides individuals with a sense of control over their environment, and it promotes a feeling of self-worth and security. Children with autism are no different." (Vacca, 2007, p. 58)

<u>Introduction</u>

Emerging in the first three years of life and defined by a pattern of qualitative distinctions in the areas of reciprocal social interaction, communication, and repetitive interests and behaviors autism was initially described in America in 1980 in the American Psychiatric Association's *Diagnostic and Statistical Manual* (*DSM-III*) under labels that included Infantile autism, Childhood onset pervasive developmental disorder, and Atypical pervasive developmental disorder. The revised, *DSM-III-R* version of the manual listed Autistic disorder and, for the first time, the more inclusive Pervasive developmental disorder not otherwise specified. A few years later updated revisions in 1994 (*DSM-IV*), and 2000 (*DSM-IV-TR*) (text revised) versions of the manual again revised the spectrum, listing five different disorders under the umbrella of autism spectrum, or pervasive development disorders. As of this writing these continue to be noted as autistic disorder, pervasive developmental disorder not otherwise specified (PDDNOS), Rett's syndrome, and childhood disintegrative disorder, a condition that had been previously known as Heller's syndrome, and is more commonly referred to as "regressive autism." Other diagnostic systems, including the *International Classification of Diseases* (*ICD-10*) published by the World Health Organization; *The Gillberg diagnostic criteria for Asperger's Syndrome*; and Szatmari, Bremner and Nagy's *Diagnostic criteria for Asperger's Syndrome*, have released systems that offer slight variations from the standard *DSM-IV* versions. Although none of the current systems list the condition of <u>high functioning</u> autism the emphasis of this book will be on identifying persons who fall at the "high" (full scale IQ of 70 or higher) end of the autistic spectrum, along with Asperger's syndrome and Non-verbal Learning Disorders. Many of the assessment instruments suggested throughout the book, however, have the capacity for identifying autism spectrum condtions ranging from the low to the high ends of the autistic hierarchy of cognitive capabiltities.

Research Gems: Early Identification of Autism

"To identify autism in very young children…look for differences in four key areas of behavior:

- Social isolation…."ignoring others," "doesn't respond to name," "fails to attend to voice," "acts as if deaf," "does not imitate."

- Abnormal play…."absence of pretend play," "playing only with parts of objects," "playing only with a few things," "inappropriate relating to toys."

- Lack of joint attention, or a lack of "showing," "sharing," "commenting," "directing other's attention," "protodeclarative pointing." (indicating objects of interest rather than to obtain an object)

- Difference in eye contact described as "abnormal gaze," "difficulty getting or sustaining eye contact." (Kope et al., 2001, p. 3)

Assessment Instruments Designed to Evaluate Autism

Checklist for Autism in Young Children (CAYC)

Administration: Individual

Intended to be completed by: Parent/caregiver

Purpose: Checklist is designed as a standardized tool for gathering information to determine if the child meets DSM-IV-TR criteria for autism, AS, or PDD-NOS. This checklist is not designed to make a diagnosis but merely to gather information on autistic symptoms.

Consists of: Thirty autistic symptoms that are scored as present or absent.
Twelve of which correspond with the DSM-IV-TR diagnostic criteria for autism, and sixteen as associated features of autism as described in same.

Checklist symptoms are divided into six categories:

- problems with social interaction (social isolation, withdrawal, limited peer interaction, and limited eye contact)
- perseveration (obsessive preoccupations, stereotyped and repetitive play, and sterotypies such as hand flapping or toe walking),
- somatosensory disturbance (hypersensitivity to certain sounds, tactile defensiveness, high tolerance for pain)
- atypical developmental pattern (language delay, difficulty with reciprocal conversational speech, idiosyncratic and perseverative speech, splinter skills or special abilities)
- mood disturbance (emotional lability, over-reactivity, difficulty expressing and recognizing emotions)

- problems with attention and safety (hyperfocusing on activities or topics of interest to self and inattention at other times)

(Tryon et al., 2006, p. 3)

Research Gems: The Autism Spectrum Quotient as Identification Tool

"We wish to underline that the AQ is not diagnostic, but may serve as a useful instrument in identifying the extent of autistic traits shown by an adult of normal intelligence. A score of 32+ appears to be a useful cut-off for distinguishing individuals who have clinically significant levels of autistic traits. Such a high score on the AQ however does not mean an individual has AS or HFA, since a diagnosis is only merited if the individual is suffering a clinical level of distress as a result of their autistic traits." (Baron-Cohen et al., 2001, p. 17)

The Autism-Spectrum Quotient (AQ)—Adolescent Version

Intended ages: 9.8–15.4 years
Testing time: 5–10 minutes
Administration: Individual

Intended to be administered by: Self

Purpose: To help quantify where an adolescent is situated on the continuum from autism to normality.

Consists of: 50 questions, made up of 10 questions assessing five different areas:
- social skill
- attention switching
- attention to detail
- communication
- imagination

Other information: Early studies have shown the AQ-Adolescent Version to have excellent test-retest reliability. The authors recommend that, due to its communication subscale, the instrument be used primarily with individuals with some speech, and with an intelligence in the borderline average range (70) or above. Further, as of this writing, they suggest the instrument be used for research purposes until it undergoes more extensive evaluation as a screening instrument in the general population.

Research Gems: The Autism-Spectrum Quotient (AQ)—Adolescent Version

"AS predicted, adolescents with Asperger Syndrome (AS)/high functioning autism (HFA) or with classic autism scored significantly higher on the AQ than matched controls. Eighty percent to 90% (mean = 89.3%) scored above a critical minimum of 30+, whereas none of the controls did so….Within the control group, males score slightly but significantly higher than females, both overall, and at intermediate and high levels of autistic traits. This is consistent with the extreme male brain theory of autism and may have implications for the marked sex ration in autism and AS." (Baron-Cohen et al., 2006, p. 347)

Research Gems: "High AQ is not Necessarily a Debilitating Factor"

"If the AQ were being used in a general population screen (and the ethical case for such a use has yet to be demonstrated) the higher cut off of 32 is likely to minimize false positives. We suspect that this is because in the general population there may be a percentage of individuals who have many autistic traits but who do not require any clinical support (and are not seeking this) because of a good cognitive match between their cognitive style or personality, and their family or occupational or social context." (Woodbury-Smith et al., 2005, p. 334).

The Autism-Spectrum Quotient (AQ)
(Baron-Cohen et al., 2001)

Intended ages: Adults
Testing time: 5-10 minutes
Administration: Individual
Intended for: Adults of normal intelligence

Purpose: To assist in rapidly quantifying where a given individual is situated on the autism-normality continuum. Helpful for screening adults of normal intelligence adults who may present with "autistic traits"—or the "broader autistic phenotype"—as well as those with autism spectrum conditions.

Consists of: 50 questions, made up of 10 questions designed to assess five different areas:
- Social skill
- Attention switching
- Attention to detail
- Communication
- Imagination

Research Gems: The AQ's Generalizability

"These results suggest that autistic conditions at clinical levels of severity are expressed in very similar ways across widely differing cultures. The results also demonstrate the reliability of the AQ in terms of generating very similar patterns of results in otherwise very different samples....An identical result in both cultures was that a talent for the mathematical or physics end of science is particularly associated with a higher number of autistic traits. These results are also consistent with the extreme male brain (EMB) theory: sex difference in autistic traits may be a universal characteristic." (Wakabayashi et al., 2006, p. 269)

Other information: A self-administered instrument designed to measure the degree to which adults with normal intelligence have traits associated with autistic spectrum conditions. Adults with Asperger and high-functioning autism received a mean score of 35.8, with 80% receiving scores of 32 or higher. Scores range from 0–50. Follow-up research indicates that this test is "a valuable instrument for rapidly quantifying where any given individual is situated on the continuum from autism to normality" (Baron-Cohen et al., 2001, p. 2).

AQ is available at: http://autismresearchcentre.com/docs/paper/2001_BCetal_AQ.pdf
(Baron-Cohen, Wheelwright, Skinner, Martin, & Clubley, [2001]).

Research Gems: The AQ's Cross-Cultural Relevance

"In a study comparing AQ data from samples in the United Kingdom and Japan "the UK results were replicated in every respect: (1) The AS/HFA group scored at a similar high level (UK cut-off > 32, Japanese cut-off > 33); (2) A sex difference (males > females) was found in both general populations and student populations, but not among the individuals with AS/HFA; (3) Among the students, scientists scored significantly higher than non-scientists in both countries; and (4) mathematicians and physicists scientists scored higher than medical scientists in both countries." (Wakabayashi et al., 2006, p. 269)

Gilliam Autism Rating Scale – Second Edition (GARS-2)

Intended ages: 3–22
Testing time: 5–10 minutes
Administration: Individual
Intended to be administered by: teachers, parents, and clinicians

Purpose: To assist in estimating the severity of the autism spectrum condition.

Consists of: A behavioral checklist consisting of 42 items describing typical characteristic behaviors of persons with autism. Three subscales examine stereotyped behaviors, communication, and social interaction. Designed to screen for autism, recommend treatment goals, and monitor intervention responses. DSM-IV-TR diagnostic definitions of autism.

Other information: The GARS-2 helps to discriminate persons with autism from persons with other behavioral disorders, such as mental retardation. The earlier GARS consisted of 56 items that were grouped into four subtests that examined early development, stereotyped behaviors, communication skills, and social interactions.

Research Gems: The CARS

"Results indicated high concordance between the CARS and clinical diagnosis using DSM-IV (including excellent sensitivity and specificity)…there were significant sensible differences in mean CARS score for different diagnostic groups, including a substantial difference between the Autistic Disorder and PDD-NOW groups (p. 625)….Best practice necessitates using a behavioral observation measure as part of a comprehensive diagnostic assessment, and the CARS continues to be well suited to this task." (Perry et al., 2005, p. 631)

Research Gems: "The Gilliam Autism Rating Scale"

"The data suggested caution when using the GARS as a screening or diagnostic tool….The instrument should be used with care when assessing higher functioning individuals and a lower AQ cutoff is recommended when screening for ASDs….The GARS does have a number of positive features. Its administration and scoring are quick and simple and a significant amount of data has been collected. The instrument could be used as an index of severity of autism for selected populations. It could also be used to measure specific behavior (repetitive motor behaviors) and it may prove to have good discriminant validity with lower functioning individuals." (Lecavalier, 2005, p. 804)

Childhood Autism Rating Scale (CARS)

Intended ages: 2 through adult
Testing time: 15 minutes
Administration: Individual

Intended to be administered by: Physicians, special educators, school psychologists, speech pathologists, and audiologists. Minimal training is required.

Purpose: To help identify children with autism and distinguish them from children with developmental disabilities who are not autistic. Also distinguishes mild to moderate from severe autism.

Consists of: Items drawn from five prominent systems for diagnosing autism, each covering a particular characteristic, ability, or behavior. Uses a 7-point scale to indicate the degree to which the child's behavior deviates from that of a non-disabled same-aged child. Combines information from various sources including direct observation, parent report, and chart review.

Other information: Provides quantifiable ratings based on direct observation of the person's behaviors. High sensitivity, with DSM diagnostic criteria for autism reflecting the CARS cutoff score.

Research Gems: Diagnostic Instrument Comparison

"Results indicated that the ADOS-G, CARS and clinical judgment agreed with each other but not with the ADI-R. Many of the children classified with ASD by the other measures were not classified with autism by the ADI-R because they did not display enough repetitive behaviors and stereotyped interests. These results indicate that young children with ASD may not display repetitive behaviors and stereotyped interest, and for toddlers, the ADI-R would have a higher sensitivity if revised to include a diagnosis of PDD-NOW, for which the requirement of repetitive behaviors is less stringent." (Ventola et al., 2006, p. 839)

Research Gems: CARS Effectiveness Measuring Autistic Symptomology

"When comparing the two groups of children on the CARS, all of the social communication items as well as some of the atypical sensory-related items differentiated the ASD group from the groups with other delays. For all items, the ASD groups scored higher (more significant degree of impairment) than the DD/DLD (developmental delay/developmental language disorder) group. When language level was controlled, the results were very similar, indicating that the CARS is relatively robust to developmental level and in measuring autistic symptomology, as opposed to developmental level." (Ventola et al., 2007, p. 434)

Autism Behavior Checklist (ABC)

Intended ages: 18 months to 35 years (most effective for older children and adults)
Testing time: 20 minutes or less
Administration: Individual

Intended to be administered by: Parents/caregivers, teachers.

Purpose: To measure varying levels of autism symptoms whereas high (67 or above) scores reflecting greater degrees of impairment and lower (53 or less) scores indicating low probability of autism. Scores falling in the in-between range are suggestive of the need for further assessment.

Consists of: A 57-item behavior rating scale that examines behaviors and symptoms of autism in five areas: sensory (sensory related behaviors), relating (social relations), body and object use (repetitive behaviors), language (use of language and communication skills), and social and self-help (level of social and adaptive skills).

Other information: Emphasizes autistic symptomatology and observable features associated with, but not limited to autism, rather than pro-social behaviors. The development phase of the ABC included information from professionals working with the developmental spectrum of typically developed children through adults as well as populations presenting with autism, mental retardation, visual and hearing impairments, and emotional disturbance.

The ABC is a component of the ASIEP (see elsewhere in this chapter) and draws from various sources including Kanner's criteria for autism, The Behavior Observation Schedule, and the BRIAAC.

Research Gems: "The Need for Multiple Sources for Diagnosis"

"Studies show that the ADI-R does not agree with other diagnostic measures in all cases, either due to over- or under-classification, which may be because it relies solely on parent-reported behaviors, whereas other measures rely at least in part on observation. This finding highlights the need for clinicians to use multiple sources of information when diagnosing a child." (Ventola et al., 2006, p. 846)

RECOMMENDED
Autism Diagnostic Interview – Revised (ADI-R)

"The ADI-R is the most widely used diagnostic instrument in autism research….Original studies of the ADI-R found that all children with autism appropriately exceeded ADI-R cutoffs in all three domains for a sample of 25 children with autism and 25 mentally handicapped or language-impaired children." (Mazefsky & Oswald, 2006, p. 535)

Intended ages: 2.0 years and above.
Testing time: 1 ½ to 2 ½ hours
Administration: Individual

Intended to be administered by: Trained professionals

Purpose: To provide a thorough assessment of individuals suspected of having autism or other autism spectrum disorders. Useful for formal diagnosis as well as treatment and educational planning.

Consists of: Ninety-three items focusing on three functional domains:
- Language/Communication
- Reciprocal Social Interactions
- Restricted, Repetitive, and Stereotyped Behaviors and Interests

Interview questions cover eight content areas:
- Subject's background, family, education, previous diagnoses, and medications
- Overview of the subject's behavior
- Early development and milestones
- Language acquisition and loss of language or other skills
- Current functioning in regard to language and communication
- Social development and play
- Interests and behaviors
- Clinically relevant behaviors, such as aggression, self-injury, and possible epileptic features

Other information: Results can be used to support a diagnosis of autism or to determine the clinical needs of various groups in which a high rate of autism spectrum disorders might be expected. Very effective in differentiating autism from other developmental disorders and assessing syndrome boundaries, identifying new subgroups, and quantifying autistic symptomatology.

Research Gems: The ADOS + ADI-R in Diagnosis

"The ADOS is a reliable and sufficiently sensitive diagnostic tool in the assessment of autistic disorders. For ICD-10/DSM-IV classification and to ensure a high specificity of diagnosis additional information concerning repetitive, stereotyped behavior and early development (e.g., taken from the ADI-R) has to be collected." (Bolte & Poustka, 2004, p. 45)

RECOMMENDED
Autism Diagnostic Observation Schedule (ADOS)

"The ADOS-G is unique in providing diagnostic cutoffs for both autism and pervasive developmental disorder not otherwise specified." (Mazefsky & Oswald, 2006, 534)

Intended ages: Toddlers through adulthood.
Testing time: Each of four modules requires 35–40 minutes of administration.
Administration: Individual

Intended to be administered by: Trained professionals

Purpose: A semi-structured assessment used to evaluate anyone suspected of having autism, including nonverbal toddlers through verbally fluent adolescent and adult populations.

Consists of: Various activities that allow the clinician to observe social and communication behaviors related to the diagnosis of Pervasive Developmental Disorders. Composed of four modules, each requiring 35-40 minutes to administer. Module 1 is used with children who do not consistently use phrase speech, module 2 with those who use phrase speech but are not verbally fluent, module 3 with fluent children, and module 4 with fluent adolescents and adults. It does not address nonverbal adolescents and adults. Modules 1 and 2 require movement around the room, while modules 3 and 4 involve more conversation and are typically administered at the examination table.

Module 1 consists of:
- Free Play
- Response to Name
- Response to Joint Attention
- Bubble Play
- Anticipation of a Routine with Objects
- Responsive Social Smile
- Anticipation of Social Routine
- Functional and Symbolic Imitation

- Birthday Party
- Snack

Module 3 consists of:
- Construction Task
- Make-Believe Play
- Joint Interactive Play
- Demonstration Task
- Description of a Picture
- Telling a Story from a Book
- Cartoons
- Reporting a Nonroutine Event/Conversation
- Emotions
- Social Difficulties/Annoyance
- Break
- Friends/Loneliness/Marriage
- Creating a Story

Other information: An extensive package containing training and practice videos and materials is available for clinicians in lieu of a two-day clinical training course offered by Western Psychological Services. The ADOS provides standardized materials and ratings that measure ASDs regardless of language impediments. "The ADOS-G has the most empirical support among play-based diagnostic assessment procedures for autism….Using a sample of 78 individuals with autism, 69 with PDD-NOS, and 66 with non-PDD diagnoses, the ADOS-G correctly identified 95 percent of those with autism and 92 percent not in the autism spectrum." (Mazefsky & Oswald, 2006, p. 535)

Research Gems: ADOS-G (Generic)

"Because the focus of the ADOS-G is on observation of social behavior and communication, the goal of the activities is to provide interesting, standard context in which interactions occur. Standardization lies in the hierarchy of behavior employed by the examiner and the kinds of behavior taken into account in each activity during the overall ratings. The activities serve to structure the interaction; they are not ends in themselves. The object is not to test specific cognitive abilities or other skills in the activities, but to have tasks that are sufficiently intriguing that the child or adult begin assessed will want to participate."
(Reference: http://www.agre.org/program/aboutadosg.cfm?do=program)

Neuroanatomical Abnormalities in Autism
(Baron-Cohen, 2004)

♦ Anatomical abnormalities in the cerebellum, the brain stem, frontal lobes, parieteal lobes, hippocampus, and the amygdale.

♦ Epilepsy occurs commonly among classic autism populations

♦ Abnormally low number of Purkinje cells in the cerebellar cortex, effecting disinhibition of the cerebellar deep nuclei and overexcitement of the thalamus and cerebral cortex

♦ Abnormal density of neurons in the hippocampus, amygdale, and other parts of the limbic system

♦ Abnormally low degree of dendritic branching in the hippocampus

♦ A reduction in the size, coupled with an increase in the dispersion of cells, of cortical minicolumns, leading to increased connections between the minicolumns

---

Research Gems: Biological Impairments in Autism
(Jepson, 2005, p. 18)

o Chronic Diarrhea/Constipation
o Inability to clear heavy metals
o Leaky gut syndrome
o Mineral deficiencies (zinc, magnesium, selenium)
o Impaired neuronal development
o Gluten/Casein sensitivity
o Impaired detoxification
o Omega-3 fatty acid deficiency
o Impaired pancreatic function
o Vitamin deficiencies
o Neurotransmitter imbalance/dysfunction
o Seizures impaired methylation

o Yeast/bacterial overgrowth of bowels
o Impaired sulfation
o Imbalanced immune system
o Malabsorption/Malnutrition
o Disrupted hippocampus/Amygdala
o Impaired secretin signaling
o Impaired antioxidation
o Significant food allergies
o Frequent viral and bacterial infections
o Autoimmunity
o Sensitivity to vaccinations

Neurophysiological Abnormalities in Autism
(Baron-Cohen, 2004)

♦ Decreased ability between competing sensory stimuli, coupled with a hyper arousal triggered to sensory input, effecting fluid selectivity

♦ Decreased activity in brain areas related to higher cognitive processing coupled with hyper-activity in sensory areas associated with stimulus driven processing revealed via functional neuroimaging studies

- High activity in ventral occipital areas couple with low activity in both prefrontal and parietal areas

- Abnormally high P1 evoked potential to events at the point of attention, vs abnormal orientation to surrounding stimuli revealed via EEG studies

- Abnormal hemispheric activation during attentive shifting, accentuated by deficits in rapid shifting to stimuli between different modalities, spatial locations, and object features.

Research Gems: Autism – "The Male-Brain Syndrome"

"The adults with AS/HFA had a mean AQ score of 35.8 (sd = 6.5), significantly higher than Group 2 controls (x = 16.4, sd = 6.3). 80% of the adults with AS/HFA scored 32+, vs. 2% of controls. Among the controls, males scored slightly but significantly higher than women. No females scored extremely highly (AQ score 34+) whereas 4% of males did so. Twice as many males (40%) as females (21%) scored at intermediate levels (AQ score 20+). Among the AS/HFA group, males and female scorers did not differ significantly." (Baron-Cohen et al., 2001, p. 2)

Morphometrical Abnormalities in Autism
(Baron-Cohen, 2004)

- Reduced volume in the cerebellum, the brainstem, and posterior corpus callosum revealed via magnetic resonance imaging (MRI)

- Postnatal macroencephaly, revealed by either MRI volumetric analysis, or measures or head circumference, apparent between the ages of two and four among 90% of neonates later diagnosed with autism or PDD-NOS, with evidence of larger than average brain volumes

- Enlarged cerebellar and cerebral white matter, and cerebral grey matter resulting in an abnormally large cerebellar vermis size by which up to 95% of toddlers with autism can be distinguished from normal controls. Measurements can also assist in predicting if the child will present with high or low functioning autism

- Anterior to posterior overgrowth—with frontal lobe areas showing the largest abnormal increases—reflecting cortical grey matter volumes that could indicate failures in synaptic pruning as well as excesses of synaptogenesis (note: the formation of a neurotransmitter's release site in a presynaptic neuron and a receptive field at the postsynaptic partner, along with the precise alignment of pre- and post-synaptic specializations).

Four Lines of Evidence for Amygdala Deficit in Autism
(Baron-Cohen, 2004)

◆ Increased cell density revealed via postmortem microscopic pathology
◆ A pattern of deficits similar to those of amygdale lesion patients
◆ Reduced amygdale volume revealed via structural MRI
◆ Significantly reduced amygdale activation—compared to normal controls—among adults with both HFA and AS

Research Gems: PDD Subtypes

"Significant differences between the groups existed on many PDD (Pervasive Developmental Disorder) symptoms, adaptive behaviors, and cognitive measures of language competence, but not on aspects of nonverbal communication, nonverbal cognition, or motor development. Subtypes of children with PDD can be identified that differ in variable relatively independent of defining characteristics. These findings should provide a firm foundation into research to determine whether children with autism and Asperger's syndrome also differ on outcome, etiology, and response to treatment." (Szatmari et al., 1995, p. 1662).

The Broad Autism Phenotype

Research Gems: The Autism Phenotype – Three Distinct Domains

"The autism symptom phenotype is indeed made up of three factors or domains that are somewhat different than those used in DSM-IV. Rather, domains include social-communication, inflexible language and behavior, and repetitive sensory and motor behavior. For the three factors, only a small amount of variance was accounted for by cognitive and adaptive functioning. Only inflexible language and behavior showed familial correlation between siblings." (Georgiades et al., 2007, p. 188)

The Broad Autism Phenotype (BAP) is a term that refers to those persons who have some of the characteristics, or brain differences, that are similar to those of persons with autism spectrum disorders. Usually identified in family members or relatives of persons with autism or Asperger's, the term can also refer to those persons who may be diagnosed with Pervasive Developmental Disorder, NOS, or, in other words, persons who have some autistic, or autistic-like tendencies but either have not been formally diagnosed with autism, or Asperger's syndrome, those who have learned to "mask" or "cloak and cover" these symptoms (particularly during evaluations), or those who share some of the characteristics, but not enough to obtain a formal diagnosis.

Research Gems: The Broad Autistic Phenotype

"It has previously been suggested that in a general population study a cut-off of 32 or above should be employed for correctly identifying individuals with 'autistic traits'. However, examination of the receiver operating characteristics for the total AQ suggested that for this clinic referred sample a threshold score of 26 resulted in the correct classification of the greatest numbers. At this cut off the sensitivity is 0.95, specificity 0.52, positive predictive value 0.84, and negative predictive value 0.78....and, at a cut-off of 26, its sensitivity and specificity were such that 83% of patients were correctly classified." (Woodbury-Smith et al., 2005, 35, p. 333)

The Friendship Questionnaire (FQ)

Intended ages: Adults
Testing time: 5- 10 minutes
Administration: Individual

Intended for: Self-administered

Purpose: To help identify persons with the broad autistic phenotype related to friendship variables. Suggested applications include the measurement of (a) individual differences related to levels of friendship for research, (b) change in an person's style of relating to others pre- and pos-treatment, (c) differences across special populations, such as those with AS/HFA from those with "normal" (neurotypical) profiles, and (d) specific markers that might help to identify, or screen for, various autistic phenotypes relating to friendship.

Consists of: 35 questions, extracted from the sex differences literature with the goal of identifying whether a quantitative self-report questionnaire would yield results consistent with related observational studies. The FQ uses a forced choice ("agree" vs. "disagree") format and is designed for self-administration.

Other information: "A high FQ score is achieved by respondents who report enjoying close, empathic supportive friendships; who like and are interested in people; who enjoy interaction with others for its own sake; and for whom friendships are important. In the general population women scored significantly higher than men (Study 1), the results replicating the findings from previous observational studies concerning the differences in friendships experienced by men and women. And in line with the EMB (Extreme Male Brain) theory of autism, adults with AS/HFA scored significantly lower on the FQ than unaffected males (Study 2)." (Baron-Cohen & Wheelwright, 2003, p. 513)

> ### Research Gems:
> ### Broader Phenotype Autism Symptom Scale (BPASS)
> ### vs. Social Responsiveness Scale (SRS)
>
> "The BPASS differs from the SRS in three key respects. First, whereas the SRS is completed by parents and teachers about a child with whom they are familiar, the PBASS is administered by trained clinicians experienced in assessing psychopathology and clinical interviewing….Second, whereas the SRS is a questionnaire, the BPASS requires direct observations of the adult or child….Third, the BPASS provides scores in four separate domains (social motivation, social expressiveness, communication, and flexibility), whereas the SRS yields one score reflecting degree of overall social reciprocity." (Dawson et al., 2007, p. 525)

Broader Phenotype Autism Symptom Scale (BPASS)

Intended ages: Children and Adults
Testing time: Varies
Administration: Individual

Intended for: Trained professionals

Purpose: To assess autism symptom-related traits in parents, probands, and siblings via parent interview regarding self-functioning, or the functioning of a child, in addition to direct observation of the child and parent carried out during interactions with a clinical examiner. Direct observation of nonverbal behaviors (eye contact, body language, facial expressions) and repetitive, restricted, and routine behaviors are further assessed during the clinical interview.

Consists of: Assessment of traits in four domains:
- Social motivation
- Social expressiveness
- Conversational skills
- Repetitive/restricted behaviors

Designed to separately measure autism-related traits in the four above domains (two related to social behaviors, one to communicative behavior, and one to flexibility/range of interest, each of which relate to specific autism symptoms as defined in the DSM-IV.

Research Gems:

Effectiveness of the Broader Phenotype Autism Symptom Scale (BPASS)

"It was found that, of the four BPASS trait domains, social motivation and flexibility/range of interests showed the highest heritability, suggesting that these traits are most promising for gene mapping. Moreover, these two traits also showed strong genetic correlation (.92), suggesting a shared genetic basis for the two traits. Results of this initial study suggest that the BPASS shows promise as an effective quantitative measure of autism symptom-related traits that bridges the continuum between affected and non-affected status as well as characterizing the severity of impairment of those who are affected." (Dawson et al., 2007, p. 534)

Pervasive Developmental Disorder

"Currently, the best available estimate of a 'gold standard' in the diagnosis of pervasive developmental disorders (PDDs) is the consensus opinion of at least two or more experts." (Mazefsky and Oswald, 2006, p. 533)

Research Gems: PDD-NOS vs. Autism and/or Asperger's

"No overall differences between VIQ and PIQ were found in PDD-NOS and autism. Peaks in the subtest scores on Information, Similarities, Picture Arrangement, and Mazes, and troughs in the subtest scores on Comprehension, Digit Span, and Coding were demonstrated in children with PDD-NOS. Their score on the Freedom from Distractibility factor was lower than the scores on the Verbal Comprehension factor and the Perceptual Organization factor. Children with PDD-NOS seemed to have a similar VIQ-PIQ profile as children with autism, and on the subtest level children with PDD-NOS showed some similarities to children with Asperger syndrome or autism." (de Bruin et al., 2006, p. 263)

Pervasive Developmental Disorder Behavior Inventory (PDDBI)

Intended ages: 1 year 6 months to 12 years 5 months
Testing time: Extended form: 30-45 minutes; Standard form: 20-30 minutes
Administration: Individual or group

Intended to be administered by: Parents/Caregivers, teachers, and therapists

Purpose: Assess responsiveness to intervention in children with a pervasive developmental disorder. An informant-based rating scale designed to assist in the assessment of children who have been diagnosed with a PDD. Developed to assess both problem behaviors and social communication skills as well as provide age-standardized scores for both parent and teacher ratings.

<u>Consists of</u>: Clinical-based items for assisting in diagnostic and treatment recommendations as well as assessing change over time. The Extended Rating Forms include 10 domains for both parent and teacher versions, the Standard forms both consist of 6 domains. Each domain consists of a variable number of behavioral clusters that that help to identify behaviors that contribute most to a child's score on a given domain.

Domain scores are divided into two sections:
- <u>Approach/Withdrawal Problems</u>
  - Sensory/Perceptual Approach Behaviors
  - Ritualisms/Resistance to Change
  - Social Pragmatic Problems
  - Semantic/Pragmatic Problems
  - Arousal Regulation Problems
  - Specific Fears
  - Aggressiveness

- <u>Receptive-Expressive Social Communications Abilities</u>
  - Social Approach Behaviors
  - Expressive Language
  - Learning, Memory, and Receptive Language

<u>Other information</u>: Can be used in educational settings for placement decisions, intervention planning, evaluating outcomes, and research applications. Each of the parent and teacher rating forms include extended sets of items, allowing the clinician to decide on a case-by-case basis how items are to be administered. The extended form is appropriate for assessing aspects of a child's behavior extending beyond those specifically associated with autism, while the standard form is appropriate if the primary concerns are related to autism. Clinical validity was assessed via comparison with the Autism Diagnostic Observation Interview Revised, the Autism Diagnostic Observation Schedule-Generic, and the Vineland Adaptive Functioning Level.

<u>Research Gems: The PDD Phenotype – Three Distinct Domains</u>

"The pervasive developmental disorder symptom phenotype is composed of three domains or factors: social-communication, inflexible language and behavior, and repetitive sensory and motor behavior. Each child with pervasive developmental disorder can be characterized by these dimensions, which give an informative picture of the clinical presentation and a quantitative estimate of the severity of the disability." (Georgiades et al., 2007, p. 188)

Chapter 5

Asperger's Syndrome

Introduction

The purpose of this section is to assist professionals, as well as laypersons, in recognizing a large number of signs that may signal the possibility of a high-functioning autism or Asperger's syndrome condition. Although, in general, many of these challenges are also evident across the full neurodevelopmental spectrum (i.e., everyone has some of these to different degrees) they tend to be more apparent, more pronounced, and/or present greater obstacles to daily functioning for persons throughout the Asperger's spectrum.

> "Asperger syndrome in adults presents with particular, and often subtle, difficulties, especially in communication, social relationships and interests….In some it is questionable whether they simply fall within the normal range of variation, particularly male, and whether their behaviour represents psychiatric disorder or isolated, specific developmental characteristics." (Berney, 2004, p. 347)

In all cases, the reader should keep in mind the notion of the "bell curve" (see chapter 9, "AS, HFA, and NLD – Standard Distributions"), whereas the degrees of difficulty may range anywhere from mild, through moderate, and into severe. Additionally, the severity of any of these issues will most typically be exacerbated depending on any number of factors, such as the immediately presenting situation (severity will likely increase when in stressful situations or new settings), the nature of the event (an individual seating in a clinician's office undergoing an assessment may react completely differently in a more relaxed, informal social situation), sensory triggers (noises, fluorescent lights, hunger, uncomfortable chair)—all of which will contribute to the individual's capacity to tolerate or react to presenting events. As such, the antecedent "may be," "often," "may have a tendency to," and so on, are used consistently to indicate that various factors can help to exacerbate or ameliorate these symptoms.

> "Ideally, an experienced pediatric neurologist, child psychologist or psychiatrist, or developmental psychologist should diagnose Asperger's disorder. It cannot be identified by a single test, and an interview in an office can be misleading because these children often handle themselves well in a one-on-one situation with an adult. It's important to learn about the child's history and how he or she behaviors with other children in school and at play. Screening questionnaires for teachers, parents, and children may help." (Reference: Harvard Mental Health Letter, February 2005, p. 5, www.health.harvard.edu)

Although the condition currently known as Asperger's syndrome (AS) (formally Asperger's Disorder) was initially recognized by the Austrian doctor Hans Asperger in 1944, awareness to the syndrome, and the distinction between it and autism in particular, did not surface until Lorna Wing widened attention to Hans Asperger's work through her epidemiological research of childhood psychosis in London in1981. A decade later, Uta Frith's 1991 translation of Asperger's original papers made his observations readily available to the English speaking world, influencing its inclusion in the 1994 DSM-IV as one of the autism spectrum, or pervasive developmental disorders. As of this writing, there are only two characteristics noted in the DSM-IV that serve to formally distinguish autism from AS. These are (1) delayed language development in autism but not in AS, and (2) no delay in intellectual abilities—as well as average or better cognitive capacity—in AS in comparison to autism which can range from the severe and profoundly impaired, to moderate, mild and high functioning ranges of intellectual capabilities. Although awareness of AS and autism began to grow immediately after their revised inclusions in the DSM-IV the late 1990's early 21st century attention to these conditions in the popular media, fueled by exponential numbers of educated, resourceful parents, caregivers, educators and professionals has raised both the familiarity and responsivity to these condition to unprecedented heights in an extraordinary short period of time. Regardless, actual understanding of the intricacies of these two high functioning versions of autism, and their formal identification for clinical, scientific and practical purposes, remains elusive with attempts at finding the keys to their screening, assessment and diagnosis still in their infancy. As such, the goals for this chapter in particular, and this book in general, are to assist all of us involved in the identification and eventual diagnosis of AS, as well as autism and Non-verbal Learning Disorders, through a comprehensive combination of research, presented in numerous, extensive checklists, tables, and diagrams, as well as anecdotal information gathered from years of clinical experience working with these populations.

Diagnosing AS in Adults

Problems with planning and organization may persist from childhood into adulthood. However, many learn to compensate by being extremely organized and meticulous in their planning and keeping extensive written or mental checklists.

<u>Communication</u>: Conversations are typically one-sided, long-winded, circumstantial, lecture-like, and robotic.

<u>Social relationships</u>: Relationships tend to be one-sided, distant, or absent. Personal objectivity leads to difficulties differentiating friends from acquaintances as well as developing romantic and sexual relationships.

<u>Interests</u>: Lives often described as "eccentric," with strict routines and a systematic, narrow focus on activities and/or hobbies such as stamp collecting, baseball statistics, or railway timetables. Interests typically remain circumscribed and enjoyed in solitude.

(adapted from Muscari, M. E. http://www.medscape.com/viewarticle/531750)

"The line between a normal boy's fascination with the latest computer game and a symptom of Asperger's disorder can be difficult to draw. But the more unusual and intense a restricted interest is, and the earlier in life it appears, the more it suggests Asperger's. It is also a possible diagnosis if a child seems to look through rather than at other people, if his voice seems to lack normal emotional inflections, of if he is unusually sensitive to loud sounds or the feel of clothes." (Reference: Harvard Mental Health Letter, February 2005, p. 5, www.health.harvard.edu)

JMO-7 Checklist© For Asperger's Syndrome

Topic Area 1: Social Interaction Differences

	OFTEN	SOMETIMES	RARELY
Difficulties reading or interpreting intent			
Limited ability to describe emotions			
Difficulty interpreting emotions in photographs			
Difficulty interpreting emotions in animations			
Difficulty interpreting emotions in caricatures			
A focus on detail vs. gestalt			
Difficulties interpreting social rules			
Difficulties interpreting metaphors & analogies			
Difficulties interpreting slang & cultural idioms			
Difficulties interpreting cultural expressions			
A tendency to make impulsive comments			
Appearing younger than (about 2/3) actual age			
Inability to filter thoughts or emotions			
Common use of scripted/memorized responses			
Displaying "out-of-sync" reactions to events			
Displaying exaggerated or dramatic reactions			
Appearing rude, disrespectful, or insensitive			
Displaying inappropriate emotions			
Ritualistic politeness that seems superficial			
Ritualistic politeness that seems sycophantic			
Appearing insincere, phony, or artificial			

Appearing deceitful, condescending, or rude			
Described as childlike, gullible, or naïve			
Described as candid or direct			
Described as immature or unsophisticated			
Out-of-context use of metaphors & analogies			
Out-of-context use of common phrases			
Foiled attempts at deceiving others			
Foiled attempts at impressing others			
Foiled attempts at influencing others			
Foiled attempts at manipulation			
Foiled attempts at social gossip			
Hoarding of apparently trivial possessions			
Lack of attachment to typically prized possessions			
Apparent lack of empathy toward others			
Inability to read or interpret social messages			
Inability to read or interpret nonverbal messages			
Describing emotions or feelings in logical terms			
Apparent detachment from emotional events			
A pattern of intellectualizing			
A pattern of dominating conversations			
Difficulties forming affective connections			
A preference for social isolation			
A pattern of disregarding social conventions			
A preference for "things" vs. people			

A pattern of not seeking social support			
Rarely complains about significant maladies			
Often complains about minor maladies			
Obsessive about deadlines and timeliness			
Lack of tolerance for those who break rules			
Unkempt grooming and poor hygiene habits			
Exquisite grooming and good hygiene habits			
Appears narcissistic, selfish, or conceited			
A pattern of "needing to be in control"			
A pattern of making social faux pas			
Problems with problem solving			
Difficulties with brainstorming			
Described as stubborn, inflexible, or tenacious			
Described as amenable, compliant, cooperative			
A pattern of being bullied or coerced			
A pattern of isolating self in social events			
A pattern of dogged determination			
Difficulties interpreting veiled social messages			
A pattern of taking things literally			
A pattern of explaining via concrete examples			
A pattern of making insensitive comments			
Lack of, awkward, or strained eye contact			
Apparent insincerity			
Problems reading the "bottom line"			

	OFTEN	SOMETIMES	RARELY
Common use of "out-of-context" voice tones			
Common use of "out-of-context" body language			

Topic Area 2: Adherence to Routines and Consistency

	OFTEN	SOMETIMES	RARELY
Prefers strict routines			
Prefers precise schedules			
Dislikes minor changes to routines/schedules			
Dislikes spontaneity			
Difficulties with flexible timetables			
A pattern of clutter in surroundings			
Described as pedantic, painstaking, or finicky			
Described as nitpicky, rigid, or fastidious			
Problems dealing with inflexible standards			
Adheres to routines that appear to lack purpose			
A pattern of elaborate practices			
An inclination for habitual behaviors			
Lack of imagination in personal pursuits			
Lack of imagination in professional pursuits			
A pattern of inflexible consistency			
A pattern of aligning objects in groups or rows			
A pattern of fastidious practices			
A pattern of uncompromising attitudes			
A pattern of unyielding resolve			

A pattern of fixed belief systems			
A pattern of arrangement by category, size, etc.			
Described as stubborn or obstinate			
Described as "set in own ways"			
Described as "narrow minded"			
Described as demanding or hardheaded			

Topic Area 3: Aptitudes, Skills, and Talents

	OFTEN	SOMETIMES	RARELY
Perceived as of average or above intelligence			
Test results yield average intelligence or above			
Test results indicating high aptitude for detail			
Test results indicating high sequencing aptitude			
Test results indicating high deciphering aptitude			
Test results indicating high decoding aptitude			
Test results indicating high aptitude in logic			
Test results indicating high aptitude for designs			
Test results indicating high aptitude for graphics			
Test results indicating high mechanical aptitude			
Extensive vocabulary at a young age			
Sophisticated use of language at a young age			
Early speech described as scripted			
Early speech rich with memorized scripts			
Early speech contained movie/TV dialogues			

Good and above-average ability to recall scripts/dialogues			
A pattern of using atypical phrases			
A pattern of using arcane or obscure language			
Early ability to read or decode phonetically			
Good and above avg. memory for distant events			
Good and above avg. for facts and details			
Vast knowledge of obscure characters			
Vast knowledge of exotic locales/practices			
Vast knowledge of mechanical/descriptive			
Vast knowledge of concrete facts			
Unusual logic and reasoning patterns			
A pattern of meticulous attention to detail			
Consistency in personal and work habits			
Lifelong patterns of self-learning			
An adherence to non-traditional approaches			
Unique or unusual areas of special interest			
Good and above ability for deductive reasoning			
Good and above ability for logical reasoning			
Good and above ability for mechanical reasoning			
Good and above ability for technical reasoning			
Good and above mathematical reasoning ability			
A pattern of thinking "outside the box"			
Ability to focus on the "trees" vs. "the forest"			
An ability to detach from emotional situations			

Described as intellectual or a thinker			
Described as rational or academic			
A pattern of using unusual words or phrases			
Good and above ability to systematize			
Good and above ability for categorization			
Excellent abilities in specific, "splinter" areas			
A pattern of intellectual pursuits			
A preference for reading non-fiction			
A pattern of reading manuals and texts			
Good and above ability for sequencing			
Above average ability to find embedded figures			
Good and above ability with electronics			
Good and above ability with computers			
Good and above ability with lab sciences			
Good and above ability with material sciences			
Good and above ability with graphic design			
Good and above ability with editing			
Good and above ability with spelling			
Good and above ability with reading			
Good and above ability with cataloging			
An attraction for working in research			
An attraction for working in laboratories			
An attraction for working in forensics			
A preference and aptitude for board games			

A preference and aptitude for computer games			
A preference and aptitude for video games			
A preference and aptitude for intellectual games			
A preference and aptitude for pattern recognition			
A preference and aptitude for virtual games			
A preference and aptitude for scientific hobbies			
A preference and aptitude for decoding games			
A preference and aptitude for math-related games			
A preference and aptitude for games of routine			
A preference and aptitude for detailed hobbies			
A preference and aptitude for games of focus			
A preference and aptitude for games of repetition			
A preference and aptitude for games of detail			
A preference and aptitude for scholarly games			
A preference and aptitude for information games			

Topic Area 4: Communication Skills and Eccentric Language Characteristics

	OFTEN	SOMETIMES	RARELY
A pattern of naïve communication			
A pattern of immature communication			
A pattern of shying away from physical touch			
Prefers well-delineated physical boundaries			
Awkward two-way interpersonal communication			
A pattern of one-sided communications			
Communicates through a didactic style			
Communicates through intellectualizing style			
Communicates through rational style			
Uses emotionally detached communication style			
Described as being "out-of-sync" socially			
Described as being "emotionally distant"			
Described as being "in different wave-length"			
Described as being "in a zone" or "preoccupied"			
Communication rich with "special topic" data			
Communicates as if addressing audience			
Gives impression of "needing to be in control"			
Gives impression of "being bossy"			
A pattern of unyielding communications			
Described as "difficult to get along with"			
Described as "having an attitude"			
Described as "being up to something"			

Described as "untrusting"			
Described as rude or insensitive			
Described as superficial or phony			
Described as "politically incorrect"			
Described as "inappropriate" or "offensive"			
More comfortable with literal communication			
More comfortable with unembellished messages			
More comfortable with direct interactions			
More comfortable with exact instructions			
More comfortable with factual detail exchanges			
Difficulties reading nonverbal communications			
Difficulties with abstract interactions			
Difficulties reading body gestures			
Difficulties reading facial expressions			
Difficulties interpreting fluctuating voice tones			
Difficulties reading body proximity			
Difficulties reading emotional expressions			
Difficulties interpreting subtle messages			
Difficulties making or maintaining eye contact			
Difficulties interpreting slang expressions			
Difficulties deciphering metaphors/analogies			
Difficulties understanding cultural idioms			
Difficulties understanding unwritten social rules			
Difficulties with "insight-oriented" discussions			

Difficulties with objective communications			
Difficulties embellished personal accounts			
Difficulties with fictional accounts			
Difficulties with objectivity			
Difficulties with superficial communications			
Difficulties with cursory social interactions			
Difficulties with trivial discussions			
Difficulties with frivolous "chitchat"			
Difficulties with social or office "gossip"			
More comfortable with honest communication			
More comfortable giving direct, succinct answers			
More comfortable with technical conversations			
More comfortable with formal interactions			
More comfortable over telephone than in person			
More comfortable online than over telephone			
More comfortable text messaging vs. phoning			
More comfortable with e-mails vs. phoning			
More comfortable written vs. verbal			
More comfortable with rule-based interactions			
More comfortable with well-defined relations			
More comfortable with descriptive accounts			
More comfortable with imparting information			
Described as having "a sense of entitlement"			
Described as being "aloof"			

Described as being "submissive"			
Described as having "a sense of superiority"			
Described as being "narcissistic"			
Described as being "slow"			
Described as being "unfriendly"			
Described as being "patronizing"			
Described as being "oppositional"			
Described as having a "conduct" problem			
Described as having "spoiled child syndrome"			
Described as being "passive" or "inactive"			
Described as being "lazy"			

Topic Area 5: Outward Appearance

	OFTEN	SOMETIMES	RARELY
Described as "unkempt"			
Described as "odd"			
Described as "different"			
Described as "unusual"			
Described as "clumsy"			
Described as "awkward"			
Described as quiet			
Described as respectful			
Described as mannerly			

Described as highly talkative			
Described as socially inept			
Described as "absent minded"			
Described as if "looking right through you"			
Described as if "mind is elsewhere"			
Wears "uniform" type outfits			
Wears odd clothing combinations			
Distant eye-gaze			
Sideways eye-gaze			
Peripheral eye-gaze			
Uses scripted responses and greetings			
Appears to be "in a zone"			
Appears to be "lost in thought"			
Appears distrustful			
Comes across as shifty or guarded			
Comes across as anxious or nervous			
Comes across as fidgety			
Displays tic behaviors			
Displays a pattern of repetitive movements			
Displays awkward motor movements			
Appears robotic or stiff			
Appears gawky or gangly			
Appears un-animated or emotionally detached			
Appears dys-rhythmic or uneasy			

Appears "uncomfortable in own skin"			
Described as being a follower			
Described as "always having to be in control"			
Described as stubborn			
Behaviors appear dramatized or exaggerated			
Facial gestures contradict verbal discourse			
Body language out-of-sync with verbal discourse			
Begins and ends conversations abruptly			
Lack of self-aggrandizement			
Appears to lack self-esteem			
Appears worried or depressed			
Appears hesitant or restrained			
At school, described as "weird kid, class clown"			
Social presentation is overtly formal			
Social presentation is overtly friendly			
Social presentation is textbook-like			
A pattern of imitating or mimicking others			
Laughs or smiles at inappropriate times			
Inserts long, awkward pauses in conversations			
Speaks in monotone or metric-like phrases			
Inserts seemingly endless loops in conversations			
Perseverates on particular topics			
Dominates conversations with favored themes			
Displays idiosyncratic physical gestures			

Exhibits finger twisting or nervous tapping			
Exhibits hand flapping or wringing			
Exhibits muscular jerks or spontaneous moves			
Exhibits poor body posture			

Topic Area 6: Sensory Challenges

	OFTEN	SOMETIMES	RARELY
Exhibits strong reaction to tactile stimuli			
Exhibits strong reaction to visual stimuli			
Exhibits strong reaction to auditory stimuli			
Exhibits strong reaction to olfactory stimuli			
Exhibits strong reaction to gustatory stimuli			
Exhibits strong reaction to stimuli			
Complains about certain types of fabrics			
Displays problems swallowing certain foods			
Displays problems with balance			
Displays problems with coordination			
Displays problems using tools			
Displays problems with mechanical assembly			
Appears to have a "sixth sense"			
Displays an over-sensitive startle response			
Displays an under-sensitive startle response			
Displays a strong sensitivity to certain lighting			
Displays a strong preference for certain lighting			
Displays a preference for certain colored lights			

Displays a strong sensitivity to certain sounds			
Displays a lack of sensitivity to certain sounds			
Displays a strong sensitivity to certain scents			
Displays a strong preference for certain scents			
Displays a strong sensitivity to certain foods			
Displays a strong preference for certain foods			
Displays a strong aversion to certain textures			
Displays a strong preference for certain textures			
Displays a strong aversion to certain colors			
Displays a strong preference for certain colors			
Displays an uncanny sense of direction			
Displays a delayed response to auditory warnings			
Displays an uncanny ability to distinguish scents			
Displays an uncanny ability to discern music pitch			
Displays an uncanny ability to distinguish taste			
Displays a strong aversion to off-key singing			
Displays a pattern of squinting or rubbing eyes			
Difficulty reading text printed on colored paper			
Displays an awkward gait (way of walking)			
Displays unusual thermal preferences			
Appears unaware of thermal extremes			
Displays strong sensitivity to thermal changes			
Displays lack of awareness to bumps & bruises			
Displays strong sensitivity to mild stimuli			

Appears unaware of surroundings			
Appears to notice everything in surroundings			
Displays difficulty with parallel body mechanics			
Displays difficulty with fine dexterity			
Displays difficulty with balance			
Displays difficulty with body awareness			
Displays difficulty with rhythmic movements			
Displays difficulty with motor planning			
Displays difficulty with body lateralization			
Displays difficulty with body position			
Displays difficulty with visual-spatial skills			
Displays difficulty with judging distances			
Displays "sensory-seeking" (daredevil) activities			
Displays passive approach to physical play			
Displays difficulties with daily activities (ADLs)			
Displays sleeplessness			
Displays restless behaviors			
Displays awkward running ability			
Displays awkward dancing ability			
Displays lack of focus on areas on non-interest			
Displays extreme focus on special interest areas			
Displays worries or fears about "silly" events			
Displays lack of concern over serious events			
Delves thoughtlessly into hazardous situations			

Exhibits extreme caution in harmless situations			
Displays great stamina for certain events			
Displays lack of stamina for certain events			
Displays lack of tolerance for certain events			
Displays extreme tolerance for certain events			
Displays overall lack of physical strength			
A pattern of allergies or allergic reactions			
A pattern of stomach problems			
A pattern of skin rashes or skin problems			
Displays overall lack of athletic ability			
Seems to endure thirst/hunger without complaint			
Seems to endure pain/sickness without complaint			

Topic Area 7: Executive Dys-Function Areas

	OFTEN	SOMETIMES	RARELY
Problems with organization			
Problems with structuring activities			
Problems with planning			
Problems with multitasking			
Problems with shifting attention			
Problems with making transitions			
Problems with adjusting to changing events			
Problems with accommodating change			

Problems with switching topics			
Problems with flexibility			
Problems with processing speed			
Problems with time management			
Problems with tolerating frustration			
Problems with integrating work tasks			
Problems with seeing the "big picture"			
Problems with seeing the long-term goal			
Problems with rigidity or perfectionism			
Problems with becoming easily overwhelmed			
Problems with handling stress			
Problems with returning to and completing tasks			
Problems with judging time variables			
Problems with perseverating on topics			

Research Gems: "Onset as Inclusion/Exclusion Criteria"

"Using onset as an inclusion/exclusion criteria, whereby individuals are considered for a diagnosis of AS only in the absence of early speech delay or impairments of self-help skills, adaptive behavior or curiosity about the environment, has several disadvantages. A fundamental concern is that this tends to 'tilt' the diagnosis towards autism on the basis of vague developmental phenomena, such as the developmental onset of words and phrases, rather than on the basis of true research on developmental pathways to social disabilities. This approach fails to capture important and more subtle developmental phenomena that might earmark true differences between social developmental phenotypes." (Woodbury-Smith, Klin, & Volkmar, 2005, p. 238)

Assessment Instruments Designed to Evaluate Asperger's Syndrome

The Adult Asperger Assessment (AAA)

Intended ages: Adults
Testing time: 5-10 minutes
Administration: Individual

Intended to be administered by: Self

Purpose: To diagnose adults with Asperger's Disorder (Syndrome)

Consists of: Four sections each of which describes a group of symptoms, and a fifth section that describes five key prerequisites relating to Asperger's Syndrome. The AAA incorporates all of the symptoms from the DSM-IV diagnosis of Asperger's Disorder (Syndrome) in addition to other relevant symptoms that draw from current literature and which reflect impairments of adults who present with Asperger's Disorder (Syndrome).

- Section A: Qualitative impairment in social interaction
- Section B: Restricted, repetitive, and stereotyped patterns of behavior, interests, and activities.
- Section C: Qualitative impairments in verbal or nonverbal communication
- Section D: Impairment in imagination

Other information: Properties of the AAA include:

- An electronic, data-based, computer-scorable format
- The ability to link with two screening instruments: The Autism Spectrum Quotient (AQ), and the Empathy Quotient (EQ)
- Employing a more stringent set of diagnostic criteria than the DSM-IV in order to help avoid false positives.

Prior to completion of the AAA, examinees are asked to complete the Autism Spectrum Quotient (AQ) and the Empathy Quotient (EQ) screening questionnaires.

> "Rutter et al.'s (2003) suggestion that the ADI-R algorithm cutoffs will identify most children with Asperger's disorder was supported in this study; current findings indicate that this is true with younger children as well, which expands on Gilchrist et al.'s (2001) findings with adolescents with Asperger's disorder." (Mazefsky & Oswald, 2006, p. 545).

The Childhood Asperger Syndrome Test (CAST)
(See online: http://drrobertkohn.com/forms/CAST.pdf)

Intended ages: 4 – 11 years of age
Testing time: 5–10 minutes
Administration: Individual

Intended to be administered by: Parents or caregivers

Purpose: designed to screen for Asperger's syndrome and subtler manifestations of autism spectrum conditions and help identify these conditions among primary school-aged children enrolled in mainstream academic settings.

Consists of: A thirty-seven item parent-rating scale of behavioral indicators of AS that are scored as either present or absent. A cut-off score of 15 or greater indicates the need for further, formal assessment for AS. Items comprising this scale were selected from behavioral descriptions found in ICD-10 and DSM-IV diagnostic manuals that pertained to the core features of AS, in addition to items from the ASSQ, and the Pervasive Developmental Disorders Questionnaire (PDD-Q). The CAST also contains a supplemental "Special needs section."

Other information: Can distinguish between autism spectrum disorders and typical children.

Concerns identified by the CAST include:
- Language delay, hearing, and behavior
- Autism spectrum learning disabilities
- Speech and language, autism spectrum
- Asperger's syndrome
- Behavior, hyperactivity
- Social interaction with peers
- Social development, unusual behavior
- Hearing difficulties
- Hearing difficulties, behavior

NOTE: As of early 2007, the CAST was not recommended for national or comprehensive screening in public health or educational settings due to lack of evidence for screening in the population. However, research had demonstrated good test sensitivity and specificity suggesting its usability for screening autism spectrum conditions in epidemiological studies. (Williams et al., 2006, pp. 415-427)

Research Gems: The CAST

"The CAST has previously demonstrated good accuracy for use as a screening test, with high sensitivity in studies with primary school aged children in mainstream schools….The CAST shows moderate test-retest reliability in a high scoring sample, further evidence that it is a relatively robust screening tool for epidemiological research." (Allison, 2007, p. 173)

Gilliam Asperger's Disorder Scale (GADS)

<u>Intended ages</u>: 3.0 through 22.0
<u>Testing time</u>: 5 – 10 minutes
<u>Administration</u>: Individual

<u>Intended to be administered by</u>: Parents/caregivers and professionals

<u>Purpose</u>: Norm-referenced and designed to evaluate children with unique behavioral problems who may have AS. Designed for documenting behavioral progress, targeting IEP goals, research purposes, and documenting behavioral characteristics to assist with establishing a diagnosis.

<u>Consists of</u>: Thirty-two items divided into four subscales that describe specific, observable, and measurable behaviors. Eight additional items to assist parents in contributing data about their child's development during the first three years of life.

<u>Other information</u>: Discriminative ability helps to differentiate between persons with AS and persons with autism and other behavioral disorders. Differentiates between AS, autism, other disability groups, and non-disabled peers. Correlates with the GARS. The scores are not dependent on either age or gender.

Research Gems: AS and the Rorschach

"Persons with AS were found to have higher scores on conventionality (P), self-image (3r + (2)/R), and number of primary contents (PrimCont). Also, AS subjects were more often classified as Introversive, while HFA subjects were categorized as Extratensive…AS subjects tended to be more focused or tuned into their unique internal experiences compared to the HFA group…the subgroups were differentiated on three variables (the number of popular responses, the Egocentricity Index, and the number of content categories)…in conclusion, AS patients were found to have higher scores on measures of conventionality, self-image, and on primary contents based on the Rorschach test." (Ghaziuddin, Leininger, & Tsai. 1995, pp. 315-316)

Asperger Syndrome Diagnostic Scale (ASDS)

<u>Intended ages</u>: 5 through 18
<u>Testing time</u>: 10–15 minutes
<u>Administration</u>: Individual

<u>Intended to be administered by</u>: Parents/caregivers, teachers, siblings, para-educators, speech-language pathologists, psychologists, psychiatrists, and other professionals.

<u>Purpose</u>: Provides an AS Quotient that reveals the likelihood that an individual has AS.

<u>Consists of</u>: Fifty yes/no items drawn from five specific areas of behavior: cognitive, maladaptive, language, social, and sensorimotor. Items represent behaviors symptomatic of AS.

Other information: Based on observations that help to compare an individual's performance with that of others with AS. Helps to differentiate between AS, autism, learning disabilities, ADHD, and behavior disorders. Correlates with the GARS. The scores are not dependent on age.

Research Gems: "Neuropsychological Examinations for Asperger"

"The neuropsychological examination can be an essential component of treatment planning and school programming for children with Asperger syndrome (AS)…although children with AS share many core features, their individual pathways to learning or cognitive profiles are likely to have unique characteristics. The objective of a thorough neuropsychological evaluation is to promote an understanding of the child with AS to the fullest extent possible. This includes identifying vulnerable areas as well as assessing areas of strength. Goals can then be selected to be relevant for the individual child and the child's strengths can be used to address areas of need." (Volkmar & Tsatsanis, 2005, p. 259)

Krug: Asperger's Disorder Index (KADI)

Intended ages: 6 to 21 years
Testing time: 10 – 15 minutes
Administration: Individual
Intended to be administered by: Diagnosticians

Purpose: To accurately distinguish individuals with AS from those with other forms of high-functioning autism. Also a pre-screening scale that immediately identifies persons who do not have AS.
Consists of: Validity studies that include content-descriptive validity, criterion-predictive validity, and construct-identification validity. Reliability tests included content sampling, time sampling, and inter-scorer differences.

Other information: Each item on the KADI has a weighted score, determined via statistical analysis of the item's predictive ability to differentiate AS from HFA and non-disabled populations. The scores are not dependent on either age or gender.

Research Gems: Eye Contact as an Early Marker for AS

"The aim of study 2 was to test if dyadic eye contact in infancy is intact in a child later diagnosed with Asperger syndrome. The same child's eye contact was measured at three time points (3, 6, and 9 months) over her first year of life and compared with that of age-matched controls. Although the child had low rates of eye contact at 6 months, it was within the normal range at all three points in the first year of life. We conclude that low levels of eye contact are not predictive of later development of Asperger syndrome." (Baron-Cohen, 2006, p. 351)

<u>Recommended Intelligence Tests for students with</u>
<u>ASD and spoken language</u>

In one of the most clear and comprehensive reviews of assessment strategies currently available, Dr. Stephen E. Brock—in a paper delivered at the California State University in Sacramento on January 21, 2004—suggested the following intelligence tests for children with autism spectrum disorders presenting with both spoken language and communication challenges:

Wechsler Preschool & Primary Scale of Intelligence-3rd Ed	3–7 years
Wechsler Intelligence Scale for Children-4th Ed	6–16 years
Wechsler Adult Intelligence Scale-3rd Ed	16 years & up
Wechsler Abbreviated Scale of Intelligence	6–89 years
Stanford-Binet Intelligence Scale-5th Ed	2 years–adult
Differential Ability Scales	2–17 years

(Brock, 2004, p. 32)

<u>Recommended Intelligence Tests for students with ASD</u>
<u>and communication challenges</u>

Leiter International Performance Scales-Revised	2–21 years
Bayley Scales of Infant Development-II	1–42 months
Mullen scales of Early Learning	1–60 months
Columbia Mental Maturity Scale-3rd Ed.	3.5–10 years
Merrill-Palmer Scale of Mental Tests	1–6 years
Raven's Coloured Progressive Matrices	5–11 years
Test of Nonverbal Intelligence-3rd Ed	5 years & up
Kaufman Assessment Battery for Children	2–12 years

(Brock, 2004, p. 32)

Asperger's Syndrome's Pro-Active Criteria Checklist

Persons with Asperger's syndrome typically have remarkable strengths in various vocationally viable areas that are often not actualized due to any number of reasons. Among these are poor social skills, awkward personality characteristics, poor pragmatic communication skills, perseveration on special topics, lack of early identification of their talents resulting in low self-esteem, lack of a support system, obstruction of their realization due to comorbid deficits, learned helplessness or hopelessness due to being trapped by misunderstanding systems, and many others. In effect, the following checklist of diagnostic *strengths* was designed to assist those who work with or serve these populations, in focusing on identifying their talents, strengths, gifts, and overall potential.

A.S.I. Asperger's Syndrome's Pro-Active Criteria Checklist©
John M. Ortiz, Ph.D.

Diagnostic *Strengths* — Section 1: Social Attributes

<u>Individual can be described as displaying a pattern of:</u>

	OFTEN	SOMETIMES	RARELY
Loyalty and steadfastness			
Non-judgmental attitudes			
Consistency and reliability			
Sincerity in spite of potential social backlash			
Decisive confidence in his/her own beliefs			
Determination in his/her own perspectives			
Treating everyone equally, regardless of sex, religion, race, financial or authority status, etc.			
Resoluteness in the face of opposing views			
Objectivity without personal judgment			
Avoiding gossip or spreading social rumors			
Avoiding trivial and artificial conversations			
Few, but honest and trustworthy friends			
Lack of interest in "what's in" among peers			
Keeping complaints about minor aches, pains, bruises, and health problems to self			
Not bragging about own accomplishments			
Being happy in pursuit of personal hobbies regardless of subjective judgments			
Not impeding on others' personal condition by assuming to know their thoughts or feelings			

Not giving false assurances (e.g., "I'm sure everything will be just fine!")			
Not assuming to know how others may feel at any given time			

A.S.I. Asperger's Syndrome's Pro-Active Criteria Checklist©

Diagnostic *Strengths* — Section 2: Verbal Strengths

Individual has a history of:

	OFTEN	SOMETIMES	RARELY
Early speech development			
Acquiring an extensive vocabulary			
Good to excellent rote memorization			
Sophisticated use of language			
Early reading skills			
Good to excellent spelling skills			
Liking to read aloud			
Mastery with verbal "tricks" such as rhyming, playing with pronunciations, using rare words, inventing word combinations, etc.			
Language-based humor			
Giving direct and succinct responses			
Little to no use of deceit or false representation			
Rich elaboration on areas of special interest			
Self assurance regarding how things are said			

Asperger's Syndrome's Pro-Active Criteria Checklist©

Diagnostic *Strengths* — Section 3: Intellectual Skills

Individual can be described as displaying a pattern of:

	OFTEN	SOMETIMES	RARELY
Good to excellent skills in math or science			
Good to excellent skills in art or music			
Good to excellent skills with computers			
Good to excellent skills with technology			
Good to excellent skills with mechanical toys			
Good to excellent skills with construction toys			
Figuring out how things work			
Mechanical and/or technical exploration			
Discovering and learning new knowledge			
Seeking and learning new information			
Developing expertise on specialized topics			
Having a keen eye for details			
Using unique paths to problem solving			
Off-beat originality			
Steadfast approach to structure			
Superiority in finding embedded figures/shapes			
Compiling and classifying information			
Superior focus when involves interest area			
Objective detachment from emotions			
Fair play			

Giving sincere feedback without considering social repercussions or benefits			

Asperger's Syndrome's Pro-Active Criteria Checklist©

Diagnostic *Strengths* — Section 4: Sensory Advantages

Individual can be described as displaying a pattern of:

	OFTEN	SOMETIMES	RARELY
Acute sensitivity to toxicity			
Superior olfactory ability (able to detect small differences in scents)			
Superior auditory ability (able to detect small differences in sounds)			
Superior visual ability (able to detect small differences in details, lights)			
Superior tactile ability (able to detect small differences in textures)			
Superior gustatory ability (able to detect small differences according to taste)			
Above average to superior ability to focus on special interest areas in spite of distractions			
Above average to superior ability to shut out unwanted disturbances when engaged in special interest area			
Above average to superior ability to detect small mechanical differences (weight, shapes, dimensions, distances, speed, direction)			
Affinity and sensitivity to animals			
Keen awareness of climactic conditions			

Synesthetic (cross-modal association of sensory modalities) abilities or experiences			
"Sixth-sense" type abilities			
Keen awareness of thermal fluctuations			

Chapter 6

Non-Verbal Learning Disorder/Disability (NLD)

NLD - Definition and Diagnosis

"NLD is a developmental neurobehavioral disorder characterized by a primary core deficit in the processing of nonlinguistic perceptual information. The deficit produces receptive problems in the decoding of such information and may also result in expressive problems. The diagnosis is warranted if, and only if, this deficit produces concomitant social impairments." (Palombo, 2006, p. 128)

Introduction: Non-Verbal Learning Disorder/Disability (NLD)

Typically, the first problem that people have when they hear the term "Nonverbal Learning Disorder, or Disability" (NLD) is that they immediately infer that one is referring to persons who are, well, "nonverbal," or who lack the ability to speak or communicate verbally. In actuality, and making it perhaps even more difficult to understand, is that persons with NLD are more often than not quite verbal, and tend to orient themselves through verbal and auditory means. With NLD, the main problem areas lie in nonverbal—such as visual and kinesthetic—domains. In other words, the majority of people with NLD tend to have problems when learning involves watching or doing instruction, and prefer, or are more able to learn, through verbal and auditory means. As a *pervasive syndrome*, NLD involves a number of skill deficits all of which can vary in terms of intensity and degree from person to person leading to impediments that can range from mild to profound and which invade and effect many areas of the person's life personally, socially, academically, and professionally.

Since the primary areas of strength for persons with NLD fall under auditory and verbal domains, children with this syndrome will typically develop rich, extensive vocabularies by the time they begin school, often impressing their classmates as well as adults who, based on their ability to verbalize, sophisticated word knowledge, auditory memory, and ability to focus on verbal communication, tend to think that they are often more intellectually capable than they actually are. As the child grows up, however, their NLD related deficits begin to creep in, and the verbal advantages that earlier on set them ahead and apart from their same age peers are not able to compensate for their global tapestry of deficits and shortcomings. Among others, and varying from person to person, these weaknesses typically include one or more problems in areas involving;

- Psychomotor coordination
- Emotional and affective expression and stability
- Spatial and visuo-spatial orientation
- Ability to multitask
- Ability to act spontaneously

- Ability to react to change and transitions
- Sensory related challenges
- Ability to adapt to rapid changes
- Generalizing learning and adaptive strategies
- Pragmatic language
- Nonverbal communication (picking up on facial expressions, voice tones, and body language)
- Organization skills
- Social and interpersonal skills
- Various secondary conditions such as depression, anxiety, stress, worries, fears, and others that can, and typically do, lead to an assortment of misleading labels

Just as it is with autism and Asperger's syndrome, proper, formal identification, assessment, and diagnosis of NLD is quite difficult and typically requires a diagnostician who is not only well educated and trained in recognizing the different forms and expressions of this disability, but also one who is *experienced* at recognizing, screening, and pursuing a comprehensive evaluation of the NLD syndrome while distinguishing it from similar, and/or related conditions—or confounding comorbities—such as Asperger's syndrome, Turner syndrome, de Lange syndrome, right hemisphere dysfunction, or brain damage—all of which makes a proper diagnosis quite complex. Unfortunately, such as in the case with autism and AS, children presenting with NLD are very often misdiagnosed with ADHD, Oppositional Defiant Disorder (ODD), Conduct Disorder (CD), or, simply "lazy kid syndrome" or "difficult kid disorder," as, to the untrained eye, their cluster of deficits is difficult to understand in the presence of such early promise illustrated by their initial verbal advantages.

The goal of this chapter, then, is to assist all of us who serve persons with NLD in better understanding the condition, including its strengths and deficits, so that we can better identify and either assess and diagnose, or refer the suspected individual for those services to a qualified diagnostician. Although NLD cannot be diagnosed using checklists, tables and flowcharts, both laypersons and professionals can utilize these to help screen persons who may present with NLD as well as distinguishing their symptoms from the very similar condition of AS in particular. Through early identification of their presenting symptoms persons with NLD will have a far better chance of obtaining a proper diagnostic label facilitating their access to helpful resources and services. Since, to date, the syndrome of NLD is not currently listed in any of the various formal diagnostic systems discussed in earlier chapters (DSM-IV, ICD-10) clinicians need to apprise themselves to their state by state regulations and adapt a corresponding label (such as "Other Health Impaired") that can assist the NLD child, or adult, to qualify for necessary services.

Nonverbal Learning Disability and Speech-Language Pathologists

Although children with NLD are typically highly verbal, fluent speakers who present with sophisticated vocabularies and appropriate sentence structure, they are often impaired with regard to the content, or semantics, and functional use, or pragmatics, so essential in social communications. It is these very issues that often make speech-language pathologists (SLPs) one of the initial points of referral for children across the NLD spectrum. Although children who struggle with NLD-related deficits present with problems that extend well beyond language domains, parents, caregivers, and teachers alike are most apt to pick up on NLD challenges such as understanding inferences in conversation, failure to recognize slang and metaphors, and an awkwardness in social discourse, all of which signal for intervention from SLPs.

As such, when encountering children presenting with NLD, SLPs can expect a diverse set of language, and non-language, related challenges that can vary both in number of symptoms and level of intensity. A number of related areas are briefly reviewed below.

Phonology, or the ability to blend sounds together and connect words into sound composites, is typically not a problem for children with NLD. Syntactic and morphological skills, drawing from both grammar and sentence structure, are likewise not a problem area. In short, problems with rules underlying language, word formation, and general language structure are not typically an area of difficulty.

Semantics, on the other hand, is a common problem among children with NLD. Difficulties in terms of the practical meaning of language, the interrelationships of words, phrases and sentences, and how these are used to communicate intention in conversation, and particular social settings, tend to be common challenges for these populations. In contrast to general expectations of improvement as these children become older, these semantic difficulties become ever more apparent as they enter middle and high school age and language begins to involve increasingly complex layers that include unwritten social rules, cultural slang, contextual cues, pre-adolescent and adolescent humor, irony, jargon, analogies, and similes that require more intricate, sophisticated, and faster modes of processing.

Pragmatics, as well, presents a significant problem for children with NLD, and, again, problems in this area become increasingly more problematic as they enter puberty and adolescence. Pragmatics, or the appropriate and practical use of language essential to navigating day-to-day social discourse, typically present one of the biggest hurdles that children with NLD have to cross in daily interactions at home, school, and the community.

Simple requests, responses, greetings, the rhythmic timing of back and forth discourse, beginning and ending sentences, introducing relevant conversational themes, and recognizing patterns of interest or non-interest in the midst of conversations are all problems that often lead to children with NLD becoming isolated, misjudged, alienated, and misunderstood by their peers, laypersons, and many professionals alike. The fact that these children are equipped with such rich vocabularies, and eloquent mechanical language skills, makes it very difficult for those whom they engage in attempts at communication to realize that these semantic and pragmatic language problems do not encompass poor attitudes and rude behaviors, but rather a syndrome of difficulties that create a very real set of impairments at social and interpersonal levels.

> "The speech-language pathologist would do well to evaluate semantic and pragmatic skills carefully. Semantic skills to be evaluated include nonliteral language (e.g., metaphor, irony, absurdities, and humor), and comprehension of abstract, sophisticated concepts. Some standardized tests (e.g., The Word Test-R, Test of Problem-Solving-Revised-Elementary, Test of Language Competence-Expanded Edition) that tap these high-level semantic skills are suggested." (Volden, 2004, p. 137)

Volden notes the need for "evaluating the pragmatic skills of turn-taking, sensitivity to cues provided by the interlocutor, coherence and contingency in conversation, metalinguistic skills, and rules of conversation." Nonverbal forms of communication, such as eye gaze, body proximity, underlying word meanings, body postures, and facial expressions, as well as suprasegmental aspects of communication, including inflection, speech stress and modulation, and prosody, also need to be considered. She suggests that SLPs use a "core-tool-kit," outlined by Adams (2002), a comprehensive checklist of pragmatic behaviors, parent-caregiver checklists such as the CCC (Bishop, 1998, 2003), assessing pragmatic language comprehension via tests such as the Test of Language Competence-Expanded Edition (Wigg & Secord, 1989), the Assessment of Comprehension and Expression (ACE

6-11), by Adams et al., 2001, and detailed, behavioral observations in order to gain a comprehensive picture of a child's level of impairment (Volden, 2004).

Assessment Instruments Designed to Evaluate NLD Syndrome

"Social-Emotional Learning Disability" (SELD)

Considering these myriad obstacles, Palombo (2006) suggests a distinct label, which he terms "Social-Emotional Learning Disability" (SELD) that would serve to distance us from the constraints noted above and subsequently facilitate movement toward differentiating the children with the above conditions, from those who have other, specific neurocognitive impairments. As such, Palombo proposes that NLD and AS are distinct disorders, and suggests that the SELD label, by comprising many of the developmental deficits currently defining Pervasive Developmental Disorders, and those characterizing NLD, could prove helpful in establishing necessary diagnostic guidelines.

Research Gems: NLD Assets

"The principal neuropsychological asset of children who exhibit the NLD syndrome is their capacity to deal with information delivered through the auditory modality. Virtually all other assets of such children appear to flow from this basic strength." (Tsatsanis & Rourke, 1995, p. 8)

Assets and Deficits of the NLD Syndrome
(Tsatsanis & Rourke, 1995, p. 7)

Primary Neuropsychological Assets
- Auditory Perception
- Simple Motor
- Rote Material

Primary Neuropsychological Deficits
- Tactile Perception
- Visual Perception
- Complex Psychomotor
- Novel Material

Secondary Neuropsychological Assets
- Auditory Attention
- Verbal Attention
- Tactile Attention
- Visual Attention
- Exploratory Behavior

Terciary Neuropsychological Assets
- Auditory Memory
- Verbal Memory

Terciary Neuropsychological Deficits
- Tactile Memory
- Visual Memory
- Concept Formation
- Problem Solving

Verbal Neuropsychological Assets
- Phonology
- Verbal Reception
- Verbal Repetition
- Verbal Storage
- Verbal Associations
- Verbal Output

Verbal Neuropsychological Deficits
- Oral-motor Praxis
- Prosody
- Phonology-Semantics
- Content
- Pragmatics
- Function

Research Gems: The NLD Syndrome

"The NLD syndrome would be expected to develop under any set of circumstances that interferes significantly with the functioning of right-hemisphere systems, as in the case of any general deterioration of white matter or with substantial destruction of white matter within the right hemisphere, and/or access to neuronal intercommunication with these systems, as in the case of callosal agenesis." (Tsatsanis & Rourke, 1995, p. 23)

The Three Principal Types of White Matter Fibers

a. <u>Commissural fibers</u> (right <-> left). These nerve fibers cross the midline and interconnect similar regions in the two cerebral hemispheres. There are three sets of such fibers: the corpus callosum; the anterior, posterior, and habenural commissures; and the hippocampal commissural fibers.

b. <u>Association fibers</u> (back <-> front). These are fibers that interconnect cortical regions of the same cerebral hemisphere.

c. <u>Projection fibers</u> (up <-> down). These fibers project from the diencephalon to the cerebral hemispheres and from the hemispheres to the diencephalon, the brain stem, and the spinal cord. (Tsatsanis & Rourke, 1995, p. 21)

The "V-KD ALA" Syndrome
One way of conceptualizing NLD is to think of it as a
"Visual-Kinesthetic Deficit with an Auditory Learning Advantage"

NLD: Suggested Assessment Protocols
(adapted from Rourke [2007]; www.NLD-BPROURKE.CA)

Protocol One: Ages 9 – 15 Years

Dr. Rourke strongly suggests that the following protocols be administered by a clinical neuropsychologist with extensive expertise in the assessment of children and background in Nonverbal Learning Disabilities.

Note: **Bold** lettering indicates tests or measures of relative NLD deficits.

Primary Assets and Deficits

	Simple (Rote)	Complex
Motor & Psychomotor	Grip Strength	**Maze**
	Static Steadiness	**Grooved Pegboard**
Tactile-Perceptual	Tactile Perception	**Finger-Tip Number Writing: Tactile Form Recognition**
Visual-Spatial-Organizational	Visual Perception	**W Object Assembly**
	Trail Making Test, Part A	**W Block Design**
Auditory-Perceptual	Speech-Sounds	**Sentence Memory**
	Auditory Closure	**W Digit Span Backward**

Attention/Memory

Auditory:	Visual:
W Digit Span Forward	**Target Test**
Seashore Rhythm	**Rey-Osterrieth**
Serial Digits	**Complex Figure**
Problem Solving,	**Category Test**
Hypothesis Testing,	**Wisconsin Card Sorting Test**
Symbolic Shifting, etc.	**Tactual Performance Test**

Trail Making Test, Part B

Language	W Similarities W Vocabulary	**W Comprehension** **Verbal Fluency** **(Phonemically Cued)**
Academic Achievement	WRAT Reading WRAT Spelling	**WRAT Arithmetic** **Reading Comprehension***

*Note: (Reading Comprehension is not a test, but an area of functioning that can be measured in various ways.)

Psychosocial Functioning	**Vineland Adaptive** **Behavior Scale**	**Personality Inventory** **for Children**

Protocol Two: Ages 5 – 18 Years

Motor & Psychomotor	Grip Strength Grooved Pegboard Test
Tactile-Perceptual	Tactile Perception (simple) Finger Agnosia Finger-Tip Number Writing
Visual-Spatial-Organizational	W Object Assembly subtest W Block design subtest Target Test
Auditory-Perceptual	Speech-Sounds Perception Test Auditory Closure Test W Digit Span subtest
Language I (rote)	W Similarities subtest W Vocabulary subtest
Language II (complex)	Sentence Memory Test Verbal Fluency (Phonemically Cued)
Problem Solving, Hypothesis Testing, etc.	Children's Word-Finding Test Tactual Performance Test Matching Pictures Test
Academic Achievement	WRAT Reading, Spelling, and Arithmetic subtests
Psychosocial Functioning	Vineland Adaptive Behavior Scale Personality Inventory for Children

The "SAVME" NLD Protocol

According to Liza Little (2001), the characteristics of children with NLD can be divided into five areas that she has handily categorized under the acronym SAVME. These include problems in areas involving social competencies (S), academic performance (A), visual-spatial abilities (V), motor coordination (M), and emotional functioning (E), although, as she points out, one of many difficulties in making a diagnosis is the fact that not everyone shows deficits across every domain. The SAVME characteristics are further broken down under each categorical area:

- Social
  - Problems understanding nonverbal communication
  - Problems with social judgment and interaction

- Academic
  - Problems with math, reading comprehension, and handwriting
  - Problems with organization, problem solving, higher reasoning
  - Strengths in verbal and auditory attention and memory
- Visual-Spatial
  - Problems with image and visual recall
  - Problems with spatial perception and spatial relations

- Motor
  - Poor coordination
  - Poor balance
  - Poor fine motor skills
- Emotional
  - Problems with tantrums, self-soothing, and becoming overwhelmed
  - Problems with routine changes and being in new places
  - A high incidence of depression and anxiety

Diagnosing NLD
(Adapted from, Stewart, 2002, pp. 161-163)

The following tests are recommended:
- Wechsler Intelligence Scale for Children-III
  Expect a significant difference between verbal and performance scores, with verbal over performance by 20 or more points over performance.
  Particular subtests relevant to NLD include:
  - visual-spatial organization (object assembly, block design, and coding…which appear to be consistently low for NLD students)
  - auditory perception (digit span)
  - language skills/general understanding of language (comprehension, vocabulary, and similarities)

- K-ABC (Kaufman)
Offers information on learning style and on nonverbal functioning.

- Vineland Adaptive Behavior Scale
- Personality Inventory for Children
- Rey-Ostereith Complex Figure Test
- Category Test
- Sentence Memory Test
- Trail Making (forms A and B)
- Specific subtests from neuropsychological assessments
  - Halstead Reitan
  - Grooved pegboard
  - Grip strength
  - - Tactile form recognition
  - - Fingertip number writing
  - - Target test

Educational assessment
- WIAT – all subtests
- Wide Range Achievement Test
- Test of Written Language
- Woodcock Johnson – all subtests
- Writing Sample

Occupational Therapy assessment
- sensory integration
- balance
- perceptual abilities
- motor skills

Speech Therapy assessment
- pragmatic language
- TOPL (Test of Pragmatic Language)
- Pragmatic language checklist
- CASL
- A language sample in different settings

Nonverbal and Social Skill Level
- The DANVA (Diagnostic Analysis of Nonverbal Accuracy, S. Nowicki)
- Social skill assessment by a clinical psychologist

Research Gems: NLD in Middle School

"By middle school, parents may describe the child with NLD as persecuted by peers, misunderstood by teachers, coming home with stories of social conflict at school, and having problems with work habits, organization and memory, math, writing sports, and reading comprehension. These difficulties often are mislabeled by teachers as motivational issues or issues in the home. Children with NLD can be misdiagnosed with ADD and put on medications. When the behavior doesn't change, the child can be labeled as resistant or oppositional. This is the age where secondary psychiatric symptoms may begin to appear; depression and anxiety are common." (Little, 2001, p. 118)

NLD: When is a comprehensive neuropsychological evaluation necessary?

The following list of rules has been proposed as guidelines that would indicate the need for a comprehensive neuropsychological assessment among children ages 7 – 8 (Drummond, Ahmad, and Rourke, 2005).

- Memory for visual sequences is impaired.
- Complex visual-spatial-organizational skills and speeded eye-hand coordination are impaired.
- Straightforward and/or rote verbal skills are superior to those involving more complex processing.
- Complex tactile-perceptual and problem-solving skills under novel conditions are impaired.
- Simple motor skills are superior to those involving complex eye-hand coordination, especially under speeded conditions.
- Verbal skills are superior to visual-spatial-organizational skills.
- Single-word reading is superior to mechanical arithmetic.
- Simple tactile-perceptual skills are superior to complex tactile-perceptual skills.

Research Gems: NLD and Central Coherence

"There is a difference between having gaps in one's self-narrative and having an incoherent self-narrative.… Children with NLD have the capacity to generate self-narratives, but not necessarily ones that are entirely coherent. The question, then, is whether their failure is related to an impairment in central coherence or whether they have intact central coherence but cannot generate a coherent self-narrative for other reasons. I would lean in the direction of the position that they do possess central coherence but have gaps in the information they acquire and fail to integrate the nature of their disability." (Palombo, 2006, p. 175)

The following list of rules has been proposed as guidelines that would indicate the need for a comprehensive neuropsychological assessment among children ages 9 – 15 (Pelletier, Ahmad, & Rourke, 2001).

- Simple tactile-perceptual skills are superior to complex tactile-perceptual skills.
- Single-word reading is superior to mechanical arithmetic.
- Straightforward and/or rote verbal skills are superior to those involving more complex processing.
- Complex visual-spatial-organization skills and speeded eye-hand coordination are impaired.
- Memory for visual sequences is impaired.
- Simple motor skills are superior to those involving complex eye-hand coordination, especially under speeded conditions.
- Complex tactile-perceptual and problem-solving skills under novel conditions are impaired.
- Verbal skills are superior to visual-spatial-organizational skills.

Research Gems: NLD and Theory of Mind

"What appears as a deficit in a theory of mind may be secondary to the child's concrete interpretation of the verbal exchanges.…Children with NLD do have the capacity for second-order mental representation but may not have the pragmatic language skills to understand what is being asked of them.…Regarding pretend or imaginative play, the anecdotal clinical data indicated that children with NLD are quite capable of dealing with metarepresentations of reality." (Palombo, 2006, p. 78)

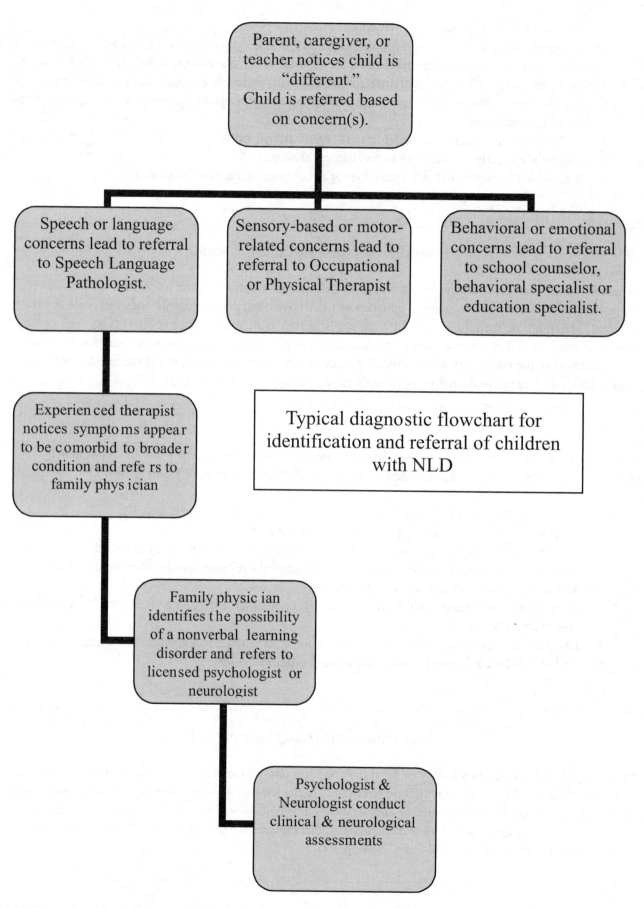

Parent, caregiver, or teacher notices child is "different."
Child is referred based on concern(s).

Speech or language concerns lead to referral to Speech Language Pathologist.

Sensory-based or motor-related concerns lead to referral to Occupational or Physical Therapist

Behavioral or emotional concerns lead to referral to school counselor, behavioral specialist or education specialist.

Experienced therapist notices symptoms appear to be comorbid to broader condition and refers to family physician

Typical diagnostic flowchart for identification and referral of children with NLD

Family physician identifies the possibility of a nonverbal learning disorder and refers to licensed psychologist or neurologist

Psychologist & Neurologist conduct clinical & neurological assessments

Assessment Instruments Recommended for Screening and Evaluating Typical NLD Characteristics

Although, to date, there are no assessment tools specifically aimed at evaluating nonverbal learning disorders, the following standardized measures are recommended as some that are designed to measure various deficits and characteristics that contribute toward different aspects NLD.

Wide Range Assessment of Memory and Learning, 2nd Edition (WRAML2)

Intended ages: Ages 5 – 90
Testing time: Less than one hour
Administration: Individual

Intended for: Trained Professionals

Purpose: To assess an individual's *memory functioning* and acquisition of new learning skills.

Consists of: A core battery composed of:
- Two Verbal, two Visual, and two Attention/Concentration subtests
- Yields a Verbal Memory Index, Visual Memory Index, and an Attention/Concentration Index
- Yields a General Memory Index
- New version includes a Working Memory Index comprised of a Symbolic Working Memory and Verbal Working Memory subtests
- New version also includes four new recognition subtests:
  - Design Recognition
  - Picture Recognition
  - Verbal Recognition
  - Story Memory Recognition

Other information: The battery includes a Screening Battery component, which consists of four subtests from the Core Battery and provides an overview of memory functioning. Available from Psychological Assessment Resources.–

The Beery-Buktenica Developmental Test of Visual-Motor Integration, 5th Edition (BEERY-VMI)

Intended ages: Ages 2 – 18
Testing time: Short Format and Full Format tests: 10 – 15 minutes each
Supplemental Visual Perception Test and Motor Coordination tests: 5 minutes each
Administration: Individual – long format; Individual or groups – Short format

Intended for: Psychologists, learning disability specialists, school counselors, teachers, and other professionals.

Purpose: To screen for *visual-motor deficits* that can lead to learning, neuropsychological, and behavior problems.

Consists of: With age-specific norms from birth through age 6, the 5th edition manual yields information on areas designed to help parents to better understand a child's current developmental levels.

These include:
- Basic gross motor
- Fine motor
- Visual
- Visual-fine motor developmental "stepping stones"

Other information: The Beery VMI series provides supplemental Visual Perception and Motor Coordination tests, designed to be administered after screening results indicate the needed for further testing, helping to compare a person's test results with relatively pure visual and motor performances. Culture-free, nonverbal assessment, the Beery VMI is appropriate for persons of diverse environmental, educational, and linguistic backgrounds. Available from Pearson Assessments.

Wechsler Individual Achievement Test – Second Edition (WIAT-II)

Intended ages: Ages 4 – 85 years/PreK–16
Testing time: PreK–K: 45 minutes; Grades 1–6: 90 minutes; Grades 7–16: 1 &1/2 – 2 hours
Administration: Individual

Intended for: Trained professionals

Purpose: Described as a *comprehensive and flexible assessment* instrument designed to yield information on achievement skills, learning disability, special education placements, curriculum planning, and clinical appraisal for preschool children through adults.

Consists of:
- Three measures of reading:
  - o Word Reading
  - o Reading Comprehension
  - o Pseudoword Decoding
- Two measures of numerical attainment:
  - o Numerical Operations
  - o Mathematical Reasoning
- Two measures of written language attainment:
  - o Spelling
  - o Written Expression
- Two measures of oral language attainment:
  - o Listening Comprehension
  - o Oral Expression

Other information: Described as the only achievement battery empirically linked with the Wechsler Intelligence Scale for Children-4th Edition; The Wechsler Preschool and Primary Scale of Intelligence-3rd Edition, and the Wechsler Adult Intelligence Scale-3rd Edition. The WIAT-II is further described as practical for schools, clinics, private practices, and residential treatment facilities in terms of assisting with diagnosis, eligibility, placement, and decisions regarding interventions. Available through Harcourt Assessment.

The Booklet Category Test

Intended ages: Adolescents and Adults.
Testing time: 30–60 minutes
Administration: Individual
Intended for: Trained professionals

Purpose: To help predict *general neurological dysfunction* and help determine a person's ability to learn from both negative and positive experiences as a basis for modifying one's subsequent behaviors.

Consists of: A booklet version of the Category Test originally introduced by Hastead and Reitan as a subtest within the Halstead-Reitan Neuropsychological Battery. It is designed to test Concept Formation and Abstract Reasoning skills, and to help distinguish individuals aged 15 and older with brain damage from normal individuals.

The BCT is composed of two portable easel binders containing 2208 Category Test designs, eliminating the need for the more expensive, non-portable format that also requires projection equipment.

Other information: The booklet version is described as a functional adaptation of the Halstead-Reitan version that helps to reduce equipment cost as well as increase the test's portability. The publisher (Psychological Assessment Resources, Inc.) describes the BCT as the "most sensitive indicator of brain dysfunction in the Halstead-Reitan Neuropsychological Test Battery," and "nearly as valid as the complete battery in detecting brain damage." Available from Psychological Assessment Resources.

Benson Visual Retention Test – Fifth Edition

Intended ages: 8 years to adult
Testing time: 15 – 20 minutes to administer and 5 minutes to score
Administration: Individual

Intended to be administered by: Trained professionals

Purpose: To assess visual perception, memory, and visuoconstructive abilities

Consists of: Ten designs presented one-by-one requiring the examinee to reproduce them. Contains three alternate, equivalent forms.

Other information: Described as containing proven sensitivity to populations presenting with:

- Reading and nonverbal learning disabilities
- Traumatic brain injury
- Attention Deficit Disorder
- Alzheimer's and other forms of dementia

The Hayling and Brixton Tests

Intended ages: 18 – 80 years
Testing time: 15 minutes
Administration: Individuals

Intended to be administered by: Trained professionals

Purpose: To obtain a clinical assessment of executive functioning from individuals presenting with reading, visual perception, or movement problems.

Consists of:
- The Hayling Sentence Completion Test: Entirely spoken, it yields three different measures of executive functioning that can be considered separately or combined into an overall score.
- The Brixton Spatial Anticipation Test: Two sets of 15 sentences, each missing the last word, which yields measures of response initiation speed, response suppression ability, and thinking time.

Other information: Designed for quick and simple administration to minimize testee resistance, the tests can be given individually or in combination depending on testing time.

Research Gems: NLD in High School

"If the NLD teen reaches high school without any intervention or remediation, a typical scenario is to find a worsening of symptoms as the child attempts to negotiate even more complicated social interactions and situations. Children may drop out of school as a coping strategy. They may enter the psychiatric system for depression, anxiety, or acting-out behaviors as they fail to succeed or achieve normal developmental and academic adolescent milestones….Diagnosis cannot be made from a checklist alone, but it can be the first step to establish a problem in need of further evaluation." (Little, 2001, p. 118)

(See Noverbal Learning Disability - JMO:NLD-8–Checklist©, chapter 22, "Red Flags.")

NLD as a "Social Imperception"

A major authority in the study of NLD, Dr. Joseph Palombo, suggests an integration of some of the major theories relevant to this condition into a coherent system of related domains. As such, he suggests three: (1) the complex and nonlinguistic perceptual function domain, (2) the attentional/executive functions domain, and (3) the social cognition domain.

The first domain pertains to functions related to visual-perceptual/sequential information-processing functions as well as visual-spatial organizational functions. The second concerns those with neuropsychological deficits in attention and executive function areas.

The third involves right hemisphere functions of paralinguistic or nonverbal communication and the perception of affective states. In addition to these domains, Palombo suggests the coexistence of nonlinguistic perceptual deficits and the social impairments associated with those conditions—which he refers to as *social imperceptions*—constitute the necessary and defining features that result in NLD (Palombo, 2006, p. 126).

In effect, Dr. Palombo posits that although persons with NLD are alternatively challenged anywhere in the range from mild to moderately severe impairments in terms of reciprocal social interactions, they retain the ability for theory of mind. Relationship problems, he suggests, are a result of difficulties with interpreting nonverbals, and adds that even though moderately significant problems in emotional functioning tend to be present in these populations, those are not disabling enough to eliminate the possibility of successful, intimate social relationships.

Palombo further suggests that each of the above domains plays contributing parts to what results in different sets of behaviorally manifested issues. As noted above, problems with complex and nonlinguistic perception result in the construct of social imperception. The cluster of challenges posed by deficits in attentional and executive function domains lead to social problems which are, in fact, secondary to the complex of obstacles posed by those spheres of disorder. Likewise, problems experienced by persons with NLD in the area of social cognition in turn results in impairments related to reciprocal social interactions, communication, and emotional functioning all of which can help determine the extent in which NLD symptoms are manifested as well as that individual's self identify.

Palombo's Four Subtypes of NLD

Drawing from the many different theories, domains of influence, and neurobiological, social, and intrapersonal permutations that contribute to the syndrome of NLD, Palombo (2006) suggests that the condition should actually be divided up into four subtypes.

NLD Subtype I refers to those children whose primary neuropsychological challenge involves the processing of complex and nonlinguistic perceptual tasks and whose concomitant problems within this domain leads to social relationship problems. Subtype I, then, refers to children who exhibit problems in terms of neuropsychological deficits and social impairments. Neuropsychological deficits would involve perceptual consequences occurring in some of the areas including auditory, visual discrimination, visual-spatial, visual-motor, memory for complex spatial relations, and time perception capabilities. Social impairments, or his social imperceptions construct, would involve obstructions related to social communication that would involve difficulties in nonverbal communication (auditory perception, visual discrimination, visual-spatial processing, and visual-motor functions) and reciprocal social interaction.

The second NLD Subtype, Subtype II, would refer to children who meet the criteria for NLD Subtype I, in addition to neuropsychological deficits related to his second proposed domain, that involving attention, executive function, and psychomotor problems. As often seen in clinical practice, neuropsychological deficits in the area of attention—involving inattention, impulsivity, or hyperactivity issues—can lead to many of these children receiving a diagnosis of ADHD. Whether this impression meets the formal criteria for the latter condition or needs to be relegated to a comorbid condition depends on additional diagnostic factors. Likewise, difficulties resulting from executive dysfunction, as would be expected, would tend to both exacerbate the condition and add various layers to the diagnostic impression.

NLD Subtype III would pertain to children who, again, would meet the criteria for NLD subtype I, in addition to being challenged with social cognition impairments, including problems with reciprocal social interactions, social (pragmatic and nonverbal language) communication, and affective functioning. These children, as Palombo points out, would struggle not only with an awareness of social rules, but with cognitively deciding the socially selective things to include, or leave out, during typical conversations.

The most severe of the four subtypes, NLD Subtype IV, would comprise those children who meet Subtype II criteria, as well as struggling with the social cognition impairments that characterize the children who fall under Subtype III, therefore including all of the issues presented by each of the first three subtypes.

Popular Misconceptions About NLD

(adapted from Rourke, http://www.nld-bprourke.ca/NLDMisconceptions.html)

Persons with NLD…
- are manipulative or lazy
- have very well developed language of excellent quality
- exhibit excellent reading skills
- are simply deficient in mechanical arithmetic
- will all exhibit at least a 10-point discrepancy between Verbal (higher) over Performance (lower) IQ
- are exceptionally rare, too rare to warrant practical diagnostic consideration
- will mostly grow out of it
- should be left alone as they will likely grown into their social selves
- can be easily "treated" by setting a system of discipline with clear rewards and consequences
- say rude and disrespectful things because they want attention
- can be easily diagnosed with a simple checklist or rating scale

(See Characteristics Comparing/Differentiating NLD from AS as detailed in Byron Rourke's system – Appendix B.)

Chapter 7

Asperger's Syndrome vs. High-Functioning Autism

Research Gems: The Need for AS as a Separate Dx Category from Autism

"Compared to high-functioning autistic children of equivalent IQ, Asperger's syndrome children have better social and language skills....For purposes of recognition and research, Asperger's syndrome should be considered a separate entity. This ensures that such children are identified for treatment and included in research protocols. This, in itself, would be of considerable benefit, even if it is acknowledged that Aspeger's syndrome and autism probably represent different end points of a similar pathogenic mechanism. Asperger's syndrome represents a type of developmental disability that profoundly limits a child's participation in the process of growing up." (Szatmari, 1991, p. 81)

"The different diagnostic systems have provided different sets of criteria but have not resolved the key issue dominating research on AS since the early 1970's, namely, its validity status relative to autism.... There is a need to go beyond the current sterile impasse fueling so much of the current classification debate, which is still based on rather arbitrary decisions and vague semantics rather than empirical validation of operationalized definitions that reflect more sophisticated developmental constructs." (Volkmar et al., 2005, p. 95)

Research Gems: Diagnosis Notwithstanding

"Regardless of the diagnostic category, a significant number of children and adults with social communication learning disability require intervention." (Freeman, Cronin, & Candela, 2002, p. 145)

Introduction: Asperger's Syndrome (AS) vs. High Functioning Autism (HFA)

The quest for the similarities and differences between AS and high-functioning autism (HFA) has ridden the crest of the autism spectrum wave since long before 1994 when AS was initially introduced into the DSM-IV.

Although the text revised DSMIV-TR, published in 2000, does not include any revisions to the diagnostic criteria for AS, it does include updated information based on more recently acquired empirical data. Among these the updated edition includes variable cognitive functioning, overactive behavior, mild motor clumsiness or awkwardness, inattention, and associations with secondary emotional issues (anxiety, depression). Rather than the sense of social or emotional indifference typical in autism, those with AS are more apt to display eccentric and egocentric characteristics. The revised version also indicates that significant language delays may not necessarily be evident while deficits in subtle social communication features may be indicated. Preoccupations involving particular topics on which the AS person gathers remarkable amounts of fact-based information, limited self-monitoring capabilities, excessive verbosity, pragmatic communication issues, unusual behaviors during early development, and deficits with social norms and nonverbal cues are further indicated. This text revision, at least, seems to be a step in the right direction.

In 1998, Gillberg and Ehlers identified four primary, controversial areas that needed to be addressed regarding the potential differences between Asperger's syndrome as a distinct diagnostic category from autism (http://www.nas. org.uk, "What is high-functioning autism and Asperger syndrome?"). These were:

(1) Level of cognitive functioning
(2) Motor skills
(3) Language development
(4) Age of onset

Ten years have passed since this proposition brought forth by Gillberg and Ehlers, and, although much effort has been exerted in attempts to find differences that may help to distinguish these two conditions over that period of time, the same controversies continue to confound both clinicians and researchers.

In general, findings over the past two decades tend to highlight the following differences in the above areas of controversy.

Cognitive functioning. Whereas children with AS display high cognitive functioning abilities, those with high-functioning autism fall anywhere along the cognitive spectrum, ranging from profound intellectual impairments to IQs well into the gifted range.

Motor skills. Whereas most children with AS tend to struggle with poor fine and gross motor coordination, the majority of those with autism tend to exhibit average to, at times, better than average motor skills.

> "While many children with Asperger's syndrome acquire an impressive vocabulary, children with autism tend to find their strengths in motor skills and manipulating objects…the participants with a diagnosis of autism performed well on tasks requiring visual-spatial perception—such as puzzle-solving—or motor skills. Those with Asperger's syndrome tended to show deficits in these areas, though they outperformed the participants with autism on vocabulary, auditory perception and verbal memory tasks." (Dingfelder, 2004, p. 49)

<u>Language development</u>. For a child to be diagnosed with AS, spoken language development must be in the neurotypical ("normal") range. Nonetheless, these children typically exhibit idiosyncrasies and pedantic language peculiarities that have earned them the title "little professors." Children with autism, on the other hand, tend to struggle with language development and, even those who fall in the high-functioning range typically exhibit significant language delay. In fact, the use of pedantic speech at an early age has even been suggested as a potential diagnostic feature of AS (Ghaziuddin & Gerstein, 1996, p. 593).

> "These are kids who talk before they walk, Volkmar says, language is their lifeline." (Dingfelder, 2004, p. 49)

<u>Age of onset</u>. Although children with autism are typically diagnosed around the age of 18 (and sometimes as early as 12) months via a number of delayed developmental milestones, those with AS are most often not diagnosed until they enter kindergarten or first grade. In effect, it is not until these children must begin to use social skills in a peer-related social environment that most of their deficits and challenges become apparent.

> "Results suggest that pedantic speech is common in AS and may help differentiate AS from high-functioning autism." (Ghaziuddin & Gerstein, 1996, p. 585)

> "Thus the same child may be diagnosed as having HFA in one locality but having Asperger's Syndrome in another." (Atwood, 1998, p. 151)

Although an enormous amount of work, in terms of research and funding, has gone toward the deciphering of distinctions between these two, overlapping conditions, the verdict is still out. In the meantime, clinicians and therapists who serve these populations, and researchers who conduct scientific investigations, continue to keep up with the latest findings in order to identify how to best understand, and serve, these populations. Some of the difficulties in finding a verifiable distinction between the two conditions include the definition of AS, inconsistent criteria for assigning AS vs. HFA to group studies, overlapping criteria and circularity between autism and AS, comparison groups, and different sets of diagnostic criteria that are used for AS, as well as HFA. In addition, many authors and clinicians refer to AS interchangeably as "autism spectrum disorder, pervasive developmental disorder, high-functioning autism, high-IQ autism, more-able, or mild autism."

Research Gems: HFA's Local Processing Bias Superiority

"Individuals with autism evidence a local bias in processing visual hierarchical stimuli in a divided attention condition, construct a graphic figure beginning with local features and are less sensitive to the global 'impossibility' of a figure, detect a geometric figure embedded in a larger one with greater facility than a comparison group, and detect the modification of a single note in a melody more easily than typical participants." (Gagnon et al., 2004, p. 687)

Examining the AS vs. HFA fray Volkmar and colleagues (2005) reviewed three separate approaches that suggest further attempts at clarifying the essence of these diagnostic classifications.

AS vs. HFA: Three suggested approaches (Volkmar et al., 2005, pp. 95-96)

The Spectrum Approach
- equates AS with HFA
- all early-onset and chronic social vulnerabilities share some common factors
- research time is best spent in quantifying these factors into dimensions composing the autism spectrum

The Early Language Approach
- distinguishes AS from HFA
- AS = a child who achieves single words by age two, and phrase speech by age three
- Autism = the child does not meet the above criteria for AS

The Unique Features Approach

- emphasizes the AS features highlighted by Asperger and other authors
- distinguishes between children who isolate themselves (autism) and those who seek others (social motivation), but in an awkward manner (AS)
- children with delayed, echolalic, or stereotyped language (autism) and those with adequate to precocious language, but have pragmatic language problems (AS)
- the presence of one-sided verbosity (AS)
- the presence of factual, circumscribed interests that interfere with learning and reciprocal conversation (AS)

Research Gems: Autism and Math Skills

"The students in Cambridge University did not differ from the randomly selected control group, but scientists (including mathematicians) scored significantly higher than both humanities and social sciences students, confirming an earlier study that autistic conditions are associated with scientific skills. Within the sciences, mathematicians scored highest….The Mathematics Olympiad winner (scored) significantly higher than the male Cambridge humanities students, 6% of the student sample scored 32+ on the AQ. On interview, 11 out of 11 of these met 3 or more DSM-IV criteria for AS/HFA, and all were studying sciences mathematics, and 7 of the 11 met threshold on these criteria." (Baron-Cohen et al., 2001, p. 2)

"HFA vs. AS Checklist – '08"©
John M. Ortiz, Ph.D.

Research Gems: AS vs. HFA – Inadequacy of Current Diagnostic Systems

"Clinicians appear to be diagnosing AsD (Asperger's Disorder) and AD (Autistic Disorder) on the basis of published research and case study accounts. The findings question whether DSM-IV and ICD-10 criteria adequately describe the AsD individual, particularly in the communication domain." (Eisenmajer et al., 1996, p. 1523)

The ongoing controversy regarding the "different entities vs. overlaps vs. need for more data" attempts at differentiating or equating AS and HFA is further confounded by familial observations and case histories (where many parents share anecdotal evidence citing distinctions between the two conditions) vs. clinical experiences (where practicing clinicians cite overlaps as well as similarities and differences) vs. laboratory-controlled research findings (where "the need for more data" is typically indicated). The battle, as they say, rages on.

In effect, the following "HFA vs. AS Checklist – '07" draws from a comprehensive review of current scientific research, familial case histories, and anecdotal clinical observations in an attempt to facilitate making a distinction between persons with the characteristics that define high-functioning autism vs. those with Asperger's Syndrome.

It is divided into four subsections including:

- Section 1: Developmental Characteristics
- Section 2: Clinical Characteristics
- Section 3: Individual test scores – Wechsler
- Section 4: Individual test scores – Other Tests

"HFA vs. AS Checklist – '08"©

Section 1: Developmental Characteristics

Code:

R = Rarely   AS = Asperger's Syndrome
S = Sometimes   HFA = High-Functioning Autism
O = Often

Nothing is Always

Developmental Characteristics	HFA			/	AS		
	R	S	O	/	R	S	O
Single words prior to age two	X						X
Simple phrases prior to age three	X						X
Social isolation by choice			X		X		
Seek social engagement-socially motivated	X						X
Echolalic language			X			X	
One-sided verbosity	X						X
Circumscribed interests		X					X
Preoccupation with a favorite subject/topic	X						X
Precocious language	X						X
Orient to environment through objects			X				
Orient to environment through data							X
Not typically identifiable until preschool	X						X
Kinesthetic/Visual learning preference			X			X	
Visual/Kinesthetic learning preference		X					X
Delayed general milestones[1]			X			X	
Poor fine motor skills[2]	X						X
Poor visual motor integration skills[2]	X						X
Poor spatial perception skills[2]	X					X	

Poor nonverbal concept formation[2]	X				X	
Poor gross motor skills[2]		X			X	
Poor visual memory[2]		X			X	
Good or better articulation[2]	X					X
Good or better verbal output[2]	X					X
Good or better vocabulary[2]	X					X
Good or better verbal memory[2]	X					X
Average to good personal prognosis*	X+				X+	
Average to good professional prognosis*	X+				X+	
Problems making direct eye contact			X		X	

Superscript references refer to findings described in articles:

[1] Ozonoff, South & Miller, 2000.

[2] Klin et al., 1995.

Non-superscript references: Dingfelder, 2004; Howlin et al., 1998; Klin et al., 1995; Lotspeich et al., 2004; Lovecky, 2004; Ozonoff, South & Miller, 2000; Schopler et al., 1992; Szatmari et al., 2000; Volkmar et al., 2005; Walker et al., 2004; author's clinical sample (N = > 900; 1994-2007)

* The degree of a positive prognosis will depend on a number of developmental variables including early identification of strengths and deficits, early identification of preferred learning style(s), parental/caregiver involvement and nurturing, educational and clinical support systems, extent of sensory challenges, community and ecological support networks, nurturing of special interest topics and/or savant-splinter skill areas, vocational counseling and proper career placement, identification and so on.

"HFA vs. AS Checklist – '08"©

Section 2: Clinical Characteristics

Code:

    R = Rarely   AS = Asperger's Syndrome

    S = Sometimes   HFA = High-Functioning Autism

    O = Often

Clinical Characteristics	HFA			/	AS		
	R	S	O		R	S	O
Cognitive delays during early childhood			X		X		
Identifiable as early as 18 months			X		X		
High percentage of parent with AS/BAP*		X					X
(Mis)diagnosed with ADHD	X						X
(Mis)diagnosed with OCD	X						X
(Mis)diagnosed with ODD		X					X
(Mis)diagnosed with Conduct Disorder		X					X
(Mis)diagnosed with MR			X		X		
(Mis)diagnosed with Schizoid Disorder	X					X	
(Mis)diagnosed with Schizophrenia	X					X	
(Mis)diagnosed with Psychotic Disorder	X					X	
Mis-Dx w/ Semantic-Pragmatic Lang. Dis.		X					X
(Mis)diagnosed with Selective Mutism			X			X	
(Mis)diagnosed with Reactive Attach Dis.	X						X
(Mis)diagnosed with Central Auditory Processing Disorder			X			X	
(Mis)diagnosed w/ Social Anxiety Disorder	X						X
(Mis)diagnosed w/ Somatoform Disorder	X					X+	
(Mis)diagnosed w/ Personality Disorders	X						X
(Mis)diagnosed w/ Narcissistic Pers. Dis.	X						X

(Mis)diagnosed w/ Multiple Pers. Dis.	X				X	
(Mis)diagnosed w/ PTSD			X		X	
(Mis)diagnosed w/ Voyeurism	X				X+	
(Mis)diagnosed w/ Relational Problem(s)		X				X
(Mis)diagnosed w/ Panic Attack/Disorder			X		X	
(Mis)diagnosed w/ Acculturation Problem			X		X	
(Mis)diagnosed w/ Separation Anxiety Dis.			X		X	
(Mis)diagnosed w/ Sleep Disorders		X				X
(Mis)diagnosed with Stereotypic Movement Disorder			X	X		
(Mis)diagnosed with Vocal Tic Disorders		X				X
(Mis)diagnosed with Communication Dis.			X		X+	
Dually diagnosed with ADHD	X					X
Dually diagnosed with OCD	X					X
Dually diagnosed with ODD		X				X
Dually diagnosed with Conduct Disorder		X				X
Dually diagnosed with Nonverbal Learning Disability/Disorder	X					X
Dually diagnosed with Tic Disorders	X					X
Dually diagnosed with Tourette's Dis.	X					X
Dually diagnosed with Depression	X					X
Dually diagnosed with Anxiety	X					X
Dually diagnosed with Bi-Polar Disorder	X					X
Dually diagnosed with Developmental Coordination Disorder	X					X
Dually diagnosed with Hyperlexia	X					X
High suicidal ideation during adolescence	X				X	

Dually diagnosed with Giftedness		X					X
Dually diagnosed with Synaesthesia		X					X
Presence of savant-splinter skills		X+					X
Learning Disability - General[1]			X			X	
Learning Disability - General Math[1]			X			X	
Learning Disability - General Reading[1]			X		X		
Learning Disability - Specific[1]	X					X	
Learning Disability - Specific Reading[1]	X				X+		
Learning Disability - Specific Math[1]	X					X+	
Suffer from seizures			X		X		
Suffer from gastrointestinal problems			X			X	
Suffer from multiple sensory challenges			X			X	
Verbal IQ > Performance IQ	X						X
First Level Theory of Mind Deficits			X		X		
Second Level Theory of Mind Deficits			X			X	
Cerebral gray matter volume enlarged[1]			X			X	
Negative correlation between cerebral gray matter volume and performance IQ[1]			X			X	
Positive correlation between cerebral white matter volume and performance IQ[1]		X					X
Severity of early symptoms[2]			X		X		
Primary deficits linked to left hemisphere dysfunction[3]			X		X		
Primary deficits linked to right hemisphere dysfunction[3]	X						X
Good to superior abstract thinking ability	X						X

*BAP = Broader Autistic Phenotype

"HFA vs. AS Checklist – '08"©

Section 3: Individual test scores – Wechsler

Code:

    H = Will tend to score high on this subtest/test

    S = Could go either way—high, low, or average—on this subtest/test

    L = Will tend to score low on this subtest/test

Individual test scores: Wechsler	HFA L	HFA S	HFA H	/	AS L	AS S	AS H
Full-scale IQ		X					X
Verbal IQ	X						X
Performance IQ			X		X		
Information	X						X
Similarities		X				X	
Arithmetic		X+				X+	
Vocabulary	X						X
Comprehension	X					X	
Digit Span		X+				X+	
Picture completion		X+				X+	
Coding		X+			X		
Picture arrangement		X+				X+	
Block design			X+			X+	
Object assembly			X+			X+	
Social interaction	X					X	
Imitation			X		X		
Visual responsiveness			X		X		
Auditory responsiveness			X		X		

	L	S	H	/	L	S	H
Core autistic items	X						X
Verbal functioning	X						X
Processing speed			X		X		
Distractibility		X					X

"HFA vs. AS Checklist – '08"©

<u>Section 4: Individual test scores – Other tests</u>

<u>Code</u>:

H = Will tend to score high on this subtest/test

S = Could go either way—high, low, or average—on this subtest/test

L = Will tend to score low on this subtest/test

Individual test scores: Other tests	**HFA**			/	**AS**		
	L	**S**	**H**		**L**	**S**	**H**
Ages 6 – 8:							
TOLD Grammatical Understanding[1]	X						X
TOLD Grammatical Comprehension[1]	X						X
Peabody Picture Vocabulary Test[1]	X						X
Test of Auditory Comprehension[1]	X						X
Teacher Vineland-Communication[1]	X						X
McCarthy Oral Vocabulary[1]	X						X
Woodcock-Word Identification[1]		X					X
Ages 9 – 13							
TOLD Grammatical Understanding[1]	X						X
TOLD Grammatical Comprehension[1]	X						X
Peabody Picture Vocabulary Test[1]		X					X
Test of Auditory Comprehension[1]	X						X

Teacher Vineland-Communication[1]	X					X
WRAT-R2 Arithmetic[1]	X					X+
Woodcock-Passage Comprehension[1]	X					X+
Woodcock-Word Comprehension[1]	X					X+
Woodcock-Word Identification[1]	X					X+
Woodcock-Word Attack[1]						X+

[1]Prior, Reitzel, & Szatmari, 2003.

Above ratings are based on AVERAGES from findings across various current scientific studies (see below) based on various population samples. The statistical averages, based on cluster analysis and comparative approaches, were derived from peer-referenced, published journal articles, clinical texts, current (2005-2007) conference presentations by leading researchers, and this author's clinical sample (N = > 900; 1994-2007). Information was further substantiated by anecdotal data based on family case histories and collaborative information. Individual cases of those with HFA or AS will differ widely depending on each person's splinter, or savant-like skills in any number of areas (math, mechanical assembly, extraordinary memory, art). Subtests where savant-like "splinter" skills tend to make significant differences in individual cases are marked by "+". Individual test results will also be greatly affected by any number of environmental, sensory, interpersonal, medical, or other variables all of which need to be considered on a case by case basis.

(References: Cohen, 1988; Ehlers et al., 1997; Freeman, 1985; Ghaziuddin et al., 2004; Koyama et al., 2007; Kurita, 1997; Manjiviona and& Pryor, 1999; Siegel, Minshew, and& Goldstein, 1996; Szatmari et al., 1990.)

Research Gems: AS vs. HFA – Socialization Scores

"Children with Asperger's Syndrome had higher socialization scores than those with autism (75.6 vs. 61.8, $p = 0.0001$). Covariate analysis showed that differences in socialization at follow up were explained by differences at initial assessment ($p < 0.0001$). The diagnostic distinction, however, remained predictive of socialitzation after controlling for baseline differences in language and non-verbal IQ ($p = 0.01$). Children with Asperger's syndrome had fewer total autistic symptoms at follow up than children with autism (37.0 vs. 58.8, $p = 0.001$); these were explained by the group differences at initial assessment ($p < 0.001$)." (Szatmari, et al., 2000, p. 1980)

AS vs. HFA: A Scientific Findings Review

The following section introduces a cursory discussion based on data yielded by a number of contemporary studies published in peer-referenced journal articles searching for distinctions, or similarities, among AS and HFA.

Research Gems: HFA and AS are Empirically Distinguishable

"Both (HFA and AS) groups were impaired on executive function tests. Only the HFA group demonstrated deficits in theory of mind and verbal memory, performing more poorly than both controls and AS subjects. These results suggest that: (1) HFA and AS are empirically distinguishable on measures independent of diagnostic criteria, and (2) impairment on theory of mind measures is not universally found among individuals with autistic spectrum conditions." (Ozonoff, et al., 1991, p. 1107)

Overlaps between AS and HFA have stirred increased controversies across scientific disciplines who question whether Asperger is merely a mild form of autism, whether it should be considered a separate entity, outside of the autistic spectrum, or whether we are still a long distance away from being able to categorically make a truly educated decision on these potential distinctions. As indicated by Rinehart and colleagues, "in light of the growing body of epidemiological information, genetic, and neurobehavioural evidence that distinguishes autism from Asperger's disorder, it is premature to rule out the possibility that these disorders may be clinically, and possibly neurobiologically separate." (2002, p. 762). The fact that our current criteria for establishing diagnostic distinctions, or lack thereof, are based on symptoms, many of which are mere replications of one another in terms of defining autism and Asperger's (disorder) calls attention to the need for increased efforts from the fields of neuropsychology, genetics, and neurobiology to help modernize our current diagnostic standards.

"While there was symptom overlap between AS and autism, patients could be separated into one or other group. However, current criteria are based on symptoms, and it is argued that studies of genetics and treatment response are needed to elucidate the relationship between these developmental disorders." (Kerbeshian, 1990, p. 721)

Research Gems: AS vs. HFA – Gray Matter

"Cerebral gray matter volume in ASP (Asperger syndrome) was intermediate between that of HFA and controls, but non-significant. Exploratory analyses revealed a negative correlation between cerebral gray matter volume and performance IQ within HFA but not ASP. A positive correlation between cerebral white matter volume and performance IQ was observed within ASP but not HFA….Cerebral gray tissue findings suggest that ASP is on the mild end of the autism spectrum. However, exploratory assessments of brain-IQ relationships reveal differences between HFA and ASP, indicating that these conditions may be neurodevelopmentally different when patterns of multiple measures are examined." (Lotspeich, et. al., 2004, p. 291)

Other areas where distinctions or similarities have been found among persons with AS and HFA include suicide attempts, spontaneity, and speech and language variables. Noting higher incidence of suicidal attempts across persons diagnosed with AS, Mikami & Matumoto suggest "from a view point of clinical features, cognitive neuropsychology and neurobiology, the differentiation between HFA and AS is not clear. There are few reports on outcome in HFA and AS. Whereas, it is suggested that HFA and AS may be different in social problems such as suicide attempt." (2007, p. 487). Macintosh, & Dissanajake (2006), cite ability for spontaneity to substantiate a lack of distinction between AS and HFA, indicating that "the social behaviour of both clinical samples often deviated markedly from that of the typically developing children. The findings confirmed that although the children with high-functioning autism or Asperger's disorder are often socially isolated relative to their typically developing peers, they are capable of spontaneously engaging socially with other children. The results were supportive of the hypothesis that Asperger's disorder is on a continuum with autistic disorder." (p. 199)

Among the very few clinical variables agreed upon by most who cite true distinctions between AS and HFA, neurotypical language development is one of the most consistent. Beyond that, however, research has also suggested that timely verbalizations can be used to predict diagnosis: "a number of clinical variables predicted diagnosis. Delayed language onset was the only variable of the family and developmental variables that predicted diagnosis. The AsD (Asperger's Disorder) group was also significantly higher than the AD (Autistic Disorder) group in verbal mental age." (Eisenmajer, et al., 1996, 1523).

Other studies examining different variables related to speech, language and particular aspects of verbalizations have found additional support to distinguish autism from Asperger's syndrome. Hubbard and Tranuer (2007), for instance, indicated that "autistic subjects actually had a larger pitch range than the other groups (AS and normal controls). Other measures of intonation including amplitude, duration, and location of pitch peak revealed defects that are more complex than predicted. In spontaneous speech, autistic subjects performed more poorly on both phonetic targets and subjective ratings than controls, and AS subjects fell between autistics and normals." (p. 159). Similarly, Fine and colleagues cited results from a 1991 study which indicated that "HFA subjects less often tend to employ useful patterns of intonation for communication than the AS or OPC (out-patient controls) groups. This suggests that HFA either send random intonation signals to hearers or else demonstrate systematic misuse of the linguistic system. AS subjects differed little from the controls." (Fine, et al., 1991, p. 771)

The notion of central coherence, or local vs. global processing has also yielded substantial amounts of investigation in the quest of differentiating AS from HFA. Norbury and Bishop, for example, found that "participants with HFA were less accurate than both normal controls and a group of individuals with Asperger's syndrome, suggesting that they had particular difficulty integrating linguistic information with their own experience. The results from all three studies have been interpreted as evidence for 'weak central coherence'." (2002, p. 229). Regarding cognitive orientation favoring local vs. global processing Rinehart found that "reaction time to global targets in individuals with autism was retarded when the previous target appeared locally. This deficiency in shifting from local to global processing, however, was not observed in individuals with Asperger's disorder." (2001, p. 67). Supporting this notion, a more current study headed by the same investigator found that "children with autism displayed set-shifting deficits on the WCST (Wisconsin Card Sorting Task), while a matched group of children with Asperger's disorder displayed no such deficits" (Rinehart, et al., Autism, 2006, 71-72). Further, the same study indicated that "consistent with past research, which has shown dissociations in executive functioning between autism and Asperger's disorder, the present study revealed that the response patterns of individuals with Asperger's disorder was qualitatively different from the response of children with autism, possibly implicating differential disruption within the fronto-striatal circuitry." (Rinehart, et al., Autism, 2006, p. 82).

Extending beyond the more general social and interpersonal deficits that characterize all autism spectrum disorders, including Asperger's syndrome, the investigation of more explicit nuances that underlie day to day social communications has warranted a number of interesting scientific studies. Regarding creativity and imagination, for instance, one study revealed that "children with autism and AS could generate possible novel changes to an object, though they generated fewer of these relative to controls. Further more, these were all reality-based, rather imaginative (Craig & Baron-Cohen, 1999, 319). A second experiment within the same study examining the responses of children with autism and AS on a standardized creativity test indicated that "consistent with both the imagination deficit and executive function hypotheses, the results confirmed that the children with autism and AS showed less imaginative creativity, and they produced fewer responses overall. The tendency for the children with autism was to produce mainly manipulation type responses, and the children with AS to produce mainly addition/alteration response." (p. 323)

Two other integral aspects of daily interpersonal communication, sarcasm and empathy have also yielded research interest throughout the scientific community engaged in exploring the fine distinctions between AS and HFA. A study from Japan examining sarcasm found that "the inability to understand sarcastic situation was specific to group with AS, both group with HFA and AD/HD were differ little to understand between metaphor and sarcasm. In this study suggest differences in situational recognition among the PDD subtypes, the clinical symptoms of PDD reflects characteristics of AS." (Adachi, 2006, 38, p. 177). (author's note: the above quote is represented exactly as it appears in translation from the original Japanese article). With regard to empathy, Dyck (2001) examined gradations of distinction not only among persons with autism and AS, but also among those with mild mental retardation, ADHD and no psychological disorder.

> "Results showed that empathic ability discriminated among groups on the autism spectrum (autism < Asperger < No Psychological Disorder). Because empathic ability is not independent of intelligence (autism < Asperger < No Psychological Disorder on intelligence; Mild Mental Retardation < ADHD < No Psychological Disorder on empathic ability), both dimensions are necessary to discriminate autism spectrum from non-spectrum disorders. When intelligence is covaried, empathic ability discriminated autism, but not Asperger, from other disorders (autism < Mild Mental Retardation < ADHD < No Psychological Disorder = Anxiety Disorder = Asperger)." (Dyck, 2001, p. 105).

Another often cited point of distinction between persons with Asperger's and those with autism, or high-functioning autism, involves that of performance aptitude and/or motor skills, with persons diagnosed with autism having an advantage in these areas in comparison to persons with AS typically displaying lower overall performance vs. verbal scores, and showing little interest, or aptitude, in motor-related, coordination or athletic activities. Along these lines, one study that looked at several related issues found that "individuals with HFA were found to have difficulty in the executive functions of set-shifting and cognitive motor response inhibition, when compared with age and IQ matched controls. This was not found in individuals with Asperger syndrome. Individuals with Asperger syndrome were often characterized as being clumsy, although the same was not true for HFA....HFA was associated with left hemispheric dysfunction, but Asperger syndrome was not. Rather, Asperger syndrome has been associated with right hemisphere dysfunction....differences which emerge between the two groups in empirical studies are often the result of cognitive ability and severity of the disorder." (Blacher, et al., 2003, p. 537). A separate study, examining coordination aptitude suggested that "while coordination deficits were found in all three groups, children with AS were found to be less impaired than those with autistic disorder and PDDNOS.... These findings suggest that some patients with AS may be less clumsy than those with autistic disorder and that this difference may be the result of their higher level of intelligence. (Ghaziuddin & Butler, 1998, p. 43)

Research Gems: AS & HFA vs. Psychiatric Patients

"When the AS and HFA with FSIQ above 85 were compared to the OPC (note: psychiatric outpatient controls), outstanding deficits on motor coordination, language comprehension, and facial recognition were observed….Some evidence is presented to suggest that the pattern of deficits of AS and HFA subjects varied by developmental level." (Szatmari, 1990, p. 130).

"In terms of their early history, the autistic probands showed more social impairment, a higher frequency of echolalia and pronoun reversal, and a more restricted range of activities than the AS group….the autistic probands spent more time in special education classes but developed fewer accessory psychiatric symptoms than the AS children." (Szatmari, 1989, p. 709)

Finally, other studies attempting to distinguish AS from HFA in particular, and autism in general, have cited various clinical issues as points of potential distinction. One study, looking at insomnia, for example, found that "in children with autism even a minor disruption of stereotypic rituals before going to bed may prevent them from falling asleep. Our patients did not describe this type of behaviour (which is often less conspicuous in AS as compared to autism) but complained more of hypersensitivity to external noise, forgetting oneself in front of computer, ruminating things passed in previous days, or, most often, diffuse difficulty in falling asleep." (Tani, et al., 2003, p. 8). An older study, examining bipolar disorder, yielded findings indicating "a high incidence of Asperger's syndrome in family members of high-functioning autistic subjects only. The rate of bipolar affective disorder in family members was 4.2%, higher than in the general population; it was significantly higher in families with Aspeger's syndrome, suggesting an etiological link between Asperger's syndrome and manic depression. Positive neurological findings were concentrated in the low-functioning subgroup. These findings imply different etiologies for high-versus low-functioning autism, with high-functioning autism related to familial factors, especially Asperger's syndrome." (DeLong & Dwyer, 1988, p. 593).

Research Gems: AS vs. HFA - Subtest Results

"The AS subjects had less significant communicative abnormality on CARS-TV compared with the HFA subjects...As found in many previous HFA studies, the present HFA subjects scored lowest on Comprehension and scored highest on Block Design, suggesting the unique intellectual structure in autism (i.e., superior in visuospatial ability but inferior in skills related to so-called social intelligence)." (Koyama, et al., 2007, p. 102)

"Compared with the HFA subjects, the AS subjects scored significantly higher on Verbal IQ, Vocabulary, and Comprehension, but scored significantly lower on Coding. Although the total CARS-TV* score did not differ significantly between the two groups, AS subjects scored significantly lower (i.e., less abnormal on Verbal communication and Non-verbal communication than did the HFA subjects. A history of normal language acquisition in early childhood could predict his/her better verbal ability in mid-childhood or later." (Koyama, et al., 3007, 99)

*(CARS-TV = Childhood Autism Rating Scale – Tokyo Version)

"By adolescence, the AS group were reported to be as abnormal as the HFA group but in structured 1:1 interaction their conversation was better. IQ profile in the AS group showed relative strength on verbal measures, unlike the HFA group, but relatively good performance on the Block Design subtest of the WISC/WAIS was a feature of both the AS and HFA groups. The results indicate closely similar behavioural manifestations that may arise by adolescence despite differences in speech development." (Gilchrist, 2001, p. 227)

Overall, at the present time, it appears that the jury destined to cast the proverbial verdict on the "AS vs. HFA" distinction is still out, and may be out for some time. Are these merely different words referring to the same persons, all of whom fall along various points along the "high" end of the autistic, or pervasive developmental disorders spectrum, or do they exemplify points of divergence? Are there enough variations among persons who may be categorized with the label of autism, vs. those who might be more clearly described by the now popular name of the gentleman who first brought them to our attention, Hans Asperger? In the meantime, then, it behooves those of us committed to serving the needs of these populations, to put aside the quest for determining what the ultimate "truth" may, in fact—if there is such a thing—be with regard to Asperger's or High Functioning autism and concentrate on what's important. To me, the focus should be on (a) assigning the label that will most readily, and effectively guarantee them services; (b) concentrating on identifying their strengths, talents, motivations and natural inclinations; (c) helping them to identify their preferred learning styles in order to assist them in formulating more effective academic, personal, vocational, and life-long goals; and (d) while we are at it, why not just get rid of labels altogether?

Chapter 8

Asperger's Syndrome vs. Nonverbal Learning Disorder

Figure 5
Interrelationships between AS and NLD, and AS and HFA

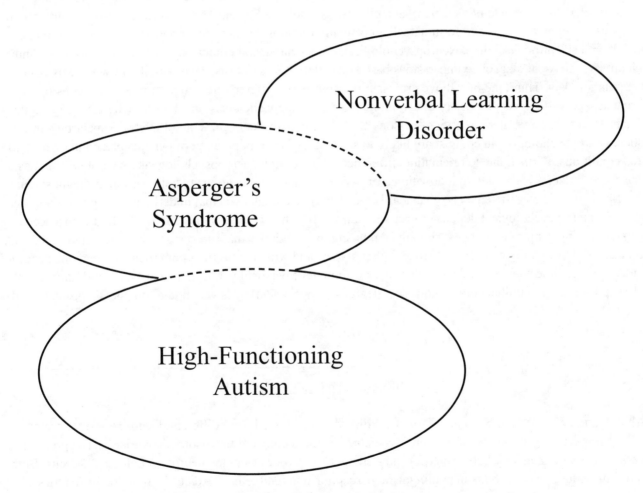

"Children with Asperger's disorder have NLD but…few children
with NLD have Asperger's disorder." (Palombo, 2006, p. 205)

Research Gems: Differentiating AS and NLD

"The process of differentiating the characteristics of AS, and NLD, and a pragmatic language disorder arguably may be the most challenging diagnostic tasks in developmental-behavioral pediatrics. Overlapping behaviors and cognitive processes and coexisting conditions challenge even the most experienced clinicians. That there are differences in these conditions is not an issue. How important a precise diagnosis is as a guide to treatment is perhaps the most important question for a clinician who treats these patients." (Stein, 2004, p. 1462)

The issues that underlie attempts to compare and contrast Asperger's Syndrome from Nonverbal Learning Disabilities are many. First, the use of a number of different diagnostic systems and diagnostic criteria make it very difficult to compare reference criteria and research findings. Basically, although many of features that characterize each of the two conditions overlap, whereas NLD derives from the discipline of neuropsychology, AS is more directly connected with the field of psychiatry and clinical psychology. Second, the two primary professions that are typically called upon to assess and formulate diagnostic impressions for these two populations differ in training, approach, and scientific discipline. Neuropsychologists, on one hand, and clinicians—such as psychologists and psychiatrists—arrive at diagnostic impressions based on different sets of tests, each with their own norms, criteria, and population data. Third, the two above professions also rely on different theoretical frameworks, considering different aspects of the overall tapestry of symptoms, to reach diagnostic decisions. Fourth, whereas, in general, clinicians tend to see a greater majority of persons across the autism, Asperger's, and PDDNOS spectrums in their practice, neuropsychologists in contrast are likely to see a much larger population of persons presenting with NLD related conditions. Further, due to orientation differences, for example, neuropsychologists may not be as apt as clinicians to consider issues related to motivational or psychodynamic implications to help base their diagnostic picture. Fifth, separated by different sets of standards regarding the core deficits that underlie and help to define each condition—neuropsychological deficits or social impairments—the two disciplines are handcuffed with a scenario akin to comparing "apples to oranges." Finally, a blurring of boundaries that run across the many continuums that encompass NLD, AS, and their related, broader phenotypes, and which are further complicated when one needs to consider a multi-dimensional approach including any number of personal variables (severity, comorbidities, age of onset vs. presentation, familial components, sex, degree of impairment) adds yet another diagnostic obstacle (Palombo, 2006).

Research Gems: The NLD – AS Overlap

"Although the diagnosis of NLD and Asperger's disorder are derived from different disciplines—the former from neuropsychology and the latter from psychiatry—some features of the disorders overlap….The greatest overlap in symptomatology between NLD and Asperger's disorder lies in the neuropsychological deficits. Both groups of children have deficits in nonlinguistic perception and tend to have executive function difficulties…. This it not the case for the other two perspectives, the social and intrapersonal." (Palombo, 2006, p. 209)

AS vs. the Four NLD Subtypes

A comparison between the DSM-IV-TR criteria for AS and Palombo's (2006) features for the four NLD subtypes proves helpful in differentiating the two conditions. The characteristics of NLD subtypes I and II, for instance, are very similar to the criteria exemplified by DSM-IV-TR's section A —"Qualitative impairment in social interaction"— for Asperger's disorder. In effect, difficulties with nonverbal behaviors, problems developing peer relations, and a lack of spontaneity and social-emotional reciprocity all run across both NLD subtypes I and II, and AS.

When one moves forward to DSM-IV-TR's section B criteria, however, a number of contrasts readily surface across the two conditions. Although some of these features are at times present in persons with NLD, they are typically of less intensity than when found in persons with AS and, in most cases, would fail to qualify as actual impairments. NLD's interest areas, for examples, rarely involve "all encompassing preoccupation," and their patterns of interest are typically seen as "abnormal in intensity or focus." Moving down the criteria under section B—"Restricted repetitive and stereotyped patterns of behavior, interests, and activities"—again, adherence to inflexible patters of behavior, nonfunctional routines or rituals, stereotyped and repetitive motor mannerisms, and preoccupation with objects, whereas common across AS populations, are rarely seen in persons with subtypes I and II of NLD. The same applies to DSM-IV-TR's section C ("The disturbance causes clinically significant impairment in social, occupation, or other important areas of functioning").

DSM-IV-TR's criteria for sections D ("no clinically significant delay in language"), E ("no clinically significant delay in cognitive development"), and F ("criteria are not met for other PDD or Schizophrenia"), on the other hand, do apply to NLD populations of subtypes I and II.

When one considers the more severe, multidimensional characteristics that pertain to NLD subtype III, and more particularly subtype IV, however, more direct comparisons are seen across persons who fall under those subtypes and those who present with AS. Still, even at this level of NLD severity, Palombo (2006) points out that a significant distinction between the two conditions surfaces when one considers that, whereas persons with NLD can function independently, those with AS are typically limited by the severity of their impairments at both personal and professional levels.

In effect, although many similarities between the two conditions are apparent, particularly across both populations who struggle with higher levels of impairment, the conclusion posed by Palombo is that AS and NLD constitute two separate diagnostic conditions.

Profiles for NLD were compiled from a combination of the following sources:

Ellis & Gunter, 1999; Fast, 2004; Keller, Tillery & McFadden, 2006; Kotulak, 1997; Levine, 1996; Little, 1999; Palombo, 2006; Pelletier, Ahman, & Rourke, 2001; Stein, 2004; Thompson, 1996; Roman, 1998; Rourke, 1995; Rourke, et al., 2002; Volden, 2004.

Profiles for AS were compiled from a combination of the following sources:

Cohen, 1988; Ehlers, et al., 1997; Freeman, 1985; Ghaziuddin, et al., 2004; Koyama, et al., 2007; Kurita, 1997; Manjiviona & Pryor, 1999; Siegel, Minshew, & Goldstein, 1996; Szatmari, et al., 1990.Dingfelder, 2004; Howlin, et al., 1998; Klin, et al., 1995; Lotspeich, et al., 2004; Lovecky, 2004; Ozonoff, South & Miller, 2000; Schopler, et al., 1992; Szatmari, et al., 2000; Volkmar, et al., 2005; Walker et al., 2004; author's clinical sample (N = > 900; 1994-2007).

The following "NLD vs. AS Checklist – '07" draws from a comprehensive review of current scientific research, familial case histories, and anecdotal clinical observations in an attempt to facilitate making a distinction between persons with the characteristics that define Nonverbal Learning Disorder (or Disability) vs. those with Asperger's Syndrome.

It is divided into five subsections including:

- Section 1: Intellectual Profiles
- Section 2: Strength & Weaknesses in Work & Academia
- Section 3: Theory of Mind & Intrapersonal Characteristics
- Section 4: Social Interaction Impairments
- Section 5: Restricted Repetitive & Stereotyped Patterns of Behaviors, Interests & Activities

NLD vs. AS Checklist – '08©
John M. Ortiz, Ph.D.

<u>Section 1: Intellectual Profiles</u>

* Fields noted as "Depends" indicate the need to obtain further information.

For example, persons with Asperger's will more typically process information much faster when related to a special interest topic, or when the subject area is connected to a relative strength. Those with a natural mathematical ability, for instance may be able to process mathematical calculations at extraordinary speeds, while others may struggle with even basic calculations. Additionally, if the subject matter is related to their preferred learning style (e.g., visual), information presented through their preferred medium will be much more quickly processed than if presented in a non-preferred (e.g., auditory) format.

<u>Research Gems: NLD vs. AS – Visual Spatial Skills</u>

"Difficulties with visual-spatial issues, a major problem area for NLDers, aren't mentioned in AS literature. In fact, many ASers respond well to visuals and diagrams, and are visual learners. Many find work as engineers or architects. In contrast, NLDers don't respond to physical demonstrations and may not understand diagrams. They can't learn by watching, and need everything explained in words. Thus NLDers tend to become wordsmiths—teachers and writers—while ASers often excel in math and find work in computer fields or engineering." (Fast, 2004, p. 27)

NLD vs. AS Checklist – '08©

Section 2: General Areas of Strength & Weaknesses Related to Work & Academia

	NLD	AS
Spelling skills	Good	Good +
Verbal skills	Good	Good
Ability to work independently	Good	Good +
Ability to process/assimilate Auditory Information	Excellent	Poor
Ability to process/assimilate Visual Information	Poor	Excellent
Ability to process/assimilate "Hands-on" data	Poor	Excellent
Ability to work in small, structured settings	Good	Excellent
Ability to work at selective, special interest areas	Good	Excellent
Attention to detail	Poor	Excellent
Flexibility in work duties or responsibilities	Poor	Poor
Rote memory skills	Good	Excellent
Ability to follow literal, concrete responsibilities	Depends	Excellent
Ability for multi-lingual skills	Good +	Good +
Ability to process words and symbols	Good	Excellent
Creative writing skills	Medium	Good
Verbal processing skills	Excellent	Medium
Ability to think in words	Excellent	Medium
Ability to think in images	Poor	Excellent
Ability to think technically	Poor	Excellent
Ability to think mechanically	Poor	Excellent
Ability for repetitive, sequential tasks	Good	Excellent
Ability for step-by-step problem solving	Good	Excellent
Rote memory ability	Medium	Excellent
Reliable, responsible, trustworthy	Excellent	Excellent

Motivation when engaged in strength area(s)	Good +	Excellent
Methodical work ethic	Excellent	Excellent
Dedicated & diligent work ethic	Excellent	Excellent
Willingness at learning new responsibilities	Good	Depends
Dependable & conscientious	Excellent	Excellent
Fine motor skills	Poor	Good
Gross motor skills	Poor	Poor
Mechanical writing skills (penmanship)	Poor	Poor
Keyboarding	Medium	Good
Ability to work in groups or teams	Poor	Poor
Ability to work at "people-related" pursuits	Poor	Poor
Ability to influence others	Poor	Poor
Leadership qualities	Poor	Poor
Emotional stability	Poor	Poor
Tolerance level	Depends	Depends
Ability to work on arts & crafts	Poor	Good
Hand-eye coordination	Poor	Poor
Ability to transition across settings	Poor	Poor
Ability to generalize information	Poor	Poor
Ability to multi-task	Poor	Depends
Ability to make quick, on the moment decisions	Poor	Poor
Ability to follow visual diagrams & charts	Poor	Excellent
Ability to work in stressful situations	Poor	Poor
Ability to follow geographic directions	Poor	Good +
Ability to decode information	Poor	Excellent
Ability to work in research settings	Poor	Good +
Ability to work in laboratory settings	Poor	Good +

* Depends – on topic area or learning medium in which information or task is presented.

Research Gems: NLD vs. AS – Interpersonal Characteristics

"It is in the affective area that NLD and AS diverge. NLDers have normal emotions but are inept at expressing them and in recognizing them in others, to the extent that they are expressed nonverbally….Though they (Aspies) may feel very deeply about many things, they may not cry or smile when it's deemed appropriate. They often have a flat aspect, and have difficulty with initiating or experiencing normal social relationships." (Fast, 2004, pp. 26-27)

NLD vs. AS Checklist – '08©

Section 3: Theory of Mind & Intrapersonal Characteristics

	NLD	AS
First-order representation*	Good	Good
Second-order representation*	Good	Poor
Ability to recognize another's interest in own topic	Medium	Poor
Reciprocal social interaction (responding to others)	Medium	Poor
Ability to sustain meaningful dialogue with others	Medium	Poor
Ability to understand another person's perspective	Medium	Poor
Ability to recognize others as independent thinkers	Medium	Poor
Ability to communicate one's own feeling state	Medium	Poor
Ability to understand emotional communications	Medium	Poor
Ability to express one's own feelings objectively	Medium	Poor
Ability to relate to another person objectively	Medium	Poor
Cohesive sense of self	Medium	Poor
Ability to see the whole vs. the small parts	Medium	Poor
Capable of taking the initiative	Medium	Poor
Ability to formulate long term goals independently	Medium	Poor

Ability to develop a coherent self-narrative	Medium	Poor
Ability to fit in comfortably in social settings	Medium	Poor

* First order representations refer to the most basic notion that different things share certain connections. Second order representations refer to the more advanced ability of thinking about our thoughts in relation to another person's thoughts, as well as what one thinks that someone else may be thinking about one's own thoughts.

Research Gems: NLD vs. AS – Social Problems

"AS individuals generally have greater social problems. Their frequently highly restricted interests create an additional obstacle to their social functioning. These restricted interests seem to be peculiar to Aspies; they're not mentioned in the literature about NLD. This is the main difference between the two disorders, as they are most frequently defined clinically. The ASers odd behavior, like rocking or flapping, can also contribute to their social problems. These are not present in NLD. In contrast, the NLDer's social ineptness is mainly due to their inability to read nonverbal communication, such as facial expressions and gestures." (Fast, 2004, p. 27)

NLD vs. AS Checklist – '08©

Section 4: Social Interaction Impairments

	NLD	AS
General ability to interpret nonverbal behaviors	*Medium<	Poor+
Ability to make direct eye contact	Medium<	Poor+
Ability to read facial expressions	Medium<	Poor+
Ability to interpret body postures	Medium<	Poor+
Ability to interpret gestures	Medium<	Poor+
Ability to regulate social interactions	Medium<	Poor+
Ability to develop peer relationships	Medium<	Poor+
Ability to be spontaneous	Poor+	Poor+
Ability to share personal interests with others	Medium<	Medium+
Ability to appreciate the interests of others	Medium	Poor
Ability to share personal achievements with others	Medium<	Poor+
Ability to demonstrate personal emotions	Medium	Poor

Ability to relate to other's emotions	Medium	Poor
Ability to make peer-related acquaintances	Medium	Poor
Ability to make acquaintances with younger children	Good	Medium
Ability to make acquaintances with older children	Medium	Medium
Ability to make acquaintances with adults	Good	Good+
Pragmatic language capabilities	Medium<	Poor+
Ability to sustain relationships	Medium<	Poor+
Ability to read subtle signals from others	Medium<	Poor
Ability to use deceit	Medium<	Poor
Ability to use social manipulation	Medium<	Poor
Ability to use social coercion	Medium<	Poor
Ability to process one's own emotional state	Medium<	Poor
Ability to understand the extent of their deficits	Medium<	Poor
Ability to explain or relate the extent of their deficits with others	Medium<	Poor
Ability to relate to members of opposite sex	Medium<	Poor
Ability to maintain opposite sex relationships	Medium<	Poor
Ability to understand work-place relationships	Medium<	Poor
Ability to adapt to work-place relationships	Medium<	Poor
Ability to understand work-place social agendas	Medium<	Poor

*(The symbol "+" refers to an upward extension of the noted ability level. For example, "Medium+" implies that ability would be "Medium or higher," and could extend into "Good" or, in some persons, "Very good." A "Medium<," conversely, indicates an ability in that particular area would be "Medium or less.")

NLD vs. AS Checklist – '08©

Section 5: Restricted Repetitive & Stereotyped Patterns of Behaviors, Interests & Activities

Characteristics Behaviors	NLD	AS
A pattern of preoccupation with certain topics	Rare	Nearly Always
A pattern of adapting certain repetitive behaviors	*Rare+	Common
A pattern of engaging in limited activities	Rare+	Common
A pattern of abnormal intensity in interest areas	Rare+	Common
Good or better ability to focus on limited areas	Common	Nearly Always
Inflexible adherence to specific routines	Rare	Common
Inflexible adherence to (apparently) nonfunctional routines	Rare	Common
A pattern of adapting to behavioral rituals	Rare	Common
Stereotyped and repetitive motor mannerisms	Rare	Common
Preoccupation with parts of objects	Rare	Common
A pattern of collecting that is of abnormal intensity	Rare	Common
A pattern of memorizing facts of abnormal intensity	Rare	Common
A pattern of hoarding of abnormal intensity	Rare	Common
An adaptation to written rules of abnormal intensity	Rare	Nearly Always
A pattern of making own rules	Rare	Common
A preoccupation with others following rules	Rare	Common
A preoccupation with details	Rare	Common
A pattern of compiling factual knowledge	Rare	Common
A stubborn adherence to set guidelines	Rare	Common
A stubborn adherence to tradition	Rare	Common
A staunch adherence to ethical principles	Common	Nearly Always
A pattern of routines impairing day to day functions	Rare	Common

*(Rare+ implies a "Rare or greater" possibility of the noted behaviors.)

An additional checklist comparing and differentiating NLD from AS, based on Byron Rourke's NLD deficits and strength model as proposed by Rourke for Consideration as ICD Diagnostic Criteria for Research in NLD, is offered in Appendix B. AS characteristics are drawn from research studies and anecdotal clinical information cited in chapter 5 in addition to research studies differentiating these two diagnostic conditions.

(Note: NLD information adapted from Rourke, 2007, www.nld-bprourke.ca)

Hiearchical Spectrum of Neurodevelopmental Disorders
with Variations of NLD Characteristics

Level 1:
Most or all of the assets and deficits associated with NLD are present.

- Callosal Genesis (uncomplicated)
- Asperger's syndrome
- Velocardiofacial syndrome
- Williams Syndrome
- De Lange syndrome
- Hydrocephalus (early, shunted)
- Turner syndrome
- Significant damage/dysfunction of the right cerebral hemisphere

Level 2:
A "considerable majority" of the assets and deficits
associated with NLD are present.

- Sotos syndrome
- Prophylactic treatment for acute lymphocytic leukemia (long- term survivors)
- Congenital hypothyroidism
- Metachromatic leukodystropy (early in disease progression)
- Fetal alcohol syndrome (high-functioning)

Level 3:
"Many" of the assets and deficits associated with NLD are present.

- Multiple sclerosis (early to middle stages)
- Traumatic brain injury (diffuse white matter perturbations)
- Toxicant-induced encephalopathies (affecting white matter)
- Children with HIV and white matter disease
- Fragile-X syndrome (high functioning)
- Triple X syndrome

- Leukodystrophies other than metachromatic
- Hamophilus influenzae meningitis
- Inventricular hemorrhage (early)
- Children with cardiac disease treated with ECMO
- Children with very low birth weight
- Congential adrenal hyperplasia
- Insulin-dependent diabetes mellitus
- Fahr's syndrome

Level 4: Ambiguous research evidence

- Neurofrimatosis I
- Noonan syndrome
- Cerebral Palsy of perinatal origin

Similar, but basically different

- Tourette syndrome
- Autism (high-functioning)

(Adapted from: Rourke et al., 2002, p. 330)

Chapter 9

AS, HFA, and NLD – Standard Distributions

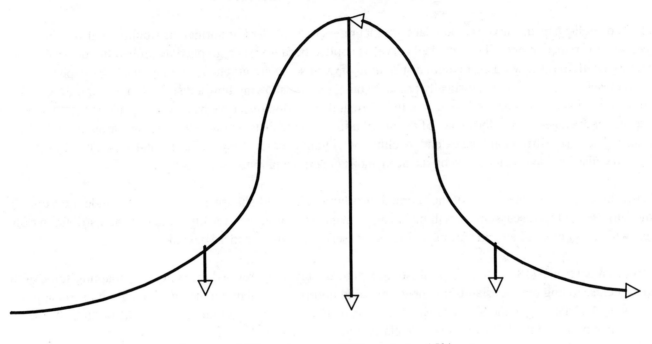

< ---15% ---> < --------70% ---- > < ---15% --->

Research Gems: The Autism Bell Curve

"Although the data collected in this study were cross-sectional, they support a new perspective on the development of psychopathology in higher-functioning people with autism. Traditional views tended to perpetuate a monolithic view of autism as involving 'pervasive lack of responsiveness to others' with very little self or social awareness. This perspective emphasized only the social deficits of people with autism. However, it appears that people with autism vary in their self and social awareness and, unfortunately, greater social awareness and motivation may bring a clearer perception of one's own difficulties in these domains." (Meyer et al., 2006, 398)

Research Gems: The Harm of Making Assumptions

"One of the biggest difficulties anyone can face is the assumption that they are either competent or not competent regarding a specific skill or task. It is fine to recognize that a person may be good or bad at certain things when there is evidence to support that. It is quite another to make the assumption that a person with a certain trait has a certain level of ability in an unrelated trait." (Smith, 2007, p. 1)

The Bell-Shaped Curve: A Quick Primer

The Bell, or Bell-Shaped, Curve is a popular term that refers to a standard or normal distribution with a mean of zero and a variance of one. The term "bell curve" is applied because when graphed its probability density resembles a bell. In other words, a random distribution of events that are graphed resulting in a bell-shaped curve, representing a normal or statistically probably outcome and showing how a distribution of samples would theoretically fall above and beyond the mean. In a normal distribution the curve has a single peak, is bell-shaped, the mean—or average—lies at the center of the distribution, and the distribution is symmetrical around the mean. The two tails of the distribution then extend indefinitely without ever touching the horizontal axis. The ultimate shape of the distribution is determined by its mean and standard deviation.

Although in recent times the notion of the "normal distribution," or bell-shaped curve, has come under question, for the purposes of this discussion we will maintain the standard notion with regard to the normal distribution of IQ scores, with an IQ of 100 being the mean, and 15 points serving as one standard deviation.

In 1916, Lewis Terman (1877-1956), a professor at Stanford University, revised the Binet test, adapting some of the standard items, adding others, establishing new age-based norms, and extending the upper age limit to encompass "superior adults," leading to the Stanford-Binet revision of 1916 and the "intelligence quotient," or "IQ." At that point, Terman proposed the following scale for classifying IQ scores:

- 140 of above – Genius or near genius
- 120-140 – Very superior intelligence
- 110-120 – Superior intelligence
- 90-109 – Normal or average intelligence
- 80-89 – Dullness
- 70-79 – Borderline deficiency
- Under 70 – Definite feeble-mindedness

(References: http://www.wilderdom.com/intelligence/IQWhatScoresMean.html; http://www.wilderdom.com/personality/L1-5KeyP;ayer.html - 8/12/2007).
In addition to the above classifications the "normal distribution and IQ scores" were noted as having the following properties:

- 50% of IQ scores fall between 90 – 110
- 70% of IQ scores fall between 85 – 115
- 95% of IQ scores fall between 70 – 130
- 99.5% of IQ scores fall between 60 – 140

More accurately, 68% of the population would score within 15 points (or one standard deviation) either above or below 100, with IQs between 85 – 115, and 96% were predicted to fall within 30 points, above or below, the mean or average of 100, or having IQs between 70 – 130.

The IQ classifications were further distinguished and specified for different levels of both mental retardation and giftedness as follows:

Mental Retardation IQ Levels:

- Mild mental retardation (85%): 50 – 70 IQ
- Moderate mental retardation (10%): 35 – 50 IQ
- Severe mental retardation (4%): 20 – 35 IQ
- Profound mental retardation (1%): 20 or below

High IQ and Genius IQ Levels:

- Above average: 115 – 124 IQ
- Gifted: 125 – 134 IQ
- Highly gifted: 135 – 144 IQ
- Genius: 145 – 154 (University Professor level)
- Genius: 155 – 164 IQ (Nobel Prize winner level)
- High genius: 165 – 179 IQ
- Highest genius: 180 – 200 IQ
- Unmeasurable genius: 200 + IQ

By comparison, the current Wechsler IQ test lists the following descriptions for the different IQ levels: (Reference: http://www.psychologicaltesting.com/iqtest.htm)

IQ	Description
10	Profound Mental Retardation
25	Severe Mental Retardation
40	Moderate Mental Retardation
55	Mild Mental Retardation
70	Borderline
85	Low Average
100	Average
115	High Average
125	Superior
130	Very Superior/Gifted

With this overview, let us apply the notion of the normal distribution, or bell curve, to try and gain a clearer understanding of AS, HFA, and NLD.

If one were to take every person with AS (or HFA, or NLD) in the world, determine all of their descriptive characteristics, and distribute them according to a statistical distribution a certain percentage would be considered at the "low" end, or "just barely meeting the criteria for AS (or HFA, or NLD)," another percentage would fit the criteria for their diagnostic classification with characteristics that would range from "just barely meeting the criteria" to "clearly meeting many of the criteria" for the classification of Asperger's syndrome (or HFA, or NLD). At the "high" end, another percentage would be found to fit most of the criteria that would define their classification, with an even smaller percentage—at the "highest" end of the spectrum—meeting so many of the criteria that there would be no doubt that those individuals would receive the diagnosis of Asperger's syndrome (or HFA or NLD).

Again, for purposes of this pragmatic illustration, let's envision that the percentage at the "low" end, or those "just barely meeting the criteria" for either of these conditions is 15%. Those ranging from "just barely meeting the criteria" to "clearly meeting many of the criteria" would encompass 70% of the AS (HFA or NLD) population, and the "high" end, or those meeting most if not all of the criteria for either of these conditions would fall at the "high" end of the AS, HFA, or NLD spectrum.

In actuality, the above illustration is not so far fetched. Whether, in fact, 15% of persons with AS (HFA, or NLD), diagnosed or not, fall at the "low," or "just barely meeting the criteria for AS (HFA, or NLD), 70% fall within the "middle" range, and 15% fall at the "high" end of each respective spectrum is inconsequential. The fact is that, in practice, people with these conditions are, first and foremost, people. They are not "Asperger…people," or "autistic…people," or "nonverbally learning disabled…people" but people who happen to have a condition that we have, for now, decided to "label" with the words "Asperger, autism, or Nonverbal Learning Disability."

To refer, or think of, persons with these conditions by their labels is akin to defining persons who have nearsighted vision by their nearsightedness, or people with non-uniform dentures by their challenged bite. Nothing, whether one's eyesight, dental structure, or diagnostic label truly defines anyone.

Let us further examine this notion from the optical perspective.

If someone shares with you that they "need to wear prescription eyeglasses," what exactly does that mean? Does that mean that they "just barely" need prescription eyeglasses? That they need eyeglasses "just to read," or "just to drive"? Is their vision 20/40 (the "low" end), 20/100 (a moderate need for glasses), or 20/800 (a "high" need for eyeglasses)? When we see someone wearing prescription eyeglasses, we do not know, without further inquiry or investigation, whether they are nearsighted, farsighted, or both, whether their vision is further challenged by astigmatism, blepharitis, color blindness, dry-eye syndrome, eye allergies, or any other eye-related problems, some of which are easily remedied, others which require much more intensive care.

Likewise, when we learn that someone has been diagnosed with "Asperger's syndrome" (HFA or NLD) what does that mean? Are they are at the "low," "moderate," or "high" end of this condition?

When assessing, and eventually diagnosing and labeling, persons with these conditions this is one of the issues with which we are confronted. Unfortunately, determining whether someone has Asperger's syndrome is not as clear-cut as determining they are nearsighted or have astigmatism, conditions that can be much more easily established by a trained, professional optometrist with the proper equipment. Regretfully, as of this writing, we have yet to come up with assessment tools that would be able to indisputably determine whether an individual should in fact be classified with the labels or conditions that we are currently referring to as AS, HFA, or NLD. Beyond the fact that the diagnostic classification systems we currently have in place are limited and sorely lacking in terms of accurately capturing the diverse intricacies of these conditions, the fact that each of them is typically confounded by a number of secondary conditions (ADHD, OCD, depression, anxiety, Tic disorder, gastrointestinal issues, speech and language disorders, motor disorders, sensory integration challenges, etc.), most (if not all) of which are almost as misunderstood makes the application of these labels a very difficult challenge. Because of the complexities of these diverse and widely misunderstood conditions, I have found that acknowledging that persons who present with these diagnostic characteristics do not only fall in a spectrum, but also flow throughout many points within a bell, or normal distribution, curve helps to clarify their condition while acknowledging their diversity as individuals.

Having worked with a representative sample (N > 900) of persons with AS over the past 12 years I have observed that, in fact, most of them, about 70%, have met a moderate number of diagnostic criteria for AS as specified by DSM-IV-TR and/or ICD-10. About 15% have met the bare minimum criteria to be classified with this condition, and another 15% have met so much of the criteria that there would be no question in anyone's mind that they would qualify as having AS, as determined by our current diagnostic systems.

In effect, a "normal distribution" for the population described above would, in fact, fall under the auspices of a "bell-shaped curve" and be illustrated as follows:

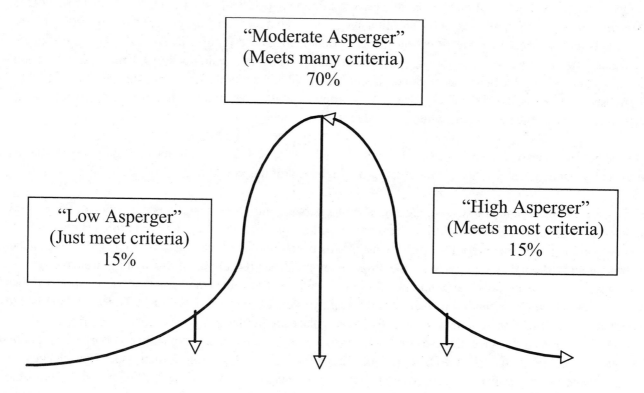

Increasingly, the notion of persons with AS, HFA, or NLD falling under a "normal distribution" curve is one which has been of great assistance to my increased understanding that the idea of a "spectrum" is not sufficient to explain the variety of characteristics exemplified by persons across these populations. The goal is to attempt to present this perspective in a manner that can help others to more clearly conceptualize these conditions as fluid, imbued with endless, personal characteristics, levels of intelligence, ambition, passion, world beliefs, degrees of "normalcy," and "eccentricities" all of which classify them under the all encompassing spectrum of "neo-normalcy.

Chapter 10

Comorbidities and Secondary Conditions

Research Gems: Recognizing Comorbid Conditions

"Aggression and self-injury are among the most common problematic behaviors that come to the attention of clinicians. In some of these children and adolescents, these disturbing behaviors are symptoms of a comorbid psychiatric condition. However, many clinicians continue to view them as part of the underlying developmental disorder. In consideration of the long-term disability associated with the pervasive developmental disorders and the absence of specific pharmacological treatments for the core deficits of this disorder, it is of paramount importance to recognize and treat comorbid psychiatric conditions in these children, which can substantially improve functioning." (Frazier, 2002, p. 13)

Introduction

The importance of making a clear distinction between comorbidities, or secondary conditions that occur commonly alongside both Asperger's syndrome and high-functioning autism is grave. In effect, being able to distinguish conditions that may have similar characteristics—such as developmental delays from autism, obsessive compulsive disorder from Asperger's, externally manifested symptoms such as AS or HFA versus conduct or oppositional disorders, or common comorbidities such tic disorders, gastrointestinal problems, anxiety and depression, which often enter the fold during adolescence—will make all the difference in terms of considering treatment strategies, medical intervention, obtaining adequate services, and making referrals to appropriate professionals.

Research Gems: The Importance of Identifying Comorbid Conditions

"We have identified a significant brain-behavior relationship between amygdala volume and anxious/depressed scores on the Child Behavior Checklist in our autistic cohort….The existing literature on human psychiatry and behavior supports our reported evidence for a neurobiologic relationship between symptoms of anxiety and depression with amygdale structure and function. *Our results highlight the importance of characterizing comorbid psychiatric symptomatology in autism.* The abundance of inconsistent findings in the published literature on autism might reflect differences between study populations regarding age at MRI, level of impairment within autistic subjects, and underlying anxiety level in the selected study groups." (Juranek et al., 2006, p. 1051)

Medical and psychological conditions often found in combination with autism or Asperger's syndrome:

- Anxiety disorders
- Mood disorders (depression, bipolar disorder)
- Epilepsy
- Post-traumatic Stress Disorder
- Celiac disease
- Attention Deficit Hyperactivity Disorder
- Obsessive Compulsive Disorder
- Food and drug allergies
- Gastro-intestinal illnesses
- Tourettes and other Tic disorders
- Dyspraxia (motor), Dysgraphia (writing), Dyscalculia (math)
- Dyslexia

Communication Disorders:

- Expressive Language Disorder
- Communication Disorder NOS
- Mixed Receptive-Expressive Language Disorder
- Phonological Disorder

Learning Disorders:

- Reading Disorder
- Mathematics Disorder
- Disorder of Written Expression
- Learning Disorder NOS
- Phobias
- Sleep disorders
- Sensory Integration Dysfunction
- Nonverbal Learning Disorder
- Lack of metallothionein protein
- Prosopagnosia (problems reading or recognizing faces)

Research Gems: "Hyperlexia among children with ASD"

"Four components of reading skill were assessed: word recognition, nonword decoding, text reading accuracy and text comprehension….There was considerable variability across the sample with performance on most tests ranging from floor to ceiling levels. Some children read accurately but showed very poor comprehension consistent with a hyperlexia reading profile; some children were poor at reading words and nonwords whereas others were unable to decode nonwords, despite a reasonable level of word reading skill. These findings demonstrate the heterogeneous nature of reading skills in children with ASD." (Nation et al., 2006, p. 911)

Diagnostic labels typically misattributed to autism or Asperger's:
- Schizoid Disorder
- Schizophrenia
- Childhood bipolar disorder
- Obsessive-Compulsive disorder
- Oppositional Defiant Disorder
- Conduct Disorder
- Selective Mutism
- Central Auditory Processing Disorder
- Developmental Coordination Disorder
- Mental Retardation
- Separation Anxiety Disorder
- Learning Disorder
- Reactive Attachment Disorder
- Personality Disorder
- Schizoaffective Disorder
- Schizophreniform Disorder
- Delusional Disorder
- Psychotic Disorder
- Disruptive Behavior Disorder
- Stereotypic Movement Disorder
- Dementia
- Eating Disorder

Special education-related labels typically assigned to autism or Asperger's syndrome:
- Behaviorally Impaired
- Emotionally Impaired
- Chronically Health Impaired
- General Learning Disabled
- Hearing Impaired

Problems with:
- Basic reading skills
- Listening comprehension
- Mathematics calculation
- Mathematics reasoning
- Oral expression or language
- Reading comprehension
- Written expression
- Physically Health Impaired
- Speech Disorder
- Trainable Mentally Impaired
- Violent and Dangerous

SCQ Items That Distinguish Between Children with Developmental Delays and Those with Autism Spectrum Disorders (Wiggins et al., 2007, p. 36)

"Sensitivity increased when the SCQ cutoff score is reduced, without compromising specificity. In our sample of children ages 17-45 months, a cut-off score of 11 yielded the highest sensitivity and specificity. These findings suggest that if a reduced cutoff score is employed the SCQ does distinguish very young children with ASD who are referred for early intervention, supporting its utility in detecting ASD in very young children with identified developmental concerns." (Wiggins et al., 2007, p. 35)

Diagnostic Group (% endorsed)

SCQ Item:	DD	ASD
Offers to share	94	53
Shows & directs attention	100	74
Seeks to share enjoyment	100	47
Social smiling	100	68
Appropriate eye gaze	100	42
Attention to voice	100	53
Range of facial expressions	100	68
Appropriate facial expressions	100	58
Imitative social play	100	53
Pointing to express interest	94	47
Head shaking to mean "no"	94	53
Head nodding to mean "yes"	78	16
Social chat	83	21
Complex body mannerisms	5	47

Research Gems: Psychiatric Disease Risk Factors

"Almasy and Blangero (2001) have described three criteria for quantitative risk factors for psychiatric disease. They argue that, ideally, a risk factor, or endophenotype, should be (a) correlated with a disease and/or disease severity, (b) unaffected relatives of an affected individual should show similar, but milder risk factor profiles, and (c) it must be established that variation in the risk factor is heritable." (Dawson et al., 2007, pp. 534-535).

Psychiatric Comorbidities Commonly Associated with Autism

The following were the most common lifetime prevalent psychiatric disorders in children with autism as found and reported by Leyfer et al. (2006, p. 854):

Psychiatric Comorbidity	Percentage
• ADHD (including subsyndromal types)	55%
• Specific Phobia	44%
• Obsessive Compulsive Disorder	37%
• Major Depression (including subsyndromal types)	24%
• Separation Anxiety	12%
• Social Phobia	7.5%
• Oppositional Defiant	7%
• Generalized Anxiety	2.4%

Research Gems: AS & HFA vs. Conduct Disorder

"The CD (conduct disorder) group were clearly different from both the AS and HFA groups. The AS group tended to have less severe early behavioural abnormalities than the HFA group, and were unlikely to have speech abnormalities, but other communicative, social, and restricted, stereotyped behavioural difficulties were largely of a similar pattern to the abnormalities in the HFA group. Eighty per cent of the AS group met criteria for autism on the diagnostic algorithm associated with the Autism Diagnostic Interview-Revised." (Gilchrist, 2001, p. 227)

AS vs. Clinical Conditions to be Ruled Out
(Brasic & Morgan, 2005; Fitzgerald Corvin, 2001; Berney, 2004; Hippler & Klicpera, 2003)

- Adrenal Hypoplasia
- Attention-Deficit/Hyperactivity Disorder
- Basic Phonological Processing Disorder
- Birth Trauma
- Callosal Dysgenesis
- Catatonia
- Cerebellar Affective Syndrome
- Cerebellar Dysfunction
- Cognitive Deficits
- Conduct Disorder
- Cornelia De Lange Syndrome
- Deficits in attention, motor control and perception
- Depression
- Developmental Learning Disability of the Right Hemisphere
- Diabetes Mellitus, Type 1
- Dissociative Identify Disorder

- Dyslexia
- Fahr Syndrome
- Fetal Alcohol Syndrome
- Fragile X Syndrome
- Head Trauma
- Hearing Impairment
- Human Immunodeficiency Virus Infection
- Hyperlexia
- Interventricular Hemorrhage
- Leukodystrophy
- Multidimensionally Impaired Disorder
- Multiple Complex Developmental Disorder
- Multiple Sclerosis
- Nonverbal Learning Disability
- Obsessive-Compulsive Disorder
- Personality Disorder
- Physical Abuse
- Posttraumatic Stress Disorder
- Pragmatic Language Disorder
- Psychosocial Dwarfism
- Reactive Attachment Disorder
- Right Cerebral Hemisphere Damage or Dysfunction
- Schizoid Personality Disorder
- Schizophrenia
- Schizotypal disorder
- Semantic-Pragmatic Processing Disorder
- Sexual Abuse
- Social-Emotional Learning Disorder
- Substance Abuse
- Toxicant-Induced Encephalopathy
- Traumatic Brain Injury
- Triple X Syndrome

Research Gems: Diagnosing Depression in Persons with AS & autism

"Autism and Asperger syndrome are associated with an increased prevalence of psychiatric disorders; the most commonly reported are depression and anxiety. Prevalence estimates of comorbid depression in autism and Asperger syndrome vary widely, from 4 to 38%. The cardinal features of autism and Asperger syndrome make the assessment and diagnosis of depression within these disorders particularly difficult. There is considerable overlap between the symptoms of autism and Asperger syndrome and those of depression and the characteristics of autism and Asperger syndrome may affect the expression of depressive symptoms." (Stewart, et al., 2006, pp. 103-104)

Clinical Instruments For Assesing Depression Secondary to AS and Autism

(Stewart et al., 2006, p. 106)

- ❋ Children's Depression Inventory (CDI)
- ❋ Disability Assessment Schedule (DAS)
- ❋ Diagnostic Interview for Children and Adolescents (DICA)
- ❋ NIMH Diagnostic Interview Schedule (DIS)
- ❋ Kiddie-Schedule for Affective Disorders and Schizophrenia—Epidemiological Version (K-SADS-E)
- ❋ Ontario Child Health Study—Revised (OCHS-R)
- ❋ Reiss Scale
- ❋ Semi-structured Interview

Research Gems: Depression Red Flags for Persons with AS and Autism

"Many of the key features of depression are reported by third-party accounts or are shown in behaviour rather than by self-report. Symptoms such as social withdrawal and abnormal speech patterns, which are symptoms of autism and Asperger syndrome, may be confused with fatigue or psychomotor retardation respectively, thereby making it difficult to discriminate between symptoms of autism and Asperger syndrome, and depression." (Stewart et al., 2006, p. 107)

Assessment Instruments Designed to Evaluate Comorbid Conditions Common to Autism, AS, and NLD

<hr>

Research Gems: AS and Antisocial/Sociopathic Characteristics

"Individuals with AS do not present with antisocial or sociopathic characteristics; the absence of empathy connotes poor insight into the social and emotional nature of other people, not an absence of compassion for their welfare. Individuals with AS often transgress rules at school, with people, and in the community at large….However, they typically do not engage in these acts willfully or maliciously." (Volkmar et al., 2005, p. 101)

<hr>

Devereux Scales of Mental Disorders (DSMD)

Intended ages: 5 – 18 years
Testing time: 15 minutes
Administration: Individual

Intended to be administered by: Educators, psychologists, guidance counselors

Purpose: To evaluate behavioral or emotional problems in children and adolescents by assessing individuals across various settings, with parents, teachers, and other informants providing relevant details regarding the child's behavioral and emotional problems.

Consists of: 111 items to help assess children (ages 5 – 12), and 110 for adolescents (ages 13-18) reflecting the full range of psychopathology including:

- Externalizing disorders: Conduct and Attention/Delinquency scales
- Internalizing disorders: Anxiety and Depression scales
- Critical Pathology disorders: Autism and Acute Problems scales

Other information: Specifically designed for treatment planning and outcome evaluation based on DSM-IV categories. Items and directions are written at the sixth-grade reading level. The autism scale helps to measure problems in areas of impaired social interaction and communication.

Research Gems: Depression vs. Obsession Among Persons with AS and Autism

"Depression in autism and Asperger syndrome may raise an interesting paradox. There is little mention in the literature of how depression impacts on repetitive and obsessional behaviours. If repetitive and obsessional behaviours are decreased in individuals with autism and Asperger syndrome when they become depressed, a reduction may be viewed as an improvement rather than a feature of depression, thereby further masking depression in this group." (Stewart et al., 2006, p. 112)

Kiddie-Sads-Present and Lifetime Version (K-SADS-PL)

Intended ages: Children and adolescents

Testing time: Unstructured Introductory Interview – 10-15 minutes

Administration: Individual

Intended for: Trained professionals

Purpose: Designed to assess current and past episodes of psychopathology in children and adolescents and generate clinical diagnoses based on DSM-IV criteria of disorders including:

Major Depression	Psychotic disorders
Panic disorder	Anxiety disorders
Enuresis	Encopresis
Tic disorders	Conduct disorder
Eating disorders	ADHD
Mania	Social Phobia
Separation Anxiety Disorders	Agoraphobia
Avoidant Disorder/Social Phobias	Anorexia Nervosa
Overanxious/Generalized Anxiety	Dysthymia
Hypomania	Cyclothymia
Bipolar Disorders	Brief Reactive Psychosis
Simple Phobia	Tourette's Disorder
Chronic Motor or Vocal Tic Disorder	Obsessive compulsive disorder
Oppositional defiant disorder	Alcohol and substanceabuse
Adjustment disorders	
Post-traumatic stress disorder	Bulimia Nervosa
Avoidant disorder of childhood and adolescence	

Consists of: A semi-structured diagnostic interview requiring completion of
- an unstructured Introductory Interview
- a Diagnostic Screening Interview
- the Supplement Completion Checklist
- the appropriate Diagnostic Supplements
- the Summary Lifetime Diagnoses Checklist
- the Children's Global Assessment Scale (C-GAS) ratings

Five Diagnostic Supplements:
- Affective Disorders
- Psychotic Disorders
- Anxiety Disorders
- Behavioral Disorders
- Substance Abuse and Other Disorders

Other information: The K-SADS-PL is available as a free Adobe PDF format version for
- Clinical usage in a not-for-profit institution
- Use in an IRB-approved research protocol

(Adobe PDF format available at: http://www.adobe.com/products/acrobat/readstep2.html.

Background information and current forms: http://www.wpic.pitt.edu/ksads/ksads-pl.pdf.)

Research Gems: Autism Spectrum Disorder vs. Obsessive Compulsive Disorder (OCD)

"Parents reported similar levels of sameness behaviour and repetitive movements in the clinical groups, although children with OCD engaged in more repetitive behaviour focused around routines and rituals. Children with OCD reported more compulsions and obsessions than children with ASD; both groups reported more compulsions and obsessions than a typically developing comparison group. Types of compulsions and obsessions tended to be less sophisticated in children with ASD than those with OCD. Sameness behaviour was more prevalent in younger children with OCD, but for children with ASD, age was not significantly related to sameness behaviour, repetitive movements, compulsions, or obsessions." (Zandt et al., 2007, p. 251)

Stroop Color and Word Test

Intended ages: 15–90 years
Testing time: 5 minutes (timed)
Administration: Individual

Intended for: Trained professionals

Purpose: To measure cognitive processing and provide diagnostic information on brain dysfunction, cognition, and psychopathology.

Consists of: A Word Page with color words printed in black ink, a Color Page with "X's" printed in color, and a Color-Word Page with words from the first page printed in colors from the second page (the color and word do not match). The test includes an Interference score, useful in determining the individual's cognitive flexibility, creativity, and reaction to cognitive pressures.

Other information: Based on the observation that individuals can read words much faster than they can identify and name colors. The cognitive dimension tapped by the Stroop is associated with cognitive flexibility, resistance to interference from outside stimuli, creativity, and psychopathology—all of which influence the individual's ability to cope with cognitive stress and process complex input. The test can be used as a screener or as part of a general battery.

Research Gems: ASD as Differential Diagnosis to OCD

"ASD (autism spectrum disorder) can be an important differential diagnosis when diagnosing OCD (obsessive compulsive disorder) and, contrary to the suggestions of some authors, the results of the current study suggest that differentiating between ASD and OCD based on the characteristics of repetitive behaviour is likely to be problematic. Differential diagnosis is most likely to be difficult in high functioning individuals, who do not exhibit such severe social and communication impairments. These impairments are not part of the diagnostic picture in OCD and are therefore useful in ruling out ASD." (Zandt et al., 2007, p. 257)

As indicated by Zandt and colleagues (2007), children who present with autism spectrum disorder (ASD) tend to be described being 'obsessed' with the collecting of facts or assimilation of knowledge regarding certain topics that brings them enjoyment and do not involve anxiety. On the other hand, obsessions seen in obsessive compulsive disorder (OCD) are typically accompanied with the provoking of varying degrees of anxiety and bring no enjoyment to the person who compulsively undertakes them. The authors add that "it is possible that children with ASD pursue their circumscribed interests in an obsessional manner as a response to anxiety, however, the language impairments and difficulties with introspection in these children make it difficult to assess this. These factors also make it difficult to assess whether children with ASD experience their repetitive behaviour as foreign and unwanted (or 'ego-dystonic'), a feature which is considered to be a defining component of OCD." (Zandt et al., 2007, p. 252)

Stroop Tasks
(Stroop, 1935)

Description:

A psychological test of our attentional-mental vitality and flexibility. The task takes advantage of our ability to read words more quickly and automatically than we can name colors. If a word is printed or displayed in a color different from the color it actually names; for example, if the word "green" is written in blue ink we will say the word "green" more readily than we can name the color in which it is displayed, which in this case is "blue." The cognitive mechanism involved in this task is called directed attention. You have to manage your attention, inhibit or top one response in order to say or do something else. The Stroop Test provides insight into cognitive effects that are experience as a result of attentional fatigue.

(See http://www.snre.umich.edu/eplab/demos/st)/stroopdesc.html.- 7/28/2007)

For examples of Stroop tasks available on the Internet visit (sites assessed 7/15/07):
http://faculty.washington.edu/chudler/sout2.html
http://www.snre.umich.edu/eplab/demos/st)/stroopdesc.html
http://www.dcity.org/braingames/stroop/
http://en.wikipedia.org/wiki/Stroop_effect#In_synesthetes
http://www.adhd.org.nz/stroop1.html
http://www.pbs.org/wgbh/nova/everest/exposure/stroopnonshock.html
http://sharpbrains.wordpress.com/2006/09/14/brain-teaser-better-than-coffee/

Research Gems: Seven Behaviors that Serve to Discriminate among Children with Autism (AD), Typical Development (TD), and Developmental Delays (DD)
(Clifford et al., 2007, p. 308)

Behavior	AD	TD	DD
Proto-declarative showing	7.1%	50.0%	62.5%
Eye contact (quality)	75.0%	0.0%	31.3%
Positive affect	78.6%	12.5%	33.3%
Gaze aversion	50.0%	0.0%	6.3%
Nestling	50.0%	0.0%	9.1%
Peer interest	90.9%	0.0%	6.3%
Conventional games	54.5%	0.0%	15.4%

The following chart identifies DSM-IV-TR diagnostic labels that can mimic symptoms of, or be comorbid with, AS, HFA and/or NLD.

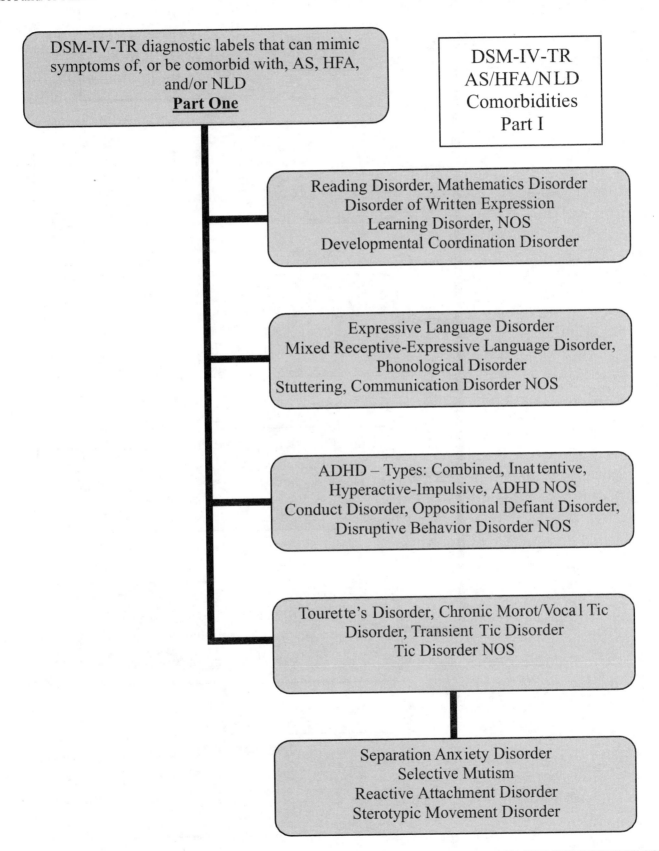

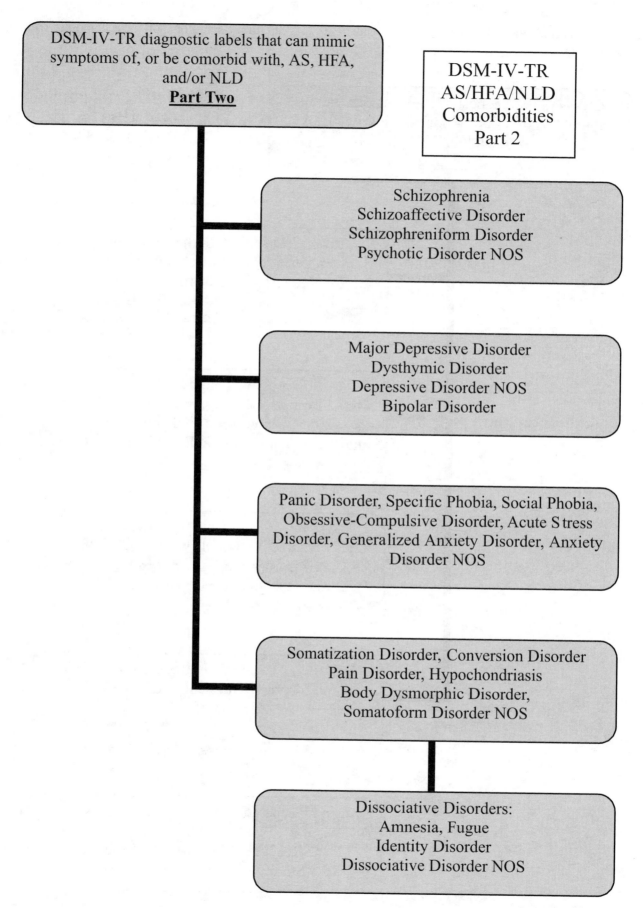

DSM-IV-TR diagnostic labels that can mimic symptoms of, or be comorbid with, AS, HFA, and/or NLD
Part Two

DSM-IV-TR
AS/HFA/NLD
Comorbidities
Part 2

Schizophrenia
Schizoaffective Disorder
Schizophreniform Disorder
Psychotic Disorder NOS

Major Depressive Disorder
Dysthymic Disorder
Depressive Disorder NOS
Bipolar Disorder

Panic Disorder, Specific Phobia, Social Phobia, Obsessive-Compulsive Disorder, Acute Stress Disorder, Generalized Anxiety Disorder, Anxiety Disorder NOS

Somatization Disorder, Conversion Disorder
Pain Disorder, Hypochondriasis
Body Dysmorphic Disorder,
Somatoform Disorder NOS

Dissociative Disorders:
Amnesia, Fugue
Identity Disorder
Dissociative Disorder NOS

DSM-IV-TR diagnostic labels that can mimic symptoms of, or be comorbid with, AS, HFA, and/or NLD
Part Three

DSM-IV-TR
AS/HFA/NLD
Comorbidities
Part 3

Sexual and Gender Identify Disorders:
Sexual Desire, Sexual Arousal, Orgasmic, Sexual Pain. Paraphilias: Exhibitionism, Fetishism, Pedophilia, Voyeurism.

Eating Disorder NOS
Sleep Disorders: Insomnia, Hypersomnia, Dyssomnia NOS; Nightmare, Sleep Terror, Sleepwalking, and Parasomnia NOS

Impulse-Control Disorders: Intermittent Explosive, Kleptomania, Trichotillomania, Pathological (collections/hoarding) Impulse-Control Disorder NOS

Adjustment Disorders; Personality Disorders: Paranoid, Schizoid, Schizotypal, Antisocial, Borderline, Histrionic, Narcissistic, Dependent, OCD, NOS

Adverse Effects of Medication NOS; Relational Problems, Problems Related to Abuse/Neglect; Noncompliance, Malingering, Adult Antisocial, Identity

Chapter 11

Learning Styles

The Importance of Preferred, or Personal Orientation, Learning Styles

Introduction

Regardless of whether one's "official DSM-IV-TR and/or ICD-10 diagnostic classification" fits the criteria of Asperger's syndrome, high-functioning autism, or the as-yet-to-be-listed nonverbal learning disorder, the labels themselves do not have much to offer regarding each labeled person's set of strengths or deficits, cognitive peaks or valleys, or vocational aptitude. Additionally, just knowing what someone's "label" may be, in spite of its accuracy and adherence to a particular set of predetermined criteria does not give a clinician, educator, or parent/caregiver much to draw from with regard to designing the most beneficial and personally congruent set of instructions, strategies, and interventions to optimize that person's potential. Identifying a person's preferred learning style, however, serves to bridge the gap between a diagnostic label and instructional program that can be designed to best fulfill that individual's needs.

Although, as long as our senses are intact, all of us obtain knowledge and experience from each and every learning modality, most of us tend to have a preferred learning style from which we gain greatest benefit and with which we feel most comfortable. From the moment that we begin to gather and incorporate information from our environment, other people, and our own reactions to passing events, each of us exercise our own natural learning proclivities orienting via two or three learning styles that tend to come more naturally. Without conscious awareness, or effort, we begin focusing on experiences and exploring our world, ourselves, and others by watching, listening, and/or manipulating objects.

Learning a particular defensive move in martial arts, for example, will typically involve a mixture of all three learning, and teaching, styles. Some instructors will first show (kinesthetic teaching) you and verbally describe (verbal teaching) the initial moves while you watch (visual learning), and listen (auditory learning) before you try out the moves (kinesthetic learning) yourself. A good instructor will typically use all three teaching styles—along with other, secondary ones—to assure that every aspect of the strategy is covered and hopefully incorporated. The student, anxious to learn, will try and focus on each and every sight, word, and movement that is shared and demonstrated hoping to optimize learning as quickly and effectively as possible. Each of us, however, will tend to lean toward gaining the biggest benefit from either the visual, auditory, or kinesthetic aspect of the instruction. Although all three are important, one will benefit us the most, another one second, the other third, and so on. As such, each morsel, and mode, of instruction becomes but a part in a summation that ends up as a gestalt of teaching and learning that adds up to a defense form, or, in martial arts terms, a kata.

Similarly, learning to play a musical instrument must at some point or another involve the three primary learning styles. Learning to play a chord on a guitar, for instance, typically involves either watching someone show you how and where to place your fingers, listening to their step by step instruction—as well as the sound the strings make when the fingers are placed and pressed correctly—and attempting to form the chord yourself. Although it is possible to learn to form and play a chord—or learn a martial art's move—without the luxury of all three modalities, having all three at one's disposal presents invaluable advantages.

Again, however, most of us have a preferred learning, or orientating, style from which we gain most benefit. While some of us may walk away from our lesson visually recalling the placement of our fingers on the guitar strings, or the angles of our feet on our martial arts' stance, others will tune in to the echoes of the verbal instruction long after the images are gone. Others, by the same account, will go to sleep that night, and wake up the following morning, with fingers, or legs, still adapting to the formation that will eventually, through much practice, hard work, and dedication, result in automatic movements each benefiting from the aggregate of all three (or more) teaching and learning modalities.

Because of problems involving central coherence, theory of mind, mirror-neuron deficits, executive dysfunction, and other alternate wiring related impediments, most people across the spectrums of AS, HFA, and NLD, however, will tend to lean much more specifically toward one learning style or orientation than those of us who are neurotypically wired. In general, persons with autism tend to be visual, then kinesthetic learners. As such, they benefit the most from watching things being done, and secondly from exploring, touching, and manipulating objects and engaging in the task themselves. Those with AS, likewise, will typically gain the most from these two primary learning modalities. On the other hand, persons with NLD will tend to gain the most from auditory instruction, learning by listening, rather than watching or doing.

In effect, verbal instruction aimed at a strong visual learner will virtually "fall on deaf ears" with the person quickly losing track of the instructional attempts regardless of how slowly, judiciously, and carefully the task may be explained. The auditory learner trying to learn via visual ("watch me do this!") or kinesthetic ("here, you try it!") instruction will most often result in wasted time and effort, and lead to frustration for both parties. Likewise, a visual or kinesthetic learner being taught via direct verbal instruction, will soon become bored, uninterested, and come across as lazy, oppositional, having an "attitude," or being a "behavioral problem."

Identifying a person's preferred learning style, or mode of primary orientation to the world, him- or herself, and others, is an essential part of being able to reach, communicate with, and succeed with persons across the AS, HFA, and NvLD spectrums.

Learning Styles Inventory©

John M. Ortiz, Ph.D.

The following checklist is offered to assist in determining one's preferred learning style or primary orientation.

JMO-LSI-'08©

I am good at and/or enjoy:	Visual	Auditory	Kinesthetic
Watching a good performance	X		
Puzzles	X		
Reading	X		
Visual organization & structure	X		
Understanding charts & graphs	X		
Recalling faces, but not names	X		
Finding my way around	X		
Painting, sketching, drawing	X		
Face to face meetings	X		
Analogies & metaphors	X		
Manipulating images	X		
Imagining scenes as I read	X		
Putting things together	X		
Designing	X		
Slides, posters, and pictures	X		
Interpreting visual images	X		
Watching people	X		
Putting things together by visualizing the end result	X		
Showing emotions with my eyes	X		
Remembering how someone looked	X		
Reading manuals and following diagrams when in need	X		
Watching sports	X		

Looking at the person I am speaking with or to	X		
Watching someone play music	X		
Finding places by recalling images in my mind	X		
Spelling by "seeing the word" in my mind	X		
Using words like "see, look, watch, picture, imagine"	X		
Watching movies, or looking at pictures of exotic places	X		
Watching the scenes in movies	X		
"Find the missing piece" games	X		
Recalling the sights after a holiday	X		
Thinking about it before diving in	X		
I prefer chatting in person	X		
Where there is something to say I prefer to say it face to face	X		
I am good at, and/or enjoy:		**Auditory**	
Remembering how someone sounds		X	
Sounding out words when spelling		X	
Listening to a good performance		X	
Using words like "hear, tune, listen, and think"		X	
Storytelling		X	
Listening to stories about exotic places		X	
Explaining things verbally		X	
Verbal humor		X	
Remembering names, not faces		X	
Word meanings		X	
Engaging in verbal reasoning		X	
Replaying conversations in my mind		X	
Convincing others of my views		X	
Analyzing language		X	

Searching for the "best words"		X	
Learning new words		X	
Listening to dialog in a movie		X	
Listening to sports		X	
Listening to someone play music		X	
Finding places by remembering or replaying verbal directions		X	
Talking on the phone		X	
Calling tech support when in need		X	
Recalling the sounds after a holiday		X	
Focusing and sitting still while I'm talking		X	
Talking about it before I dive in		X	
I prefer chatting over the phone		X	
Where there is something to say I prefer to leave a voice mail		X	
I am good at, and/or enjoy:			**Kinesthetic**
Remembering how someone moved			X
Following verbal instructions			X
Lectures			X
Group discussions			X
Verbal learning (tapes, CD, MP3)			X
Learning by reading out-loud			X
Listening to people talk			X
Using unique words when talking			X
Word teasers			X
Using gestures & expressive moves			X
Recalling what I did after a holiday			X
Talking while I'm walking			X
Using words like "feel, touch, hold, put, place, move, do"			X

Action stories, novels, movies			X
Taking part in a good performance			X
Hands-on activities			X
Going to exotic places			X
Acting			X
Diving right in			X
Charades			X
Arts and craft projects			X
Body language			X
When in doubt, just checking it out			X
Watching people move			X
Using my hands when I talk			X
Active sports			X
Playing a musical instrument			X
Eye-hand coordination			X
Finding places by "feel"			X
Coordination/balancing activities			X
Figuring it out as I go along			X
I prefer chatting over the Internet			X
Where there is something to say I prefer text messaging or e-mail			X

The following Learning Styles Inventory is recommended:

Learning Styles Inventory (LSI)

Intended ages: Junior high, high school and college students, and adults
Testing time: 15–20 minutes
Administration: Individual

Intended to be administered by: Self or other

Purpose: To help determine which learning environments—and which instructors—are best for particular students in both academic settings and industrial training programs.

Consists of: Thirty items that provide four kinds of information:
- Preferred Conditions for Learning
- Areas of Interest
- Mode of Learning
- Expectation for Course Grade

Other information: Helps to classify into one of nine learner types and includes a Learner Typology that allows the identification of students who share similar learning styles. The LSI can be used in counseling centers, classrooms, and industrial training programs to adapt instructional strategies to learner needs, to design alternative curricula, to help individuals select courses or work environments compatible with their learning styles, and to help reduce dropout rates.

Online and contact information for Learning Style Inventories:

Learning Styles Online - http://www.learning-styles-online.com

DVC Learning Style Survey for College - http://www.metamath.com/lsweb/dvclearn/html

Motivated Strategies for Learning Questionnaire
University of Michigan
610 University Avenue, Room 1323
Ann Arbor, MI 48109-1259
http://www.ldpride.net/learning_style.html

Index of Learning Styles Questionnaire
Dr. Richard M. Felder
Department of Chemical Engineering
North Carolina State University
Raleigh, NC 27695-7905
felder@ncsu.edu

Learning Styles Test - http://www.engr.ncsu.edu/learningstyles/ilsweb.html

Self Assessment - http://www.ulc.arizona.edu/learn_styl_ass.html

Three Different Learning Styles - http://www.usd.edu/trio/tut/ts/style.html

Index of Learning Styles - http://www.ncsu.edu/felder-public/ILSpage.html

The VARK Inventory - Contact: Neal Fleming, flemingn@ihug.co.nz
http://www.vark-learn.com
Learning Styles Assessment - http://www.com/assess/learningstyle.html
Ageless Learner
1075 Old Greenville Road
Staunton, VA 24401-9657
info@agelesslearner.com

Learning Styles Survey
Suzanne Miller
Diablo Valley College
321 Golf Club Road
Pleasant Hill, CA 94523
smiller@dvc.edu

Abiator's Learning Styles
http://www.berghuis.co.nz/abiator/index.html

Chapter 12

Early Developmental Markers

Research Gems: Early AS Detection

"Here we report the first-ever prospective study of a child born to two adults with a formal diagnosis of Asperger syndrome. The child's parents are both scientists (a mathematician and a chemist)….The child failed the Checklist for Autism in Toddlers at 18 months and met the criteria for Asperger syndrome at 26 months. This single case is consistent with the hypersystemizing, assortative mating theory of autism….This study also demonstrates that Asperger syndrome can be diagnosed by age 26 months." (Baron-Cohen, 2006, 21, p. 351)

The Assessment Process

Collection of Pre, Peri, and Post-natal Information

Although current and ongoing research consistently points toward a combination of genetic (familial pre-disposition) and environmental triggers as the most likely culprits that lead to autism spectrum disorders (ASD), including AS, some research has indicated that a number of pre-, peri-, and post-natal factors may exacerbate pre-existing vulnerabilities among these populations. As such, the presence of these factors may serve to increase the risk, or severity, of some ASD conditions.

Pre-, peri-, and post-natal factors that have been suggested in the literature as potential red flags include:
- Maternal infections (influenza, mumps, rubella, measles, herpes, syphilis, HIV)
- Certain drug exposures (Thalidomide, Valproate)
- Pregnancy initiated during later years
- Viral infections (herpes encephalitis, meningitis)
- Viral illnesses during the first 18 months of life (mumps, chickenpox, ear infections)
- Chemical and toxin exposures (lead, aluminum, mercury, preservatives, heavy metals)
- Vaccines containing mercury and/or thimerosal

Research Gems: Diagnostic Markers

"Children with severe language deficits received a diagnosis an average of 1.2 years earlier than other children. Hand flapping, toe walking, and sustained odd play were associated with a decrease in the age of diagnosis, whereas oversensitivity to pain and hearing impairment were associated with an increase. Children who had 4 or more primary care physicians before diagnosis received a diagnosis 0.5 years later than other children, whereas those whose pediatricians referred them to a specialist received a diagnosis 0.3 years sooner." (Mandell et al., 2005, p. 1480)

Careful Notation of Developmental Milestones

In comparison to "normally developing children," also known as "neurotypicals" (NTs), children with ASD present with myriad atypical developmental milestones that fluctuate not only from one person with a particular ASD to another, but within the same person at different times of examination. For this reason, it is essential that a history of developmental milestones be collected from not only one, or two, parents or caregivers, but from an extended number of sources to help maximize accuracy of observed behaviors.

Because persons with ASDs present with so many different levels of atypical symptoms, behaviors, and characteristics, it is often very difficult to assemble a coherent historical account of a child's developmental and health history in a cursory manner. In effect, it is not unusual for two highly qualified, highly observant clinicians to examine the same child at different times, or in two different settings, within a short time frame, and arrive at very different conclusions based on two vastly diverse sets of information. In order to maximize the acquisition of a coherent and cohesive foundation of developmental data, clinicians are advised to be patient, comprehensive, and exhaustive during these early screening and assessment periods.

That said, a number of developmental milestones that need particular attention include:

- Attainment of speech and language
- Social developmental
- Gross motor skills
- Fine-motor skills
- Possible hearing deficits
- Evidence of developmental regression
- Unusual play skills
- Lack of social interest
- Perseverative or repetitive behaviors
- Echolalia

Family History
Along with the collection of information relating to developmental milestones clinicians are advised to collect a comprehensive picture detailing an extensive family history involving not only immediate family members, but also medical, clinical, neurological, and other relevant information pertaining to the patient's extended family and relatives. Although evidence from siblings and biological parents of children with ASDs tend to show patterns

pointing toward the possibilities of a broader autistic phenotype, particularly among males with AS and their fathers, there is often the presence of conditions that are tangential, or related, to ASDs present among extended family members. Any one, or more, of these conditions extant in primary family members or extended relatives may provide additional support for the possibility of an ASD. Some of these conditions include:

- Dyslexia
- Learning Disabilities
- ADHD/ADD
- Dysgraphia
- Dyspraxia
- Nonverbal Learning Disorder
- Obsessive Compulsive Disorder
- Depression
- Anxiety
- Tourette's or Tic disorders
- Semantic Pragmatic Disorder
- Bipolar Disorder
- (often misdiagnosed) psychosis or schizophrenia
- (often misdiagnosed) schizoid or personality disorder

Medical History

A still vastly misunderstood disorder, the picture of autism is almost consistently complicated by the presence of a number of medical issues that tend to both exacerbate and mask the presence of ASD symptoms and behaviors. Physicians who are not well trained or experienced with ASD populations may at times tend to misdiagnose autism, particularly during its early stages, with any number of medical conditions that present with symptoms and behaviors that tend to closely mimic autistic characteristics. For this reason, it is crucial that pediatricians be well-versed with ASD conditions and the diversity of their presentations before an accurate medical picture can be assembled. In effect, an awareness of symptoms related to medical conditions that tend to mimic, or be related to, ASDs is always critical. Among other challenges, physicians should be aware of the fact that ASDs often mimic a number of medical conditions and several medical conditions often mimic ASDs.

Among these, red flags include:
- Hyper- and hypo-sensitivities to various sensory stimuli
- Vision and auditory problems
- Chronic ear infections
- Unusually high number of infections
- Immune dysfunction
- Autoimmune disorders such as thyroid problems and rashes
- Food or environmental allergies
- Gastrointestinal ailments

Diagnostic History

As noted above, ASDs are typically associated with a number of general medical conditions. Additionally, however, the ASD picture is further complicated by the typical presence of a number of neurological impairments and neurodevelopmental genetic syndromes. Among these, clinicians should note the presence of red flags that include:

- Epilepsy
- Seizures
- Tuberous sclerosis
- Encephalitis
- Phenylketonuria
- Fragile-X Syndrome

Educational or Vocational History

Although an enormous amount of accurate, helpful information can typically be gathered from parents and caregivers, at times information coming from these primary sources may be biased or inaccurate due to a number of factors such as a parent's lack of experience in noting age-appropriate behaviors or milestones, lack of education or awareness regarding ASDs, denial to a child's problematic symptoms, the absence of comparative benchmarks (other, neuro-typical, similar-age children), the presence of confounding familial or environmental factors (divorce, long work hours, limited time spent with the child), confounding medical conditions that may mask the presence of an actual ASD, or the presence of some of an ASD or autistic-type conditions in themselves that may make the child's condition appear "normal" or "average."

For these, and other reasons, it is always helpful to collect data from a child's educational—or an adult's vocational—networks. Although teachers, as well as employers, can at times share similar characteristics to the ones described above that may obscure the presence of an ASD, other times their feedback is invaluable in helping to assemble a comprehensive picture contributing to the accuracy of a helpful diagnosis. At times, even just a detail or two shared by an observant or caring teacher, teacher's aid, employer, or co-worker may make a significant difference in helping to identify, or solidify, an ASD leading to helpful interventions or resources that may prove invaluable with short- and long-term benefits.

In addition to information from a child's primary teacher, clinicians are strongly recommended to acquire extended information from other sources of contact within the child's network including:

- School counselors
- Principal and vice-principal
- Physical education coaches
- School nurses and medical staff
- Front office and support staff
- School custodial employees
- Bus drivers or van escorts
- Special education assistants
- Classroom aides
- Bus stop supervisors
- Hall monitors
- Classroom peer mentors
- School vocational/career counselors
- Art/music/drama teachers

Rating Scales

Over the past few years, a sizable and welcomed number of behavioral checklists and rating scales have been appearing in catalogs, at conferences and workshops, and, ultimately, in clinical settings. Closely echoing the rapidly rising numbers, and awareness, of ASD across homes, clinics, schools, medical, and other settings, the increasing quantity and quality of these behavioral scales have proven extremely beneficial in helping to identify the early appearance of ASD symptoms, in turn contributing to earlier and more accurate diagnostic impressions, the development of support networks, and practical interventions.

Although very much in their infancy, a number of rating scales are beginning to receive increased support and the "seal of approval" from parents, teachers, clinicians, and others who use them with various degrees of expectation and efficacy.

Research Gems: "Response to Joint Attention"

"Early delay in development of RJA (Response to Joint Attention) is an early marker of communication and social delays, including ASD (Autism Spectrum Disorder) and BAP (Broader Autism Phenotype). Early developmental screening should include a focus on RJA, but successful response to RJA tasks at 14 months is not sufficient to rule out an ASD. Judgments about risk for ASD must be based on more than just RJA, children who are not responding to pointing cues for RJA by 24 months of age should be considered at risk for developmental delay and should have a thorough screening." (Sullivan et al., 2007, p. 46)

General Neuro-typical* Developmental Markers

The following is a suggested checklist of "red flags" (potential warning signals) *the absence, or relative delay of which* could indicate the possibility of an autism spectrum disorder. The checklist can also be used when preparing information to share with teachers, clinicians, therapists, and other professionals who will be assisting in the care of the child. The various concerns can also be helpful across educational, therapeutic, and clinical settings when coordinating multi-modal services or considering a formal, comprehensive assessment of children presenting with the possibility of autism spectrum disorders.

*The term "neuro-typical" refers to children who are outside of the spectrum of autism, Asperger's, or NLD conditions. In other words, a child, or adult, who is "neuro-typical," or "NT," is thought of as having "neurologically typical wiring in the brain." More common words would be children ordinarily described as "normal" or "regular functioning." In effect, the following characteristics are those that a "neuron-typical," or "normally functioning" child should be demonstrating at the noted ages. Functioning that is significantly delayed, or aberrant, from those noted should be considered as potential "red flags," or potential warning signals that should be reported to the child's pediatrician.

By age three months, child should be capable of:
__ rolling
__ being alert to environmental and sensory stimuli

By age 4 – 6 months, child should be capable of:
__ executing command of head control
__ reaching for objects (by 5 months)
__ producing a social smile

By age 6 – 12 months, child should be capable of:
__ executing a consistent pattern of primate reflexes (by 6 months)
__ babbling (6 months)
__ demonstrating anxiety when in presence of strangers (7 months)
__ sitting (7 months)
__ demonstrating ability to orient to or localize sound (10 months)
__ abandoning mouthing of objects (12 months)

By age 12 – 24 months, child should be capable of:
__ executing a consistent pattern of consonant production (by 15 months)
__ executing a consistent pattern of social imitation (16 months)
__ executing a consistent pattern of protodeclarative pointing (18 months)
__ executing a consistent pattern of hand dominance (18 months)
__ demonstrating ability to execute comfortable transitions across tasks (21–24 months)
__ demonstrating ability to walk up and down the stairs (24 months)
__ demonstrating a pattern of communicative speech

Research Gems: "Age of Recognition"

"We examined factors related to parental age of recognition (AOR) or early abnormalities and the association between AOR and diagnosis and levels of functioning at 2 and 4 years in 75 toddlers with ASD. Results suggest significant differences between autism and PDD-NOS in the AOR (age of recognition) and type of first concerns. Early social and motor delays as well as maternal age was associated with AOR. Later AOR was associated with poorer social-communicative and nonverbal cognitive functioning at 2 and 4." (Chawarska et al, 2007, p. 62)

Neuro-typical Developmental Milestones

Typically, sometime between the age of 4 and 6 months, the child will:
- Engage with others by reciprocating social smiles
- Display babbling and cooing sounds (precursors to speech)
- React to the faces of other infants, children, and adults
- Explore the faces of others as if absorbing social information
- Respond to human voices

At some point between the age of 6 and 9 months, the child will:
- Point by using his or her index finger
- Seek reassurance by looking at other's faces when stressed or confused
- Initiate joint attention through the use of facial and body gestures
- Search the faces of others in search for social information

At some point between the age of 9 and 12 months, the child will:
- Begin to use combinations of consonants and vowels
- Orient to others when his or her name is called
- Show developmental increases in joint attention
- Demonstrate developmental increases in reciprocal interactions

At some point between the age of 9 and 12 months, the child will:
- Display gradual improvements in awareness of other children
- Display developmental increases in use of vocalizations and gestures
- Demonstrate gradual, more complex joint attention
- Use of words will increase in terms of purpose and vocabulary

---

Research Gems: "Early Screening Difficulties with Asperger's"

"It is most likely to be children with poor language development and/or general developmental delay who present early on for diagnosis. Children with no apparent delay in the onset of speech may not be identified or referred till later if they pass early developmental milestones on screening….Yet parents of able children with ASD mostly report in retrospect that they did have concerns before age 3, and in the case of children with Asperger syndrome, most often about their child's behaviour (especially overactivity), lack of social interest or dislike of change." (McConachie et al., 2005, p. 167)

Developmental Evaluation

(The following is adapted from the Family Practice Notebook at Family Practice Notebook.com: http://fpnotebook. com/PED43.htm.)

I.   Markers that could increase the risk for disability
- Low-income family
- Parents with limited education
- Parents with mental health concerns
- Single parent family
- Numerous siblings
- Parental unemployment
- Lack of parental concerns

II.   Survey Parental Concerns
    A.   Use Clinician Trigger Question
        1.   Ask Parent: "Please tell me any concerns you have"
           a.   Learning
           b.   Developing
           c.   Behaving
    B.   Use standardized questionnaire
        1.   Children's Behavior Checklist
        2.   Pediatric Symptom Checklist

III.   Developmental Screening Tests for Parental Concerns
- Behavior
- Speech and Language
- Gross motor
- Fine motor
- Global concerns

IV.   Tools
    A.   Developmental Screening Tests
        1.   Ages and Stages Questionnaire
        2.   Battelle Developmental Inventory
        3.   Bayley Infant Neurodevelopmental Screen
        4.   Brigance Screens
        5.   CAT/CLAMS
        6.   Denver Developmental Screening Test II
        7.   Minnesota Child Developmental Inventory
        8.   Parent's Evaluations of Developmental Status

    B.   Developmental Assessment Tools
        1.   Young children under age three years: Cognitive Test
           a.   Bayley II Developmental Assessment
           b.   McCarthy Scales of Children's Ability
        2.   Children three years and older: Intelligence Testing
           a.   Stanford-Binet Intelligence Scale
           b.   Wechsler Intelligence Scale

    C.   Behavioral Screening
        1.   Eyberg Child Behavior Inventory
        2.   Family Psychosocial Screening
        3.   Pediatric Symptom Checklist

    D.   Other Tests
        1.   Language and communication
           a. Sequenced Inventory Communication Development (4 – 48 months)
        2.   Adaptive and Social Functioning
           a.   Vineland Adaptive Behavior Scales (birth – 18 years)

Developmental Milestones

The following are neuro-typical milestones that normally developing children are expected to demonstrate at the noted ages.

(The following is adapted from the Family Practice Notebook at Family Practice Notebook.com: http://fpnotebook.com/PED43.htm.)

- Cognitive Milestones
  - Month 3-5: Attends to and reaches for objects
  - Month 4-8: Pull string to secure a ring
  - Month 8-15: Imitates patting doll
  - Month 14-20: Finds hidden object
  - Month 18-28: Completes simple puzzles

- Language Milestones
  - Month 1.5-3: Squeals
  - Month 3.5-8: Turns to locate a voice
  - Month 9-13: Says mama or dada
  - Month 14-24: Combines two different words
  - Month 21-35: Uses plurals

- Social and Emotional Milestones
  - Month 1.5-4: Smiles at others
  - Month 4-9: Seeks primary caregiver
  - Month 8-15: Stranger anxiety
  - Month 10-15: Displays two or more recognizable emotions
  - Month 11-20: Exploratory play by self
  - Month 21-36: Cooperative play in small groups

- Gross Motor Milestones
  - Month 2-4-5: Rolls over
  - Month 5-8: Sits without support
  - Month 10-14: Stands alone
  - Month 14-20: Walks up steps
  - Month 21-28: Pedals tricycle
  - Month 30-44: Balances on one foot
  - By age 6: Rhythmic skipping
  - By age 8.5: Alternates foot-hop in place
  - By age 10: Holds tandem stance for 10 seconds (eyes closed)

- Fine Motor Milestones
  - Month 2.5-4: Grasps rattle
  - Month 4.5-7: Transfers cube hand to hand
  - Month 8-12: Has neat pincer grasp
  - Month 15-20: Builds tower of four cubes
  - Month 18-24: Imitates vertical line

- Month 28-36: Copies circle
- By age 5 years: Draws a square
- By age 5.5 years: Tripod pencil grasp
- By age 7 years: Draws diagonal line
- By age9: Draws cross with same dimensions
- By age 12: Draws three dimensional cube

- <u>Self Help Milestones</u>
  - Month 4.5-8: Feeds self crackers
  - Month 10-14: Drinks from cup
  - Month 13-19: Removes clothes
  - Month 18-28: Washes and dries hands
  - Month 30-42: Dresses without supervision
  - Attained on average by age 4.5 years:
    - ⊙ Rides a Bicycle with training wheels
    - ⊙ Cuts paper with scissors
    - ⊙ Colors inside lines
  - Attained on average by age 5.5 years:
    - ⊙ Ties shoelaces
    - ⊙ Prints first and last names
  - Attained on average by age 6 years:
    - ⊙ Rides a Bicycle without training wheels

<u>Research Gems: "Early Asperger's Diagnosis"</u>

"This study suggests that, in community referred samples, early diagnosis of Asperger syndrome is not generally to be expected. The majority of children will continue to come to attention once they are introduced to the demands of educational settings and have reached the age when lack of friendships, poor self-help skills, circumscribed interests, and inappropriate conversation skills are more evident through comparison with other children." (McConachie et al., 2005, p. 175)

Assessment Instruments Designed to Evaluate Developmental Status

RECOMMENDED
Bayley Scale of Infant and Toddler Development, Third Edition (BAYLEY-III)

Intended ages: 1 month to 42 months
Testing time: 30 – 90 minutes (depending on child's age)
Administration: Individual

Intended to be administered by: Trained professionals

Purpose: To evaluate the developmental status of young children. Clinical studies included populations of premature, small for gestational age children, Down syndrome, pervasive developmental disorder, at-risk children, FAS/ploy substance use, asphyxia, cerebral palsy, and language impairment.

Consists of: Core battery of five scales:
- Cognitive: visual preference, attention, memory, sensorimotor, exploration and manipulation, concept formation
- Motor: fine motor and gross motor subtests
- Language: receptive and expressive language subtests
- Social-emotional: Communicating needs, and self-regulation using emotional signals
- Adaptive Behavior: Communication, self-care, and self-direction.

Three of the scales—cognitive, motor and language—are administered with child interaction. The other two, social-emotional and motor and adaptive behavior, require parent questionnaires. Also includes a Caregiver Report Form, Behavior Observation Inventory, Social-emotional subtest, Adaptive Behavior subtest, and Growth Scores/Charts to assist in monitoring and charting a child's intervention progress and outcome over time, and a Screening Test to assess the necessity of additional testing.

Other information: Designed to help identify an infant's or toddler's strengths and competencies, as well as their weaknesses in both lower and higher functioning infants and toddlers. Provides valid, reliable measures of a child's abilities as well as comparison information to help identify clinical risk on children with high-incidence clinical diagnoses.

RECOMMENDED
Mullen Scales of Early Learning

Intended ages: Birth through 68 months
Testing time: 25–40 minutes
Administration: Individual

Intended to be administered by: Trained professionals

Purpose: A developmentally integrated system designed to assess language, motor, and perceptual abilities.

Consists of: Five scales: Gross motor (birth to 33 months), receptive and expressive language, visual-perceptual skills, visual-motor skills (including fine motor), and an Early Learning Composite score. The scales provide a complete picture of cognitive and motor abilities, helps to identify strengths and weaknesses, and effectively helps to assess school readiness.

Other information: The manual includes suggestions for optimizing the performance of children with "uneven learning patterns." Contains ample stimulating materials and manipulative components, yields an easy profile analysis, and effectively assists to formulate successful interventions.

Mullen ASSIST computer software
Includes:
- Personal Information Summary
- Score summary
- T-score profile
- Early Learning Composite
- Score narrative
- Recommend activities

Mullen ASSIST computer software is designed to simplify measurement by calculating and converting raw scores for simple, direct interpretation. The software also provides suggestions for developmentally appropriate tasks to assist parents in planning learning activities for the children.
    Available: http://ags.pearsonassessments.com/group.asp?nGroupInfoID=a11150

RECOMMENDED
Developmental Profile II (DP-II)

<u>Intended ages</u>: Infancy through 9 ½ years.
<u>Testing time</u>: 20–40 minutes
<u>Administration</u>: Individual

<u>Intended to be administered by</u>: Trained professionals

<u>Purpose</u>: To screen for developmental advances or delays. Designed to assess development in the following five areas:

- <u>Physical Age</u>
- Large and small muscle coordination, strength, stamina, flexibility, and sequential motor skills
- <u>Self-Help Age</u>
- Ability to cope independently with the environment: to eat, dress, work, and take care of self and others
- <u>Social Age</u>
- Interpersonal abilities, emotional needs, and manner in which the child relates to friends, relatives, and various adults
- <u>Academic Age</u>
- Intellectual abilities and skills prerequisite to academic achievement—plus an IQ equivalency score
- <u>Communication Age</u>
- Expressive and receptive communication skills, including written, spoken, and gestural language

<u>Consists of</u>: 186 items, each describing a particular skill, that are typically answered by a parent, caregiver, or therapist who is familiar with the child with regard to whether or not the child has mastered the skill in question.

<u>Other information</u>: Profile assists in quickly determining advanced or delayed development in the five above areas. Computer-generated report includes individualized teaching suggestions and recommendations to assist with clinical reports.

Battelle Developmental Inventory, Second Edition (BDI-2)

Intended ages: birth – 7. 11 years of age
Testing time: 10 – 30 minutes
Administration: Individual

Intended to be administered by: Trained Professionals

Purpose: Screening, diagnosis, and evaluation of early development to help identify children with:

- Speech/Language Impairments and delays
- Social/Emotional developmental delays
- Cognitive delays and Mental retardation
- Motor Impairment and delays
- Hearing Impairment and deafness
- Other health Impairments

Consists of: Personal-Social, Adaptive, Motor, Communication, and Cognitive Ability measures. Offers two types of assessment – a full assessment (uses the complete instrument's five domains), and a screening test (an abbreviated instrument that includes 100 test items from the full BDI-2)

Additional Information:
  Adaptive Domain:
  - Self-Care
  - Personal Responsibility
  Personal-Social Domain:
  - Adult Interaction
  - Peer Interaction
  - Self-Concept and Social Role
  Communication Domain
  - Receptive Communication
  - Expressive Communication
  Motor Domain
  - Gross Motor
  - Fine Motor
  - Perceptual Motor
  Cognitive Domain
  - Attention and Memory
  - Reasoning & Academic Skills
  - Perception and Concepts

Chapter 13

Short-Form Test Scales

Research Gems: "Using Short-Form Scales"

"Attention to the task, motivation to succeed, compliance, and self-stimulatory behaviors and other disruptive behaviors all may influence the performance on intelligence tests of individuals with autism. It seems likely that shortening the test procedure could attenuate these behaviors. The short form of the intelligence test has therefore become a frequently studied and used method for solving time and cooperation problems. Most researchers agree that short forms…are most suitable for an estimation of IQ for research screening purposes or for treatment or educational re-assessment of someone who had a previous comprehensive evaluation." (Minshew, Turner, & Goldstein, 2005, p. 46)

The Use of Short-Form Scales for Evaluating Persons with AS, HFA, and/or NLD

Although most clinicians and researchers typically discourage the use of short-form assessments with both general and impaired populations, this notion may not always apply to working with persons throughout the autism spectrum. Atypical and disruptive behaviors often demonstrated by a large percentage of these populations, such as avoidance, difficulties with switching mental sets, escape behaviors, self-stimulation, limited tolerance, and non-compliance tend to make testing difficult, if not impossible. In these instances, short-form assessment protocols often provide a viable, and more realistic, option when trying to assess such a person's strengths and weaknesses. Keeping in mind that "the purpose of a short form is 'not to estimate a subject's IQ on the original scale, but his or her 'true IQ' (the average of the IQs that the subject would obtain on infinitely many independent administrations of the scale)' a number of short form assessment protocols have been attempted." In short, as many clinicians seeking creative ways of evaluating persons throughout the autism and AS spectrums have found, "reducing behaviors that contribute to sub-optimal function through reducing demands on sustained cooperation may actually provide a more accurate assessment of the individual potential than would a more detailed but lengthier procedure" (Minshew et al., 2005, p. 51).

Research Gems: "Common Assessment Approach"

"One common assessment approach is to make use of a core battery of tests and then supplement with additional measures of specific skills in view of the results from the standard battery. Other considerations in this process include the child's developmental history, the clinical interview, observations of test behavior (during more or less structured situations), naturalistic observations (adjustment in the classroom), behavioral and emotional presentation, and interviews with selected individuals in the child's everyday environment (teachers, therapists). Multiple sources of information along with clinical judgment will be used to better understand the factors that might be contributing to a child's difficulties." (Volkmar & Tsatsanis, 2005, p. 259)

One such short-form assessment protocol that has been identified was the "KAUFMAN2." In general, the researchers found "a clear indication that despite the common finding that individuals with high-functioning autism often produce atypical profiles on the various Weschsler intelligence scales, this atypicality does not compromise the use of short forms to predict IQ score values based on administration of the entire scale." More specifically, they indicate that "level of predictability is maintained even when the Verbal IQ score is significantly lower than the Performance IQ score," and, further, that "predictability level is also maintained in individuals with autism who have particularly low scores on Arithmetic and Block Design relative to other intellectual abilities (a profile which is) commonly reported in individuals with nonverbal learning disability but apparently occurs in a small portion of individuals with autism as well" (Minshew et al., 2005, p. 49).

The subtests use for this Short-Form KAUFMAN2 protocol by Minshew and colleagues included:
- Similarities
- Vocabulary
- Picture arrangement
- Block design

Entered subtests were as follows:
- Full Scale IQ: Picture arrangement, Similarities, Block design
- Verbal IQ: Similarities, Block design
- Performance IQ: Picture arrangement, Block design, Similarities-

---

KAUFMAN2 Short Form Example

	Subtests Entered	Mean	SD
Full Scale IQ:	PA, S, BD	96.48	9.57
Verbal IQ:	S, BD	87.90	9.71
Performance IQ:	PA, BD, S	107.95	8.94

Conclusions from using this short-form protocol indicated "the KAUFMAN2 short form that uses Similarities, Vocabulary, Picture Arrangement, and Block Design produced generally higher amounts of explained variance than was the case for the other short forms studied" (Minshew et al., 2005, p. 51). The researchers further suggest that, when working with children, data from the Matrix Reasoning (Wechsler Abbreviated Scale of Intelligence) subtest should be additionally considered.

Research Gems: "Using Wechsler Intelligence Scale Short Forms"

"It was concluded that short forms may be used with good predictive accuracy in individuals with high functioning autism, even when the subtest profile is atypical." (Minshew, Turner, & Goldstein, 2005, p. 45)

Assessment Short-Form Scales

Research Gems: Wechsler Short Forms Useful

"We evaluated the predictive accuracy of short forms of the Wechsler intelligence scales for individuals with high functioning autism. Several short forms were derived from participants who had received the full procedure….In all analyses the percentages of explained variance were typically in the .8-.9 range. It was concluded that short forms may be used with good predictive accuracy in individuals with high functioning autism, even when the subtest profile is atypical." (Minshew et al., 2005, p. 45)

The following is a collection of short forms with a focus on reports that have used these combinations of subtests in studies involving autism, other neurobiological disorders, and learning disorders or special populations and that were found to meet acceptable psychometric standards. The short forms chosen where those developed by Sattler (PENTAD), Efron, Herra-Graf, Dawson, Weschsler (WASI), and two developed by Kaufman (Minshew, Turner, & Goldstein, 2005, pp. 47-48):

Wechsler Intelligence Scales: Short Form Adaptation
*Entered by Minshew, Turner, and Goldstein = all but (--)

Full Scale IQ

Short Form	Subtests	Multiple Regression Analyses	
(Adults)		R	R2
PENTAD	V, BD, I, (OA), PC	93	.87
Efron	S, V, BD, I	.93	.88
Herra-Graf	V, BD	.91	.82
Kamphaus	I, PC	.83	.68
Kaufman 1	S, A, PC, BD	.93	.86
Kaufman 2	S, V, PA, BD	.93	.87
Dawson	V, C, BD, (OA)	.93	.87
WASI	V, BD, S, MR	.94	89
(Children)			
PENTAD	V, BD, I, OA, PC	.93	87
Efron	S, V, BD, I	.91	.83
Herra-Graf	V, BD	.81	.66
Kamphaus	I, PC	78	.61
Kaufman 1	S, A, PC, BD	.91	.82
Kaufman 2	S, V, PA, BD	.89	.80
Dawson	V, C, BD, OA	.90	.80

Verbal IQ

Short Form	Subtests	Multiple Regression Analyses	
(Adults)		R	R2
PENTAD	V, BD, I, OA, (PC)	.92	.84
Efron	S, V, BD, I	.92	.84
Herra-Graf	V, BD	.88	.77
Kamphaus	I, (PC)	.83	.68
Kaufman 1	S, A	.89	.80
Kaufman 2	S, V, BD	.90	.81
Dawson	V, C, BD, OA	.92	.84
WASI	V, S, MR	.91	.83
(Children)			
PENTAD	V, I, OA, (BD, PC)	.92	.84
Efron	S, V, BD, I	.95	.90
Herra-Graf	V, BD	.84	.71
Kamphaus	I, (PC)	.80	.65
Kaufman 1	S, A, (PC, BD)	.91	.83
Kaufman 2	S, V, BD, (PA)	.90	.81
Dawson	V, C, BD, (OA)	.91	.82
(Minshew, Turner, & Goldstein, 2005, p. 50)			

Performance IQ

Short Form	Subtests	Multiple Regression Analyses	
(Adults)		R	R2
PENTAD	(V), BD, I, OA, PC	.91	.82
Efron	S, (V), BD, I	.86	.73
Herra-Graf	V, BD	.84	.71
Kamphaus	I, PC	.75	.57
Kaufman 1	S, A, PC, BD	.90	.80
Kaufman 2	(S), V, PA, BD	.90	.80
Dawson	(V), C, BD, OA	.86	.75
WASI	(V), BD, S, MR	.90	.81
(Children)			
PENTAD	(V), BD, I, OA, PC	.89	.80
Efron	BD, I, (S, V)	.78	.61
Herra-Graf	V, BD	.74	.55
Kamphaus	I, PC	.62	.38
Kaufman 1	(S) A, PC, BD	.83	.69
Kaufman 2	S, (V), PA, BD	.88	.77
Dawson	C, (V), BD, OA	.85	.72
(Minshew, Turner, & Goldstein, 2005, p. 50)			

<u>Research Gems: "Short Forms for Predicting IQ"</u>

"These results provide a clear indication that despite the common finding that individuals with high functioning autism often produce atypical profiles on the various Wechsler intelligence scales, this atypicality does not compromise the use of short forms to predict IQ score values based on administration of the entire scale. This capacity…is not diminished in individuals with autism who do not have the prototypic profile marked by a high score on Block Design relative to performance on other tests. In particular, level of predictability is maintained even when the Verbal IQ score is significantly lower than the Performance IQ score." (Minshew, Turner, & Goldstein, 2005, p. 50)

WPPSI III Subtest Substitutions

The WPPSI III is designed in a manner that allows clinicians to substitute a number of "supplemental" subtests for various "core" subtests, with a maximum allowance of two substitutions for any of the seven core subtests when a Full Scale IQ score is desired.

The Comprehension or Similarities subtests can be substituted for one of the core verbal subtests for the Verbal I. The Picture Completion or Object Assemble can likewise be substituted for one of the core subtests when the Performance IQ is needed. Either the Coding or Symbol Search is allowed for computation of a Full Scale IQ. In each case only one substitution is allowed per administration. The potential seven Verbal IQ and Performance IQ combinations are as follows:

<u>Potential Verbal Combinations</u>				<u>Potential Performance Combinations</u>			
v1	I	V	WR	p1	BD	MR	PCn
v2	I	V	(C)	p2	BD	MR	(PCmp)
v3	I	V	(S)	p3	BD	MR	(OA)
v4	I	(C)	(WR)	p4	BD	(PCmp)	PCn
v5	I	(S)	WR	p5	BD	(OA)	PCn
v6	(C)	V	WR	p6	(PCmp)	MR	PCn
v7	(S)	V	WR	p7	(OA)	MR	PCn

<u>Research Gems: "Short Form Studies Involving Autism"</u>

"Short forms have been used in studies of several aspects of autism including, as examples, social understanding, lateralization, implicit and explicit memory abilities, and movement preparation abilities…. One type of short form is comprised of selected subtests of the original scale and another type is made up of a combination of selected items from each subtest of the original scale. The research literature indicates that the former type produces higher correlations between the IQ's produced on the short form and those produced on the original scale." (Minshew, Turner, & Goldstein, 2005, p. 46)

Chapter 14

Social and Communication Tests

Research Gems: Social Skills Improve with Time and Support

"This finding confirms previous results from both clinical and population-based studies suggesting that autistic social impairment has a general tendency to improve over the course of early childhood." (Pine et al., 2006, p. 350)

Difficulties with social issues are paramount across the spectrum of persons with autism, Asperger's syndrome, and nonverbal learning disorders. Listed under section 1 of the diagnostic criteria in the DSMIV-TR, these can include any combination of impairments in:

- ♦ Difficulties understanding, or interpreting, nonverbal behaviors such as
  - Eye-to-eye gaze
  - Facial expressions
  - Body postures
  - Gestures that regulate social interactions
- ♦ Difficulties developing appropriate peer relationships in accordance to one's developmental level
- ♦ A lack of spontaneity in seeking to share interests, enjoyment of one's achievements with others
- ♦ Difficulties with, or lacking of, social and/or emotional reciprocity

Although the extent to which these social impairments may manifest in individuals with one of these conditions will vary from person to person, some level of social awkwardness, inappropriateness, or social rhythmic discontinuity seems to be at the core of many of the challenges experienced by these populations. In effect, a number of instruments specifically designed to help assess the extent and depth of these impediments have surfaced over the past few years. Some of the more valid and reliable instruments intended for the measurement of these social variables are presented below.

Assessment Instruments Designed to Evaluate
Social and Communication Impairments

The Autism Social Skills Profile (ASSP)

Intended ages: Ages 6 – 17
Testing time: 15-20 minutes
Administration: Individual

Intended for: Parents/caregivers, teachers

Purpose: Designed to provide a comprehensive measure of social functioning in children and adolescents with ASD, assist with intervention planning, and provide a measure of intervention outcomes.

Consists of: Three subscales: Social Reciprocity, Social Participation/Avoidance, and Detrimental Social Behaviors. Items represent a range of social behaviors often associated with persons with ASD including initiation skills, social reciprocity, perspective-taking, and nonverbal communication skills. The items are rated on a 4-point Likert scale ranging from *never* to *very often* with high scores corresponding to positive social behaviors, designed to yield a total score of overall social functioning.

Other information: The ASSP authors (Bellini & Hopf) indicate that a major advantage of the ASSP, as well as other behavior rating scales, is their ability to obtain large amounts of data associated with social behavior from a number of sources across various settings quickly and efficiently, while a major disadvantage with behavioral scales is their sensitivity to small changes in behaviors. They add that "the ASSP has the capacity to help practitioners develop high-quality social skills programming for children with ASD in school, home, and community settings" (Bellini & Hopf, 2007, p. 86).

RECOMMENDED
The Awareness of Social Inference Test (TASIT)
Intended ages: 14 – 60 years
Testing time: 30 – 45 minutes
Administration: Individual

Intended to be administered by: Trained professionals

Purpose: To assess and treat deficits of social skills in populations presenting with autism, learning disabilities, traumatic brain injury, schizophrenia, and other clinical conditions. The test provides a systematic examination of poor understanding of emotional expressions and difficulty integrating the contextual information that is part of day-to-day social encounters.

Consists of: Three sections each of which assesses different components of social perception. Videotaped vignettes and standardized response probes used are based on recent theoretical accounts of how social cues provide meaning.

Other information: The TASIT was normed primarily on young adults and contains statistically equivalent alternate forms making it available for retesting.

Research Gems: The SCQ

"The SCQ would seem to be a useful tool for identifying young children in need of further assessment and assisting in routing them to the appropriate clinic, especially if used in conjunction with a screening by a community professional." (Eaves et al., 2006, p. 95)

The CAST vs. The SCQ

"Results of this study suggest that the CAST may be effective at screening for AS and related social-communication conditions in primary-school-age (4-11 year old) children in the general population. Compared to the SCQ, the CAST was better able to detect in this sample those children at risk for AS and related disorders who had not already received clinical diagnoses." (Scott et al., 2002, pp. 28-29)

Social Communication Questionnaire (SCQ)
(Formerly known as the Autism Screening Questionnaire, or ASQ)

Intended ages: 4.0 and above (with a mental age of 2.0 or above)
Testing time: 10 minutes or less
Administration: Individual

Intended to be completed by: Parent/caregiver

Purpose: To evaluate communication skills and social functioning in children who may have a Pervasive Developmental Disorder. A cost effective screening tool that helps to determine whether an individual should be referred for a complete diagnostic evaluation.

Consists of: Two forms—Lifetime and Current—each composed of 40 yes/no questions (available in Spanish and English). The Lifetime form focuses on the child's entire developmental history, providing a total score that is interpreted in relation to specific cutoff points. The Current form looks at the child's behavior over the most recent 3-month period and assists in treatment planning, educational intervention, and measurement of change over time. The items, drawn from ADI-R (see below) algorithms, examine reciprocal social interaction, language and communication, and repetitive and stereotyped behaviors.

Other information: In addition to screening and educational applications, the SCQ can also be used to compare symptom levels across various groups, such as children with developmental language disorders or those with medical conditions typically associated with ASDs. High developmental sensitivity with different versions for children aged 6 and under, and a separate one for children older than age 6.

Research Gems: The DISCO

"The DISCO is a 2-4 hour investigator-based interview intended for use with a parent, caregiver or someone else who has extensive information regarding the individual suspected of having evidenced an ASD since early childhood. Since its development it has demonstrated excellent interater and test-retest reliability and been found highly valid for assigning diagnoses, along with comorbid conditions, throughout the ASD spectrum. The DISCO also includes items designed to detect mild forms of ASDs and has a developmental perspective and is effective for use throughout an individual's lifespan." (Billstedt, Gillberg, & Gillberg, 2005, p. 353)

RECOMMENDED
The Diagnostic Interview for Social and Communication Disorders (DISCO)

Intended ages: Infancy through adulthood
Testing time: 2–4 hours
Administration: Individual

Intended to be administered by: Trained professionals

Purpose: An interviewer-based schedule for use with parents and caregivers for the purpose of assisting clinicians in gathering a developmental history and description of children or adults suspected of having ASDs. Helps facilitate understanding of patterns relevant to the diagnosis of autism over time by detailing the skills and impairments that underlie related symptoms and behaviors. Effective as both a clinical and research instrument, it is designed to assist clinicians in gathering developmental, descriptive, and diagnostic information related to persons with autism spectrum disorders.

Consists of: A detailed, semi-structured interview intended to help identify impairments associated with ASDs. "The DISCO uses 21 items related to sensory abnormality that are separated into three groups, proximal (e.g., touch, taste, smell, kin aesthetic) (14 items), auditory (3 items), and visual (4 items). Other items relating to atypical taste/oral, kinaesthetic, and touch responsiveness are also found in other sections of the DISCO….The type and degree of every sensory abnormality is explicitly recorded within the DISCO diagnostic profile making it possible to examine the extent to which abnormalities occur in different sensory domains" (Leekam et al., 2007, p. 896).

Other information: Particularly effective for identifying symptoms falling along the broad range of the broader autistic spectrum. Findings are relevant for children and adults and levels of ability from profound impairment through superior functioning ranges. Beyond autism, it can also help to identify conditions associated with spectrum disorders such as ADHD, tics, dyspraxia, and others. Enables information to be recorded systematically for a wide range of behaviors and developmental skills and assists clinicians in obtaining a profile of an individual's pattern of development and behavioral characteristic while identifying autistic associated features that relate to various diagnostic systems.

Research Gems: DISCO

"One clinical interview measure that assesses sensory symptoms in detail is the Diagnostic Interview for Social and Communication Disorders (DISCO)….The DISCO records in detail the patterns of sensory features seen in children of any age and with any degree of impairment. The sensory items that were originally selected for use within the DISCO reflect items that are commonly seen in clinical experience when working with children presenting with autistic spectrum disorders." (Leekam et al., 2007, p. 895)

RECOMMENDED
Infant Toddler Social Emotional Assessment (ITSEA)

Intended ages: 12 – 35 months
Testing time: 25 – 30 minutes
Administration: Individual

Intended to be administered by: Parents and caregivers

Purpose: To help identify social-emotional problems and developmental problems through age-appropriate measures for infants and toddlers aged 12 through 35 months of age.
Measures include social relatedness, atypical and maladaptive behaviors, and others that can serve as early indicators of atypical clinical disorders.

Consists of: Measures of competencies in four domains:
- Externalizing: Activity/Impulsivity, Aggression/Defiance, Peer Aggression
- Internalizing: Depression/Withdrawal, General Anxiety, Separation Distress, Inhibition to Novelty
- Dysregulation: Negative Emotionality, Sleep, Eating, Sensory Sensitivity
- Competence: Compliance, Attention, Imitation/Play, Mastery Motivation, Empathy, Pro-Social Peer Relations

Other information: Identifies key indicators of autism and pervasive developmental disorders while complying with both the DSM-IV and Diagnostic Classification: 0-3 of Zero to Three. The instrument is based on a national sample that included clinical groups presenting of children with language delays, developmental delays, and autism spectrum disorders as well as premature populations.

Research Gems: The Efficacy of the SRS with Autism

"We conclude that in preschool children, it is possible to obtain brief and reliable *quantitative* measurements of autistic social impairment, using SRS reports from parents and/or preschool teachers and daycare providers. This may be especially useful for early identification of subthreshold autistic syndromes and for measuring subtle effects of early intervention over time." (Pine et al., 2006, p. 351)

Social Responsiveness Scale (SRS)

Intended ages: 4 to 18 years
Testing time: 15–20 minutes
Administration: Individual

Intended for: Parent/caregivers, teachers, and therapists.

Purpose: Designed to provide a clear picture of a child's social impairments, assessing social awareness, social information processing, capacity for reciprocal social communication, social anxiety/avoidance, and autistic preoccupations and traits. Also functions as a screening tool in clinical or educational settings, as an aid to clinical diagnosis, or a measure of response to intervention. Particularly helpful in identifying autism, Asperger's, PDD-NOS, and Schizoid Personality Disorder of Childhood. The scale can also alert clinicians to sub-threshold autistic symptoms that may be relevant in evaluating children with a wide variety of psychological problems.

Consists of: A 65-item rating scale that measures the severity of autism spectrum symptoms as they occur in natural social settings. In addition to a Total Score reflecting severity of social deficits in the autism spectrum, the SRS generates scores for five Treatment Subscales: Receptive, Cognitive, Expressive, and Motivational aspects of social behavior, as well as Autistic Preoccupations.

Other information: The SRS is also helpful in helping to qualify children for mental health or special education services. A reliance on naturalistic observations of parents and teachers makes it easy to use in clinical, research, and educational settings.

Other Related Scales

The Communication Symbols Behavior Scales (CSBS)

A single page, parent-based questionnaire aimed at identifying communication disorders in general in children aged 6-24 months. For children testing positive a more comprehensive assessment (titled *The Behavior Sample*) and parent-caregiver questionnaire are administered.

Communication and Symbolic Behavior Scales Developmental Profile Infant-Toddler Checklist (CSBS DP)

Description: Designed to help determine the communicative competence (use of gaze, gestures, sounds, words, understanding, and play) of children with a functional communication age between 6 months and 24 months (chronological age from about 6 months to 6 years).

Reference: (sites accessed 7/21/2007)
http://www.brookespublishing.com/store/books/wetherby-csbsdp/index.htm
Free download of CSBS DP scale and scoring guide:
http://www.brookespublishing.com/store/books/wetherby-csbsdp/checklist.htm

The Social and Communication Disorders Checklist (SCDC)

<u>Description:</u>
A 12-item, first-level screening questionnaire designed as a quick checklist to identify autistic traits by measuring heritable characteristics in both male and female populations. Useful as a very brief measure for pervasive developmental disorders that can be used to help estimate the boundaries of the autistic spectrum across large community samples. It can also be used to rule out sub-threshold autistic traits in behavioral difficulties and conditions such as attention-deficit hyperactivity and conduct disorders.

Chapter 15

Academic Testing

Introduction

The challenges that confront persons with Asperger's syndrome, high-functioning autism and nonverbal learning disorders are well documented. In fact, once any effort to try and understand the extent to which these challenges involving social interaction, communication, and perseveration on repetitive and stereotyped patterns of behavior is made, our awareness of the trials that confront them, from infancy onward, imbue us with a deep sense of respect for the enormous courage with which many of them take on these seemingly insurmountable obstacles.

As soon as we get past the "areas of impairment" identified by our current diagnostic systems, and examine the complexity of their obstacles just a little deeper, this sense of respect, however, cannot fail but turn into awe. How many of us, "neuron-typicals," if faced with the limitations in areas of theory of mind, central coherence, executive dysfunction, and—perhaps most overwhelming and difficult to surpass—sensory integration dysfunction, would continue to endure our hardships and struggle to go on?

Further, as I often indicate during my workshops, these ordeals do not go away the following morning. Or week, or month. Each day, as in the movie *Groundhog Day*, it starts all over again.

Yet, they endure.

In effect, for many persons with these conditions, learning, memorizing, knowing, education, and academia provide safe havens where they can exercise their talents, gifts, and abilities to help create what they most need. Knowing how a course is laid out, what to read, how to complete their assignments, where to go from hour to hour, and other components that are segmented by regularities in structure from hour to hour, day to day, and week to week brings a sense of security within a pre-ordained, organized arrangement creating an oasis where they find internal relief from the social world. Doing well in academic areas of interest in turn leads to enhanced self-esteem, which leads to increased ability to deal with social stressors and unyielding sensory overloads.

The structure of academic settings—as long as impeded by social demands, interpersonal chit-chat, and mind-games that are learned in middle school, rehearsed in high school, and perfected in later years can be avoided—provides a sanctuary where they can exercise their abilities and, hopefully, realize their vocational potentials. Books, filled with "facts," hard data, and evenly numbered pages are retreats from communal demands. Classrooms—not playgrounds—function as refuges from peer-group demands. Libraries—filled with books that are filled with knowledge contained in crisp, rectangular configurations—are like harbors from the sensory storms of the outside world. Their bedrooms, walls aligned with books, world and astronomical maps, posters of historical characters, and flow charts of scientific formulas or mathematical theorems, bring a sense of peace and contentment where they can recharge so that, tomorrow, they can take on the pressures of the external world, one day at a time.

Because of this, and myriad other reasons, proper and careful academic testing for persons who present with Asperger's syndrome, high-functioning autism, and/or nonverbal learning disorders, conducted by well-trained professionals experienced with these populations is essential. Being versed in the art of establishing positive early alliances, within a sensory-friendly environment, and bringing in—whenever appropriate—their special interest topics into the fold, can pay invaluable dividends into acquiring a comprehensive picture of each child's (adolescent's or adult's) *true* academic, vocational, and personal potentials.

Through incorporating a routine of flexible-structure, innovative (non-traditional), standard guidelines, atypical spontaneity…in other words, our approach cannot simply be "outside the box" but rather "no-box."

> "The notion of 'no-box' is so ephemeral that when one tried to capture it, it becomes much like trying to hold an eyelash in the palm of one's hand in the middle of a windstorm. It just blows away. Although 'thinking out of the box' can be conceptualized rather easily by example, trying to capture the 'no-box' involves a sizable quantum leap, or detachment, from ordinary reasoning." In essence, then, the 'no-box' approach is something that one can only hope to accomplish by (a) being completely comfortable with oneself, (b) being completely comfortable with the population one is serving and (c) having experienced may trials and tribulations, failures and successes, and bright days and dark nights oneself. (Ortiz, 2006, p. 18)

Three Forms of Classroom-Based Assessment

Mastery Measurement:
Analyzes curriculum into component skills and orders these into a hierarchy of objectives. A criterion-referenced test is developed for each step in the hierarchy, and administered by teachers before and after instruction.

Curriculum-Based Measurement:
Teachers administer weekly probes by having students read aloud from a passage for one minute, and the student is given a score of the number of words read correctly.

DIBELS (Dynamic Indicators of Basic Early Literacy Skills):
Teachers repeatedly measure one or more phonological awareness, language and short-term memory skills related to reading acquisition.

(Reference: School Psychology Review, 28, 1999, Assessment and Treatment of Children with Autism in the Schools, site accessed 8/02/2007 http://www.nasponline.org/publications/sprsum284.htm)

Assessment Instruments Designed to Assess Academic Skills

RECOMMENDED
NEPSY

Intended ages: 3 – 12 years
Testing time: Core Assessment: Ages 3-4, 45 minutes; 5-12, 65 minutes
      Full NEPSY: Ages 3-4, 1 hour; 5-12, 2 hours

Administration: Individual

Intended to be administered by: Trained professionals

Purpose: To evaluate neuropsychological development in children and help plan treatment interventions by detecting strengths and subtle deficiencies, linking assessment results and remediation, and functioning as a base for special education and long-term follow-up care as well as treatment planning.

Consists of: A set of comprehensive subtests designed to identify strengths and analyze deficits in 5 functional domains that facilitate or interfere with a child's learning:

- Attention and Executive Functions - self-regulation, selective and sustained attention, planning, thinking flexibility, figural fluency, inhibition, maintenance of response set

- Language - phonological processing, receptive language comprehension, expressive naming under confrontation and speeded naming conditions, verbal fluency, ability to produce rhythmic oral motor sequences

- Sensorimotor Functions - tactile level sensory input, fine motor speed, imitating hand positions, rhythmic and sequential movements

- Visuospatial Processing - ability to assess position and directionality, copy 2-dimensional geometric figures, and reconstruct 3-dimensional designs from a model or picture

- Memory and Learning - assessing immediate memory for sentences and immediate and delayed memory for faces, names, and list learning, and narrative memory under free and cued recall conditions

Other information: The NEPSY is designed to be sensitive to disruptions in learning, flexible for children with learning/attention problems, autism, mental retardation, and other clinical diagnoses as well as being fair and unbiased across cultural and racial/ethnic populations. Studies have yielded high validity and reliability for learning disabled, ADHD, autistic, speech/language impairments, and traumatic brain injury populations.

Research Gems: NEPSY and HFA

"This study presents a reanalysis of the High-Functioning Autism (HFA) versus Typical samples using IQ as a covariate….Significant group differences also were uncovered for the subtests of Phonological Processing, Auditory Attention and Response Set, and Speeded Naming: Comprehension of Instructions and Narrative Memory were no longer significant after controlling for IQ….The HFA Group showed a higher rate of occurrence on each subtest, but only significantly so on the Arrows Subtest. These findings provide additional support for the phenotypic neurocognitive presentation of individuals with HFA, and they suggest that the NEPSY can contribute to the neuropsychological description of children with HFA." (Hooper et al., 2006, p. 299)

RECOMMENDED
The NEPSY - Second Edition (NEPSY-II)
(Korkman, Kirk, & Kemp, 2007)

Intended ages: 3 through 16 years of age

Testing time:
      General administration: Pre-school ages – 45 minutes; School ages – 1 hour.
      Full Assessment: Pre-school-ages – 90 minutes; School ages – 2-3 hours.
Administration: Individual

Intended for: Trained professionals

Purpose: A single measure designed to create a tailored assessment across 6 domains, specific to a child's situation in order to answer referral questions or diagnostic concerns. The test helps to identify typical childhood and adolescent disorders to assist with establishing diagnostic impressions, treatment plans, and interventions at both school and home. Provides a comprehensive evaluation of a child/adolescent's neuropsychological status.

Consists of: Six domains:
- Executive Function and Attention
- Language
- Memory and Learning
- Sensorimotor
- Visuospatial Processing
- Social Perception

New subtests, particularly related to autism spectrum conditions, include Theory of Mind, Inhibition, and Affect Recognition.

Other information: The integrated NEPSY-II allows clinicians to collect information relating to executive functions, vary the number of subtests according to each child, link results to educational difficulties, yield recommendations related to clinical interventions, and obtain a comprehensive view of both quantitative and qualitative patterns of neuropsychological performance.

RECOMMENDED
Wechsler Preschool and Primary Scale of Intelligence – Third Edition (WPPSI – III)

Intended ages: 2.6 – 7.3 years
Testing time: Ages 2.6 – 7.3: 30-45 minutes; Ages 4.0 – 7.3: 45-60 minutes
Administration: Individual

Intended to be administered by: Trained professionals

Purpose: To measure intellectual functioning, developmental delay, and giftedness.

Consists of: Subtests for two age bands (ages 2.6 – 7.3, four core and one supplemental subtests; and 4.0 – 7.3, seven core, five supplemental and two optional subtests) designed to reflect the nature of cognitive development by de-emphasizing time constraints for the assessment of acquired knowledge and performance through shorter, engaging, and play-like tasks. Seven new subtests are included for the purpose of improving fluid reasoning, receptive and expressive vocabulary, and processing speed measurement.

Other information: The WPPSI-III's group data draws from populations presenting with autistic disorder, giftedness, mild and moderate mental retardation, developmental delays and risk factors, expressive and receptive/ expressive language disorders, ADHD, motor impairment, and Limited English Proficiency. Validity studies linking the WPPSI-III to the Adaptive Behavior Assessment System (ABAS), the WIAT-II, and DAS are available.

Gifted Rating Scales (GRS)

Intended ages: Pre-school/kindergarten: 4.0 – 6.11;
        School-Age: 6.0 – 13.11 years
Testing time: 5 – 10 minutes
Administration: Individual

Intended to be administered by: Teachers

Purpose: A standardized measure designed to identify children for gifted and talented programs based on teacher observations. Areas of relative strength and specific gifted areas are identified by specific behaviors within each domain.

Consists of: Six domains that include:
- intellectual
- academic
- motivation
- creativity
- leadership
- artistic talent

Other information: The GRS-P is linked to the WPPSI-III, while the GRS-S is linked to the WISC-IV, and correlated with the WIAT-II.

School Function Assessment (SFA)

Intended ages: Kindergarten to grade 6
Testing time: 5 – 10 minutes
Administration: Individual

Intended to be administered by: Teachers

Purpose: To help determine how well disabled elementary school children may function in the nonacademic aspects of the school setting.

Consists of: A three-part assessment to help identify a student's specific functioning level:

- Part I: Participation – Used to rate the student's level of participation in six major school activity settings:
  - Regular or Special Education Classrooms
  - Playground/Recess
  - Transportation
  - Bathroom/Toiletry
  - Transitions
  - Mealtime/Snack time

- Part II: Task Supports – Four scales designed to rate the supports currently provided to the student in areas of physical and cognitive/behavioral tasks:
  - Physical Tasks Assistance
  - Physical Tasks Adaptations
  - Cognitive/Behavioral Tasks Assistance
  - Cognitive/Behavioral Tasks Adaptations

- Part III: Activity Performance – Twenty-one scales designed to evaluate the performance of school-related functional tasks.

Other information: Can be used to help develop Individualized Education Plans (IEPs) and help to determine whether a student is performing below grade expectations and is eligible for special services.

Sensory Profile School Companion

Intended ages: 3.0 – 11.11 years
Testing time: 30 minutes
Administration: Individual

Intended to be administered by: Teachers

Purpose: To help assess sensory information related to school performance reflected by teachers' observations of a child's behavior, performance, and sensory processing skills while in the school environment.

Consists of: A standardized assessment tool based on Winnie Dunn's Model of Sensory Processing, which is designed to reflect a teacher's observations of a child's performance in the school environment.

Other information: Used together with the Sensory Profile, it offers clinicians a comprehensive evaluation in addressing the child's behavior in various contexts including home, the classroom, and the community at large.

RECOMMENDED
Differential Ability Scales: Second Edition (DAS-II)
Intended ages: 2.6 – 6 years (pre-school); 5.0 – 8.11 years (school age)
Testing time: 45 – 60 minutes (core battery); 30 minutes (diagnostic subtests)
Administration: Individual

Intended to be administered by: Trained professionals

Purpose: The DAS-II is designed to provide a comprehensive understanding of a child's cognitive ability. The measure of multidimensional abilities helps to identify an examinee's strengths and weaknesses to help design IEP goals, intervention strategies, and monitor progress. Designed for exploring differences among various cognitive abilities and differences between cognitive abilities and academic achievement.

Consists of: Various cluster scores according to a number of ability domains that include:
- Verbal
- Nonverbal/Nonverbal Reasoning
- Spatial
- Working Memory
- Processing Speed
- School Readiness for children ages 5.0 – 8.11 by measuring three ability sets relating to early school success and failure

Other information: The DAS-II includes decision points to afford flexibility in customizing the evaluation protocol according to each child's needs. Revised testing procedures are designed to help reduce testing time, maximize the child's energy level, and facilitate rapport. Clinical studies for the DAS-II draw from populations presenting with ADHD and combined Learning Disabilities (Reading, Writing, Math), Learning Disorders, Expressive and Mixed Receptive/ Expressive Language Disorders, Developmental Risk, Mental Retardation and Down Syndrome, Limited English Proficiency, and Deaf/Hard of Hearing.

RECOMMENDED
Wide Range Achievement Test 4 (WRAT4)

Intended ages: 5 – 94 years
Testing time: 15–25 minutes (5 – 7 years of age); 35–45 minutes (8 years and older)
Administration: Individual or group (specific subtests)

Intended to be administered by: Trained professionals
Purpose: To measure the basic academic skills of reading, spelling, and math computation, and how these translate into effective learning, communication, and thinking as well as performing basic mathematical calculations.

Consists of: Four subtests:

- Word Reading – measures letter and word decoding
- Sentence Comprehension – measures a person's ability to gain meaning from words and comprehend ideas and information
- Spelling – measures one's ability to encode sounds into written form through the use of a dictated spelling format
- Math Computation – measures the ability to perform basic math computations through counting, identifying numbers, solving, simple oral problems, and calculating written math problems
- Additionally, the combination of the Word Reading and Sentence Comprehension standard scores yield a Reading Composite score.

Other information: The WRAT4 contains alternate forms, the Blue and Green, which can be used interchangeably while permitting retesting within short periods of time without potential practice effects or which can be administered together during a single examination. The multiple uses of the WRAT4 include:

- Psychological, educational, and vocational assessments
- Screening large groups to identify those needing more thorough evaluations
- Assessing a broad range of academic skills useful in the diagnosis of specific learning disorders
- Reevaluation of individuals diagnosed with learning and/or cognitive disorders
- Evaluation of achievement-ability discrepancies to assist in identifying specific learning disabilities
- Determining minimal levels of proficiency needed to perform in certain educational and/or vocational settings
- Assessing a person's academic progress over time

Early Language and Literacy Classroom Observation (ELLCO) Toolkit, Research Edition

Intended ages: Pre-K to third grade
Testing time: 1–1.5 hours total (see component times below)
Administration: Multi-modal

Intended to be administered by: Researchers, supervisors, program directors, principals, administrators, and/or teachers

Purpose: A three-part classroom observation system that helps schools to assess and strengthen classroom quality, develop improved literacy programs, and maximize the children's language and literacy development.

Consists of:
- Literacy Environment Checklist (15-20 minutes)
- Classroom Observation (20-45 minutes)
- Teacher Interview (10 minutes)
- Literacy Activities Rating Scale (10 minutes)
- User's Guide

Other information: Designed to assist administrators, principals, academic supervisors, and program directors in gathering data to help maximize pre-kindergarten to third grade classroom environments, develop better literacy programs, improve teacher development, and compare existing strategies.

Transdisciplinary Play-Based Assesment and Intervention (TPBA/TBBI)

Intended ages: Infancy to age 6
Testing time: 60–90 minutes for complete TPBA play session
Administration: Individual and group settings

Intended to be administered by: Trained professionals with parent involvement

Purpose: To assess cognitive, social-emotional, communication and language, and sensorimotor development to help design improved intervention approaches and translate these findings into functional educational goals and IEPs.

Consists of: Transdisciplinary Play-Based Invervention, Child and Program Summary Forms, And You Thought They Were Just Playing (video), and Observing Kassandra (video).

Other information: An integrated approach to assessment and intervention using play to encourage children's thinking skills, communication and language abilities, movement proficiency, and social-emotional development.

RECOMMENDED
The BRIGANCE Family

Intended ages: Birth through secondary level
Testing time: Varies
Administration: Individual

Intended to be administered by: Trained professional

Purpose: A consistent assessment system designed to:
- Identify performance levels
- Set instructional goals
- Report ongoing progress
- Maintain a systematic, easily interpretable history of children's assessments

Consists of: An extensive assessment system that incorporates a number of components:

Early Childhood Screening
- Infant & Toddler Screen (Birth – 23 months)
- Early Preschool Screen-II (ages 2 – 2 ½
- Preschool Screen-II (Ages 3 & 4)
- K & 1 Screen-II (Kindergarten & Grade 1)

Ongoing Assessment
- Inventory of Early Development-II (Birth – age 7)
- Comprehensive Inventory of Basic Skills-Revised (Grades Pre-K – 9)
- Employability Skills Inventory (Secondary Special Ed, Vocational, Adult Ed, ESL Programs)
- Inventory of Essential Skills (Remedial–Grade 6+, Adult Ed)
- Assessment of Basic Skills-Revised (Pre-K – 9)

Data Management comprehensive components

Early Childhood Instruction: A correlated curriculum resource emphasizing Readiness: Strategies, and Practice.

Other information: Skill areas addressed through the Readiness: Strategies and Practice component helps to address different learning styles, abilities, and developmental levels in terms of:
- general knowledge and comprehension
- gross-motor skills
- fine-motor skills
- self-help skills
- visual motor/visual discrimination skills
- general readiness skills
- early reading, writing, and math skills

The skill sections include an objective, rationale, skills sequence, teaching recommendations, and indications of any possible reasons for learning difficulties.

Research Gems: Psychoeducational Profile

"The findings of the current study indicate that the PEP-R is an instrument that is correlated significantly with estimates of cognitive functioning obtained with the Stanford-Binet Intelligence Scales—Fourth Edition. Further, the PEP-R offers some potential advantages for testing this population including flexibility, range of appealing materials, lack of timed items, and separation of language items from general assessment items that are not dependent on language and its utility for educational programming. These findings suggest that the PEP-R can be an ideal tool to use when estimating cognitive functioning of children with autism." (Demolino, L.M., 2006, p. 962)

Research Gems: Use of Multiple Measures

"Classification accuracy significantly improved to 84% when a measure of adaptive functioning (the Vineland Adaptive Behavior Scales) was included in the analysis. The findings suggest that when clinicians obtain discrepant information on the ADI-R and ADOS, assessment of an individual's adaptive functioning may reduce diagnostic errors." (Tomanik et al., 2007, p. 921)

RECOMMENDED
Vineland Adaptive Behavior Scales, Second Edition (Vineland-II)

Intended ages:
- Survey Interview Form and Parent/Caregiver Rating Form: Birth through 90 years of age
- Teacher Rating Form: 3:0 – 21:11

Testing time:
- Survey Interview Form and Parent/Caregiver Rating Form: 20–60 minutes
- Teacher Rating Form: 20 minutes

Administration: Individual

Intended to be administered by: Teachers, parents, caregivers

Purpose: Measures personal and social skills deemed necessary for everyday living. Used to help identify persons with mental retardation, autism, Asperger's, ADHD, post-traumatic brain injury, hearing impairment, dementia, Alzheimer's disease, and developmental delays. Effective in providing information to support educational and treatment plans to facilitate independent living.

<u>Consists of</u>: Content and scales organized within a three-domain structure consisting of:

- Communication
- Daily Living Skills
- Socialization

The structure corresponds to three broad domains of adaptive functioning recognized by the American Association of Mental Retardation:

- Conceptual
- Practical
- Social

It also contains a Motor Skills Domain and a Maladaptive Behavior Index.

<u>The Survey Interview Form</u> uses information provided by a parent/caregiver to assess a person's adaptive functioning at both domain and subdomain levels.

<u>The Teacher Rating Form</u> is completed by a teacher or day-care provider to provide a comprehensive assessment for students aged 3 through 21 at school, preschool, and structured day-care settings.

<u>Other information</u>: The Vineland-II boasts improved, more flexible features over the original version in its ability to:

- help support diagnostic impressions of the above populations
- yield a perspective of the child's behavior based on those with whom the child interacts on a daily basis
- help determine both qualification and eligibility for services
- track and report ongoing progress

Autism Screening Instrument for Educational Planning – Second Edition (ASIEP-2)

<u>Intended ages</u>: 18 months through adult
<u>Testing time</u>: Varies
<u>Administration</u>: Individual

<u>Intended to be administered by</u>: Diagnosticians, educators, therapists

<u>Purpose</u>: Uses five components to provide data on five unique aspects of behavior for individuals in the autism spectrum. The subtests, when looked at together, provide a profile of abilities in spontaneous verbal behavior, social interaction, education level, and learning characteristics. Can also be used to help monitor the progress of students with autism.

<u>Consists of</u>: Five components aimed at:
- examining behavior in sensory, relating body concept, language, and social self-help areas
- sampling vocal behavior
- assessing interaction
- assessing communication
- determining learning rate

Other information: Strong empirical evidence of the strong intercorrelation among the ASIEP-2 components and its use in helping to distinguish among groups of participants with a variety of disabilities. Assessments can be given frequently without practice effects.

Psychoeducational Profile (PEP-3): TEACCH Individualized Psychoeducational Assessment

Intended ages: 6 months to 7 years of age
Testing time: 45–90 minutes
Administration: Individual

Intended to be administered by: Trained professionals

Purpose: To identify the learning strengths, teachable skills, and weaknesses of children with autism spectrum disorder.

Consists of: Function domains that focus on areas of social and communication functioning yielding composite scores in the areas of Communication, Motor, and Maladaptive Behaviors, as well as 10 Performance Subtests:
- Cognitive Verbal/Preverbal
- Expressive Language
- Receptive Language
- Fine Motor
- Gross Motor
- Visual-Motor Imitation
- Affective Expression
- Social Reciprocity
- Characteristic Motor Behaviors
- Characteristic Verbal Behaviors

Other information: Designed to assist in the educational programming for young children (ages 3 through 5) with disabilities and is particularly useful in planning for older students' Individualized Education Programs (IEPs). The report consists of three subtests: Problem Behaviors, Personal Self-Care, and Adaptive Behavior.

Functional Assessment and Curriculum for Teaching Everyday Routines (FACTER)

Intended ages: Elementary- and secondary-age students
Testing time: Varies
Administration: Individual

Intended to be administered by: Teachers

Purpose: To assess and teach students with moderate to severe developmental disabilities. Addresses the ability to perform typical, everyday "routines" (eating lunch, doing academic work, socializing with friends, going shopping) while incorporating essential "related skills" for living.

Consists of: Two components: (1) a thorough student assessment across routines and related skills, and (2) a student instruction element, which combines ongoing teaching and assessment on critical steps of selected routines. The assessment and instruction cycle is repeated continually to document student progress over time and identify new areas for instruction.

Other information: The FACTER is designed for students who need to learn typical school, leisure, community, vocational, or career exploration routines. A set number of routines that serve as basic assessment units and instruction are noted by a teacher who observes how a student performs independent routines conducted in a natural environment. Routine steps are then identified that require instruction to enhance student independence. The routines and related skills assessed are those identified from the student's IEP goals and objectives as the information gathered provides student related to the student's needs from assessment, through IEP planning, and on through instruction.

TEACCH Transition Assessment Profile, Second Edition (TTAP)

Intended ages: Adolescents and young adults
Testing time: Varies
Administration: Individual

Intended to be administered by: Trained professionals

Purpose: To assist educators, parents, caregivers, and counselors to assist persons with ASD in preparing for successful, semi-independent adult lives (personal development, recreational living, adult integration into employment, and residential arrangements, etc.). Also helps providers to identify an individual's primary transition goals, strengths, and weaknesses related to academic and/or vocational pursuits.

Consists of: A "Cumulative Record of Skills" (CRS) and two data collection forms help to maintain ongoing assessment in community-based instruction. Emphasis is on evaluating six major functional skill areas:

(1) Vocational Skills
(2) Vocational Behavior
(3) Independent Functioning
(4) Leisure Skills
(5) Functional Communication
(6) Interpersonal Behavior

These skill areas are examined within three different contexts: a Direct Observation Scale (to assess general skills), Home Scale (to assess performance in a residential setting), and School/Work Scale (to assess the academic/ vocational setting via interviews with a teacher or work supervisor).

Other information: The TTAP-Second Edition is a comprehensive, newly titled and revised version of the Adolescent and Adult Psychoeducational Profile (AAPEP) aimed at adolescent and older children with ASD, with a focus on those with transitional needs. It is structured to satisfy provisions included in the Individuals with Disabilities Education Act (ACT) of 1997.

Chapter 16

Assessment of Intelligence

Research Gems: Intelligence Testing

"Intelligence test performance is (also) a powerful predictor of ASD symptom severity, with higher IQ scores being associated with a lower degree of ASD symptoms....It is important to keep in mind that it is not until age 5 that childhood IQ correlates highly with adult IQ." (Brock, 2004, p. 31)

Introduction

As discussed in the previous chapter on academic testing, assessing the intelligence levels of persons with AS, HFA, and/or NLD also takes the type of background in training, experience, and personal dedication to serving these populations that can only come from understanding their challenges, and admiring their strengths, valor, and determination to succeed. Again, structure must be provided, a sensory-friendly environment made available, and a "no-box" approach flexibly adhered to. For many laypersons, educators, mental-health, and other professionals, one of the most difficult notions to acknowledge and hang onto when working with, and testing, these populations, is that of splinter skills. Unlike neuro-typical children who will have "peaks and valleys" in more standard, globally understood patterns, children throughout the AS, HFA, and NLD spectrums will more often than not present with high crests in certain areas (math, science, reading, spelling, memorization) and troughs in others that, to the inexperienced clinician conducting the assessment, or the non-professionals attempting to conceptualize them, just simply seem to make no sense.

In other words, their collective test scores, as in a full-scale IQ, literally do not add up. More difficult, perhaps, if one has not worked with a large enough sample covering various points of skills and deficits throughout the spectrum, is understanding how one person with these conditions may be so good at math, for instance, yet the next one have no mathematical ability whatsoever. The same applies to skills in reading, science, geography, spelling, memorization, and other areas. Again, as discussed earlier in this book, we must think about people with AS, HFA, and/or NLD as *people* first, and their "label," second. The popularization of these conditions via the media, which has succeeded magnanimously in translating these conditions from the dark corridors of Hans Asperger's Austrian writings, Leo Kanner's clinical populations, and Byron Rourke's current admirable quest to resolve the mysteries of nonverbal learning disorders and the white matter syndrome, into popular magazine covers, Internet gigabytes, television specials, and movie themes, has helped to raise our collective awareness (thank you very much!).

On the other hand, like all things that face the yin and yang of the world, this increased awareness has also brought an enormous amount of confusion, mis-education, and smoke screening to cloud the reality of these conditions. As excellent a movie as *Rainman* is, and as fabulous as the portrayal of a savant individual that Dustin Hoffman admirably accomplished, it is still just a movie. A person with autism is not "Rainman." As incredibly entertaining, accurate, groundbreaking, and successful as the book *The Curious Incident of the Dog in the Night Time* by Mark Haddon is—and it is a wonderful, enlightening book—again, it does not portray all individuals with Asperger's syndrome. Another wonderful book and movie, *Mozart and the Whale*, portraying the struggles and successes of two young persons with AS in love, again, gives us only snapshots of the collective bell-curve where all persons with each of these conditions reside.

In effect, only by working with large enough samples of persons with AS, HFA, and NLD will we come to terms, and feel comfortable with, the fact that some are good at block design, and others are not. Some excel at digit span, while others will not. Some are obsessed with trains, but others could not care less about them, and be motivated by someone who shows interest in their knowledge about clocks, or transistors, or railroad spikes of the early 1900s. Some might come across quite social (!!!), or make splendid eye contact, sound and/or come across "normal," or "be into spontaneity," or display remarkable insight. Stranger still, to the inexperienced clinical novice, is that, on any given day a child with AS, for instance, may behave as described above, but on the following day, everything may be completely different. The absolute reverse. And the challenge is to be okay with that, because that is the way that it is.

> "Clinical expertise and experience with children with PDDs is a crucial supplement to the diagnostic instruments for the less 'clear-cut' cases seen in typical practice." (Mazefsky & Oswald, 2006, p. 547)

Be Zen

As I like to mention at my workshops, the best approach to adapt when working with these populations is to "be Zen." No expectations, no shoulds-oughts-musts, no "this is the way I was taught," or "what has always worked for me," or "a real clinician would not do it this way," or "what would Freud think?!" No "why"— simply what, when, where, and how. No boxes. Not "trying," but "being." Not working at it, but "flowing" with it. Not giving up, but "giving." Not challenging— they are challenged enough, but working as collaborators. No ultimatums, but space to move. Actually, once you "get it," working with, and assessing, persons with these conditions becomes much easier than working with those outside of their spectrums.

> "While 'being,' we seem to 'float' through our days. We hover over barriers and soar over obstacles. WE flow within our own stream, emerging. Solutions seem to surge from our still and peaceful minds. It's a feeling akin to sailing across calm seas, gliding at wind speed propelled by soft, gentle breezes. While in the 'being' mode we do what we do, when and where we do it, in just the way we do it." (Ortiz, 1997, p. 263)

In essence, although the assessment instruments presented below succeed in some cases, they do not in others. Before getting down to the brass of conducting the formal assessment, clinicians are strongly encouraged to consider the writings of earlier chapters in this book and recognize the issues revolving around sensory challenges, the importance of proper screening, understanding the fine differences between actual comorbidities vs. secondary threads that simply connect the colorful tapestries that are these conditions, recognizing personal learning styles, and gathering as much information as possible *before* each assessment. In most cases, following these guidelines will significantly improve our efforts and increase the efficacy of our results.

Assessment Instruments Designed to Assess Intelligence

Research Gems: Autism — No Characteristic Prototype

"We concluded that individuals with autism can demonstrate a wide range of ability levels and patterns on the Wechsler scales, without a single characteristic prototype. Use of IQ score profiles in the diagnosis and differential diagnosis of autism in high-functioning individuals is not considered valid." (Siegel, Minshew, & Goldstein, 2005, p. 389)

RECOMMENDED
Wechsler Intelligence Scale for Children – Fourth Edition (WISC-IV)

Intended ages: 6.0 – 16.11 years
Testing time: 65–80 minutes
Administration: Individual

Intended to be administered by: Trained professionals

Purpose: The WISC-IV's four domains (see below) yield clinical indicators of both cognitive strengths and weaknesses relevant to the evaluation of learning disabilities, executive functions, attention disorders, traumatic brain injuries, mental retardation, giftedness, and other medical and neurological related conditions.

Consists of: Four index scores that reflect different abilities relevant to the expression of intelligent behavior in and out of educational settings.

- Verbal Comprehension
- Perceptual Reasoning
- Working Memory
- Processing Speed

Other information: The WISC-IV also includes 10 core subtests and 5 supplemental subtests. Most current subtests include:

- Matrix Reasoning – measures fluid reasoning
- Picture Concepts – measures fluid reasoning, perceptual organization, and categorization
- Letter-Number Sequencing – measures working memory
- Word Reasoning – measures reasoning with verbal material
- Cancellation – measures processing speed

Research Gems: Uneven Profiles

"It is not unusual for the student being tested to display an uneven profile of cognitive abilities. Thus, rather than simply providing an overall global intelligence test score, it is essential to identify these cognitive strengths and weaknesses….it is important to avoid the temptation to generalize from isolated or 'splinter' skills when forming an overall impression of cognitive functioning." (Brock, 2004, p. 31)

RECOMMENDED
Wechsler Intelligence Scale for Children – Fourth Edition Integrated (WISC-IV Integrated)

Intended ages: 6.0 – 16.11
Testing time: Varies according to number of subtests administered
Administration: Individual

Intended to be administered by: Trained professionals

Purpose: To assess cognitive abilities in both educational and clinical settings through evaluation of the examinee's learning strengths and difficulties.

Consists of: Sixteen process subtests designed to augment and expand on data acquired via examination with the WISC-IV with a focus on how a child's strengths and needs may be balanced in order to maximize performance. The WISC-IV Integrated version is particularly amenable to the needs of children with special needs, with the goal of assisting clinicians in the development of treatment plans and interventions based on the examinee's cognitive challenges and providing insights to facilitate standards based educational goals.

Subtest Domains include:
    Verbal Domain
    Working Memory Scale
    Perceptual Domain
    Processing Speed Domain

Other information: Validity data are available for children presenting with autism, Asperger's Syndrome, ADHD, learning disabilities (reading, writing, math), traumatic brain injury, and receptive and expressive language disorders.

Research Gems: Consistent Prototypes in Autism are Rare

"We therefore examined WISC-R and WAIS-R profile characteristics in 81 rigorously diagnosed high-functioning (VIQ and FSIQ > 70) children (n = 45) and adults (n = 36) with autism…these groups did not reveal the presumed typical VIA< PIQ pattern. The typical subtest pattern was found, but the magnitude of profile variability was small. We concluded that individuals with autism can demonstrate a wide range of ability levels and patterns on the Wechsler scales, without a single characteristic prototype. Use of IQ score profiles in the diagnosis and differential diagnosis of autism in high-functioning individuals is not considered valid." (Siegel et al., 1996, p. 389)

RECOMMENDED
Wechsler Adult Intelligence Scale – Third Edition (WAIS – III)

Intended ages: 16 – 89 years
Testing time: VIQ, PIQ, and FSIQ: 60 – 90 minutes; IQ & Index Scores: 65 – 95 minutes
Administration: Individual

Intended to be administered by: Trained professionals

Purpose: To assess adult cognitive ability.

Consists of: Two sets of subtests grouped according to (a) verbal and performance scales (Verbal and Performance), and (b) Index Scores (Verbal Comprehension, Perceptual Organization, Working Memory, and Processing Speed).

Other information: Clinical studies are based on populations presenting with attention deficit/hyperactivity disorder, traumatic brain injury, mental retardation, hearing impairment, reading and math disabilities, schizophrenia, chronic alcohol abuse, Alzheimer's disease, Parkinson's disease, Huntington's disease, and Korsakoff's syndrome.

RECOMMENDED
Wechsler Abbreviated Scale of Intelligence (WASI)

Intended ages: 6 – 89 years.
Testing time: Four subtest form: 30 minutes; Two-Subtest Form: 15 minutes
Administration: Individual

Intended to be administered by: Trained professionals

Purpose: To provide a quick, reliable measure of a person's verbal, nonverbal, and general cognitive functioning in various settings.

Consists of: Two formats:

Four-subtest format: Provides FSIQ, VIQ, and PIQ scores
- Vocabulary
- Similarities
- Block Design
- Matrix Reasoning

Two-subtest format: Provides an estimate of general intellectual ability (FSIQ)
- Vocabulary
- Matrix Reasoning

The WASI's VIQ subtests measure crystallized abilities, while the PIQ measures nonverbal fluid ability, and the Block Design measures visuomotor/coordination skills.

Other information: Although not intended as a replacement to the more comprehensive intelligence measures (WISC-IV, WAIS-III), this brief measure is useful in helpful as a
reliable and valid screening tool to estimate cognitive functioning for examinee's referred for psychiatric, vocational, or rehabilitation evaluations.

Wide Range Intelligence Test (WRIT)

Intended ages: 4–85 years
Testing time: 20–30 minutes
Administration: Individual

Intended to be administered by: Trained professionals

Purpose: To Provide a general measure of intelligence.

Consists of: Four subtests of cognitive abilities designed to assess both verbal and nonverbal abilities via verbal and visual scales. Each scale consists of two subtests that address a group of specific abilities:

- Verbal (Crystallized) IQ – Vocabulary and Verbal Analogies subtests
- Visual (Fluid) IQ – Matrices and Diamonds subtests
- General IQ (Verbal and Visual combined)
- Diamonds subtest requires construction of specific designs using single or multiple diamond-shaped pieces
- Matrices subtest requires evaluation of a series of pictures and selection of the option that would best complete a visual array.

Effective for:
- documenting general ability levels
- providing an estimate of cognitive ability to assist with psychiatric and vocational rehabilitation evaluations
- identifying learning disabilities, mental retardation, giftedness, neuropsychological impairments, and other exceptionalities

Other information: IQs have high correlation with the Wechsler Intelligence Scale for Children – 3rd edition (WISC-III), and the Wechsler Adult Intelligence Scale-3rd edition (WAIS-III), while conforming with the Wide Range Achievement Test (WRAT).

RECOMMENDED
Kaufman Assessment Battery for Children, Second Edition (KABC-II)

Intended ages: 3–18 years
Testing time: Luria model: 25–55 minutes;
        Core battery, CHC model: 35–70 minutes
Administration: Individual
Intended to be administered by: Trained professionals
Purpose: Measurement of cognitive ability. Provides a detailed, accurate assessment of cognitive ability in children of different backgrounds and with diverse problems.

Consists of: Two different theoretical models—the Luria, and Cattell-Horn-Carroll (CHC)—are offered to help meet the needs of each examinee as determined by the reason for referral or the child's background. A further, nonverbal option allows the examiner to assess a child with limited verbal skills.

KABC-II scales include:
- Sequential Processing/Short-Term Memory
- Simultaneous Processing/Visual Processing
- Learning Ability/Long-Term Storage and Retrieval
- Planning Ability/Fluid Reasoning
- Knowledge/Crystallized Ability

Other information: Subtests are designed to minimize verbal instructions and responses via items that contain limited cultural content. The system helps to gather clinical insights regarding how a child both receives and processes information based on each person's cognitive strengths and weaknesses.

> "Nonverbal IQs were greater than verbal IQs for young children (3-7 years of age) on the Stanford-Binet: IV …with high scores on visual matching tests (Bead Memory and Quantitative Reasoning). The low- and high-WISC-III IQ groups both performed well relative to IQ on tests of lexical knowledge (Similarities, Information, and Vocabulary), but not on language comprehension and social reasoning (Comprehension). The low-IQ group did best on visuo-motor subtests (Object Assemble and Block Design), but the high-IQ group did not. The high-IQ group had significantly low scores on the Digit Span, Arithmetic, Coding, VMI, and WIAT Written Expression Tests." (Mayes & Calhun, 2003, p. 329)

RECOMMENDED
Kaufman Brief Intelligence Test, Second Edition (KBIT-2)

Intended ages: 4–90
Testing time: 15–20 minutes
Administration: Individual

Intended to be administered by: Professionals

Purpose: To measure verbal and nonverbal intelligence. The KBIT-2 provides a culturally unbiased format that can be quickly administered to help estimate intelligence, estimate a person's verbal versus nonverbal intelligence, re-evaluate the intellectual status of children or adults in various (clinical, academic, institutional) settings, screen to identify students who would qualify for gifted programs.

Consists of: Two subtests, verbal and nonverbal, each designed to measure distinct cognitive functions, provide a balanced view of a person's overall intelligence when combined. The verbal subtest contains two item types (verbal knowledge and riddles) that measure crystallized ability. The nonverbal subtest includes a matrices subtest that measures fluid reasoning.

Other information: The KPIT-2 is a quick, valid, and reliable measure that includes the assessment of receptive and expressive vocabulary items that do not require reading or spelling. It also features full-color test items that are designed to appeal to children as well as reluctant examinees.

RECOMMENDED
Stanford-Binet Intelligence Scales, Fifth Edition (SB5)

Intended ages: 2 – 85+ years
Testing time: Varies, approximately 5 minutes per subtest
Administration: Individual

Intended for: Trained professionals

Purpose: To obtain a comprehensive measurement of intelligence. The test adapts the test to the functional level of the examinee, increasing measurement precision by tailoring the item difficulty to the subject's current level of cognitive functioning. The use of a hierarchical model of intelligence with a global g factor and several broad factors at a second level is repeated in the current fifth edition.

Consists of: Comprehensive coverage of five factors of cognitive ability
- Fluid Reasoning
- Knowledge
- Quantitative Processing
- Visual-Spatial Processing
- Working Memory

Other information: Wide variety of items requiring nonverbal performance by examinee makes it ideal for assessing populations with communication disorders. Yields ability to compare verbal and nonverbal performance. Provides verbal and nonverbal assessment of working memory. Extensive high-end items designed to measure the highest level of gifted performance. Co-normed with measures of visual-motor perception and test-taking behavior. Colored artwork and manipulatives make it task-friendly for children who benefit from visual and hands-on measurement tasks. Useful in diagnosing a wide variety of developmental disabilities and exceptionalities through clinical and neuropsychological assessment, early childhood assessment, and psycho-educational evaluations for special education placements.

Chapter 17

Nonverbal Measures

Assessment Instruments Designed to Assess Persons who are nonverbal, those who are difficult to assess with verbally-based tools, or those who struggle with standard language

Introduction

Research has pointed to speech and language delays as one of the primary "red flag" areas that can help to identify children with autism. For children with autism, speech and language delays or the absence of verbal communication are typically among the earliest warning signs that prompt parents to refer their children for evaluations. Although many children with autism eventually develop expressive and receptive language skills, their basic verbal communication abilities do not often develop until much later than expected neurodevelopmentally, or in relation to their same age peers. As such, children with autism, even those who fall under the "high functioning" end of the spectrum, typically begin their therapeutic and intervention journeys through visits with Speech Language pathologists.

As mentioned in chapter 9 (Standard Distributions), every child with autism is different and falls at a specific point of his or her own respective "bell curve" in terms of their personal language deficits. In effect, treatment for each individual child must begin at the point where that child is at the time of first encounter with a Speech Pathologist and embarks on the path to language development from there forward. Depending on any given number of factors, some will show slow, laborious progress, while others—to the delight of all involved—will evidence growth that is more moderate and steady. In some cases, children with autism will even show improvement that seems to emerge "overnight," although expectations must be kept at realistic levels and—at no time—should any pressure be exerted on the child to perform. Regardless of the child's point of departure on the way to the development of adequate communicative skills in general, and verbal communication skills in particular, however, the amount of quantitative and qualitative progress that each child makes will typically reflect the degree of concentrated and coordinated efforts that are made by that child's support network. Children whose parents, extended caregivers, siblings, relatives, teachers, para-professionals, and others providing services coordinate and sustain efforts as directed and instructed by trained Speech Language professionals will consistently show greater, and more consistent gains than those who receive minimal support from their extended networks.

Although children challenged by the inability to express themselves verbally will all present with personal struggles and individual circumstances, there are certain basic similarities they will share that will receive a primary focus of attention. Often, these involve three preverbal areas, including the presence of communication functions, the means used for such communications, and nonlinguistic comprehension, each of which has been identified as essential regarding early screening of potential autism spectrum disorder. Communication functions, including behavior regulation, social interaction, and joint attention, enable children to attend to and communicate with others through voicing requests, initiating greetings, or sharing comments and observations. The means by which these communications are conveyed can include distal gestures (pointing, waving), contact gestures (showing, giving, offering), and vocalizations (crying, laughter, grunts, giggling). Nonliguistic comprehension can include understanding of nonverbal, situational, and/or paralingual modes of communication often exhibited by nonverbal children. (Prelock, 2006, pp. 186-187)

Communication and Symbolic Behavior Scales Developmental Profile (CSBS DP)

Intended ages: Functional communication age between 6– 24 months; chronological age from 6 months – 6 years.
Testing time: Varies
Administration: Individual

Intended to be administered by: Trained professionals

Purpose: To help determine the communicative competence, such as eye gaze, gestures, sounds, words, understanding and play skills of young children. Uses include:
- Screening to identify at children at risk for developmental delay or disability
- Evaluating potential social communication, expressive speech/language, and symbolic functioning delays
- Evaluating ongoing changes in a child's behavior patterns

Consists of: Seven language predictor measures:
- Emotion and Eye Gaze
- Communication
- Gestures
- Sounds
- Words
- Understanding
- Object Use

Includes: A one-page Infant-Toddler Checklist, 4-page follow up Caregiver Questionnaire
a Behavior Sample which is administered in the parent/caregiver's presence.

Other information: Can be used to assist for intervention planning, as an outcome measure, and as a guide for further assessment.

Wechsler Nonverbal Scale of Ability (WNV)

Intended ages: 4.0 – 21.11 years
Testing time: Full battery: 45 minutes; Brief version: 15-20 minutes
Administration: Individual

Intended to be administered by: Trained professionals

Purpose: To provide a nonverbal measure of ability for linguistically diverse population examinees, such as those who are not proficient in the English language or who present with other language considerations.

<u>Consists of</u>: Flexible full and brief battery versions.

Full battery subtests include:

- Matrices
- Coding
- Spatial Span
- Object Assemble
- Recognition
- Picture Arrangement

Brief version includes:

- Two subtests
- Yields a single ability score

<u>Other information</u>:The WNV was specifically designed for individuals with language difficulties or disorders, those who may be eligible for special services and support but may not have been thus far identified, and gifted individuals from linguistically diverse groups. It meets current (2007) IDEA requirements.

Universal Nonverbal Intelligence Test (UNIT)

<u>Intended ages</u>: 5.0–17.11 years

<u>Testing time</u>: 10–15 minutes (abbreviated battery); 30 minutes (standard battery); 45 minutes (extended battery)

<u>Administration</u>: Individual

<u>Intended to be administered by</u>: Professionals

<u>Purpose</u>: To assess general intelligence. Designed to provide a fair assessment of intelligence for children and adolescents who have speech, language, or hearing impairments; different cultural or language backgrounds; or those who are verbally uncommunicative.

<u>Consists of</u>: Six subtests that require multiple response modes, including use of manipulatives, paper and pencil, and pointing while helping to engage and interest children of different races, ethnicities, and cultures. The subtests have a mean of 10, and standard deviation of 3, as well as 5 quotient scores with a mean of 100 and standard deviation of 15 that provide:

- Full Scale Intelligence Quotient
- Memory Quotient
- Reasoning Quotient
- Symbolic Quotient
- Nonsymbolic Quotient

<u>Other information</u>: The UNIT provides diagnostic information relevant to common educational exceptionalities, including mental retardation, giftedness, and learning disabilities. Discriminant validity evidence reported indicates that the UNIT reliably differentiates across individuals with speech and language impairments, mental retardation, learning disabilities, and giftedness.

Test of Nonverbal Intellifence-3 (TONI-3)

Intended ages: 6.0 – 85.11 years
Testing time: 15–20 minutes
Administration: Individuals or small groups

Intended to be administered by: Trained professionals

Purpose: To measure intelligence, aptitude, abstract reasoning, and problem solving. A language-free format helps to facilitate testing for difficult to assess individuals, as well as accommodating those who are not proficient in English, have problems with handwriting, or are reluctant testers due to a lack of familiarity.

Consists of: Norm referenced, language-free measures of intelligence, aptitude, abstract reasoning, and problem solving. The test is completely nonverbal and mostly motor-free, depending only on pointing, nodding, or symbolic gestures to indicate response choices. Even the examiner is only required to pantomime the instructions. Items present a variety of problem-solving tasks that follow an ascending order of difficulty through items with abstract figural content. Each 50-item form contains problem-solving tasks that become progressively complex and increasingly difficult.

Other information: In addition to the above, the TONI-3 helps to facilitate evaluation of individuals presenting with aphasia, dyslexia, language disabilities, learning disabilities, speech problems, specific academic deficits, and similar conditions resulting from mental retardation, deafness, developmental disabilities, autism, cerebral palsy, stroke, head injury, or other neurological impairments.

Comprehensive Test of Nonverbal Intelligence (CTONI)

Intended ages: 6 – 89 years
Testing time: Under 60 minutes
Administration: Individual

Intended to be administered by: Professionals

Purpose: To assess intellectual ability. Designed for persons who are bilingual, non-English speakers, are socially/ economically disadvantaged, deaf, language disordered, motor impaired, or neurologically impaired.

Consists of: Six subtests each of which looks at different types of nonverbal reasoning abilities. In each subtest students look at a group of pictures and solve problems using analogies, categorizations, and sequences through simply pointing to alternative choices. Three cognitive abilities are measured in two separate contexts: (a) pictorial objects—which contain familiar objects, such as people toys, and animals; and (b) geometric designs—unfamiliar sketches, drawings, and patterns.

The three cognitive abilities measured include:
- Analogical Reasoning
- Categorical Classification
- Sequential Reasoning

Other information: Directions for the CTONI can be administered orally to students who are fluent in English or pantomimed to those who are not, as well as those who are deaf, aphasic, or neurologically impaired. Composite

scores are provided for:
- Nonverbal intelligence quotient
- Pictorial nonverbal intelligence quotient
- Geometric nonverbal intelligence quotient

Leiter International Performance Scale-Revised (Leiter-R)

<u>Intended ages</u>: 2/0 to 20.11 years
<u>Testing time</u>: Varies depending on battery administered
<u>Administration</u>: Individual

<u>Intended to be administered by</u>: Diagnosticians

<u>Purpose</u>: To measure intelligence and cognitive abilities. A totally nonverbal test of intelligence and cognitive abilities. Because it is nonverbal it is suitable for children and adolescents who are cognitively delayed, disadvantaged, nonverbal, non-English speaking or ESL, speech-hearing impaired, ADHD, autistic, or TBI.

<u>Consists of</u>: A game-like administration designed to hold a child's interest. Two nationally standardized batteries: a revision of the original visualization and reasoning domains for measuring IQ, and the new attention and memory domains. Both batteries include unique growth scores that measure small, but important, improvement in children with significant cognitive disabilities.

<u>Other information</u>: The revised edition includes: new attention and memory domains (AM battery) to help identify children with ADHD, LD, or neuropsychological impairments; an assessment range that covers the ranges of the WPPSI-R, and WISC-III; new growth scores for all domains that enable professionals to gage progression of improvement over time; no cultural or language bias as it includes psychometric studies on Native American, Hispanic, and African American groups.

Chapter 18

Assessment of Executive Functions

Introduction

"Your child seems to have problems with planning…organizing…shifting attention…multitasking…there are problems with focusing, listening to the teacher, taking notes. She does not seem to be able to finish a task before starting on a second. It's exasperating to the teacher! When being assessed, she insisted on not leaving a timed task until the one she was working on was finished, even after time had expired! It was very frustrating for the evaluator. She is so good at some complex tasks, but others, the ones she has no interest in, well, we just cannot find anything to motivate her unless she is interested in something. She's not like the other kids…you know…she's 'different.' She loses everything, misses appointments, and rigid! So very rigid! Will just not budge. Hard-headed as can be. Oh, and so concrete, a perfectionist regardless of how long it takes. Seems like she can't distinguish between truly important things and those that can be set aside, everything is weighed the same."

What is this child's label? ADHD? Lazy? Conduct disordered? Oppositional? Control issues? Poor parenting? In fact, the above are signs of executive dysfunction, or problems with the "executive" brain functions. When one has problems with "executive functions," it is like having a team of blue-chip, five-star football recruits, with a dysfunctional coach. A group of world-class musicians being led by a dysfunctional conductor. An envious collection of ambitious, well-motivated, dedicated employees trying to function under the "leadership" of a dysfunctional C.E.O. The end result will likely always be the same: losing football seasons…chaotic performances…bankrupt companies.

The child described above is not "bad," or "lazy," or "not trying/motivated," "stubborn…hard to get along with… difficult…disordered"…she is not broken. She is swimming upstream against a bevy of executive dysfunction symptoms that are front and center of our three conditions—AS, HFA and NLD—as well as the ever-popular ADHD. As such, the purpose of this chapter is to introduce the reader to a collection of the most current, valid, and reliable instruments to help assess executive functions.

Research Gems: The Executive Lobe

"Like a large corporation, a large orchestra, or a large army, the brain consists of distinct components serving distinct functions. And like these large-scale human organizations, the brain has its CEO, its conductor, the general: the frontal lobes. To be precise, this role is vested in but one part of the frontal lobes, the prefrontal cortex….Yet like a leaderless army, cognition disintegrates and ultimately collapses with the loss of the frontal lobes. In my native Russian language, there is an expression 'bez tsarya v golovye,' 'a head without the czar inside'." (Goldberg, 2001, p. 23)

Assessment Instruments Designed to Evaluate Executive Functions

Edgin and Pennington (2005) summarized a number of experimental studies that documented executive function (EF) deficits in individuals with ASD, including in their references the ages of the subjects and tasks administered. The primary tests and subtest tasks that were used throughout those studies to assess EF reviewed are listed below. (For a detailed review please refer to Edgin & Pennington, 2006, pp. 731-732.)

Executive Function Measures

WCST Perseverative Errors
ECST Categories
Trails B
Mazes
Tower of Hanoi
Category Test
Goldstein-Scheerer Sorting Test
A-not-B task
Delayed Response Task
Spatial Reversal Task
Alternation
CANTAB (Cambridge Neuropsychological Test Automated Battery) ID/ED Task
Tower of London
Wechsler Memory Scale
- Sentence Span
- Counting Span
TempOrder (words)
TempOrder (pictures)
Dice Counting
Odd Man Out
Sums Span Task
A-not-B Invisible Displacement
Spatial Reversal
Spatial N Back
Box Search
Spatial Location Span

Research Gems: Executive Function

"The idea of executive function comprises an 'umbrella term' used to cover a wide range of 'higher cognitive processes,' often seen as emergent from neutral operations. Theorists believe executive function deficiencies explain the obsessive routines and inflexibility of many, if not all, people with autism. According to this hypothesis, inflexibility and obsessiveness arise from the inability to generate novel responses and/or plans of actions, due to the deficiency in executive functions." (Nadesan, 2005, p. 122)

Behavior Rating Inventory of Executive Function (BRIEF)

Intended ages: 5 to 18
Testing time: 10 – 15 minutes
Administration: Individual

Intended to be administered by: Parents/caregivers, teachers, therapists

Purpose: To evaluate children with a wide spectrum of developmental and acquired neurological conditions, including learning disabilities, ADHD, Tourette's, traumatic brain injury, and PDD-autism.
Consists of: Two rating forms (parent and teacher) designed to assess executive functioning the home and school environments. Eighty-six items in eight non-overlapping clinical scales and two validity scales.

Other information: The validity scales form two broader indexes: Behavioral Regulation (three scales) and Metacognition (five scales) that combine to form a Global Executive Composite score.

Behavior Rating Inventory of Executive Function-Preschool Version (BRIEF-P)

Intended ages: 2.0 – 5.11 years
Testing time: 10-15 minutes
Administration: Individual

Intended to be administered by: Parents/ Caregivers, teachers, therapists

Purpose: To specifically measure the range of behavioral manifestations of executive function in preschool-aged children in order to help facilitate intervention at earlier stages of development.

Consists of: A single rating form to rate children's executive functions within the context of everyday environments—home and preschool. Sixty-three items that measure various aspects of executive functioning: Inhibit, Shift, Emotional Control, Working Memory, and Plan/organize. The clinical scales form three broad indexes: Inhibitory self-control, Flexibility, and Emergent Metacognition, and one composite score: Global Executive Composite. It also provides two validity scales: Inconsistency and Negativity.

Other information: Useful in assessing preschool-aged children with medical, acquired neurological, and developmental conditions such as prematurity, emerging learning disabilities and attentional disorders, language disorders, traumatic brain injuries, lead exposure, and PDD/autism.

Behavior Rating Inventory of Executive Function-Adult Version (BRIEF-A)

Intended ages: 18 – 90 years
Testing time: 10 – 15 minutes
Administration: Individual
Intended to be administered by: Researchers, clinicians, neuropsychologists, psychologists, physicians, and rehabilitation professionals

Purpose: A standardized measure designed to capture views of adults' executive functions or self-regulation in their everyday environments.

Consists of: Seventy-five items within nine non-overlapping theoretically and empirically derived clinical scales that measure various aspects of executive functioning. These include: Inhibit, Shift, Emotional Control, Self-Monitor, Initiate, Working Memory, Plan/Organize, Task Monitor, and Organization of Materials. The clinical scales form two broader indexes: Behavioral Retulation and Metacognition that lead to a Global Executive Composite. It also provides three validity scales: Infrequency, Inconsistency, and Negativity.

Other information: Two formats are used, a self-report and an informant report. The self-report is designed to be completed by adults with a wide variety of developmental, systemic, neurological, and psychiatric disorders such as attention disorders, learning disabilities, autism spectrum disorders, traumatic brain injury, depression, mild cognitive impairment, dementias, and schizophrenia. The informant report is administered to an adult by someone who is familiar with the rated individual's everyday functioning.

Delis-Kaplan Executive Function System (D-KEFS)

Intended ages: 8 – 89 years
Testing time: 90 minutes (upon administration of all nine tests)
Administration: Individual

Intended to be administered by: Trained professionals

Purpose: To assess the key components of executive functions within verbal and spatial modalities. Designed to evaluate higher-level cognitive functions in both children and adults. Can be used to assess the integrity of the brain, to determine how deficits in abstract and creative thinking may impact daily life, and to help plan coping strategies and rehabilitation programs tailored to each patient's profile of executive function strengths and weaknesses.

Consists of: Nine stand-alone tests designed to comprehensively assess primary components of executive functions believed to be mediated primarily by the frontal lobe. A game-like format designed to be interesting and engaging for examinees, encouraging optimal performance without providing "right/wrong" feedback that can lead to frustration.

The tests include:
- Sorting: Problem-solving, verbal and spatial concept formation, thinking flexibility on a conceptual task
- Trail Making: Thinking flexibility on a visual-motor task
- Verbal Fluency: Fluent productivity in the verbal domain
- Design Fluency: Fluent productivity in the spatial domain
- Color-Word Interference: Verbal inhibition
- Tower Test: Planning and reasoning in the spatial modality, impulsivity
- 20 Questions: Hypothesis testing; verbal and spatial abstract thinking, impulsivity
- Word Context: Deductive reasoning; verbal abstract thinking
- Proverb: Metaphorical thinking; generating versus comprehending abstract thought

<u>Other information</u>: The D-KEFS is correlated with the Wechsler Abbreviated Scale of Intelligence (WASI) and the California Verbal Learning Test, 2nd Edition (CVLT-II), providing information concerning the role of intellectual ability and memory on D-KEFS performance.

Tower of London – 2nd Edition (TOL-2nd Edition)

<u>Intended ages</u>: 7 – 80 years
<u>Testing time</u>: 10 – 15 minutes
<u>Administration</u>: Individual

<u>Intended to be administered by</u>: Trained professionals

<u>Purpose</u>: To assess higher-order problem-solving skills including executive planning. Information provided is designed to assess frontal lobe damage as well as attention disorders and executive functioning difficulties.

<u>Consists of</u>: Repeated trials for failed problems, 6- and 7-move problem configurations, increasing sensitivity to executive functioning across age levels, and an empirical selection of test problem configurations.

<u>Other information</u>: Useful for assessing frontal lobe damage as well as executive function difficulties encountered by populations with Asperger's syndrome, autism, and ADHD. The new (2nd) edition includes a Stimulus-bound score to facilitate the assessment of older adults. New normative data for older adults is also included in the new edition, along with recent research findings.

<u>Key areas measured include</u>:
- Task Analysis
- Cognitive Computations
- Working Memory
- Allocation and Maintenance of Attention
- Inhibition of Impulsivity
- Cognitive Flexibility
- Stimulus-Bound

Wisconsin Card Sorting Test (WCST)

<u>Intended ages</u>: 6.5 – 89 years of age.
<u>Testing time</u>: 20 – 30 minutes
<u>Administration</u>: Individual

<u>Intended to be administered by</u>: Trained professionals

<u>Purpose</u>: To assess perseveration and abstract thinking, measure executive function, and assess frontal lobe functions such as:
- strategic planning
- organized searching

- utilizing environmental feedback to shift cognitive sets
- directing behavior toward achieving a goal
- modulating impulsive responding

Consists of: Four stimulus cards that incorporate three stimulus parameters.

Other information: Provides objective scores of overall success as well as specific sources of difficulty on particular tasks such as inefficient initial conceptualization, perseveration, failure to maintain a cognitive set, and inefficient learning across stages of the test.

Behavioral Assessment of the Dysexecutive Syndrome (BADS)

Intended ages: 16 – 87 years
Testing time: 40 minutes
Administration: Individual
Intended to be administered by: Self and caregivers

Purpose: To help predict day-to-day problems typically associated with dysexecutive syndrome by measuring executive deficits that reflect everyday life. Sensitive battery to skills involved in problem solving, planning, and organizing behavior over extended time periods.

Consists of: A series of tests that examine:
- Temporal judgment: Four questions assess subjects' ability to estimate how long various complete events last
- Action program: Tests practical problem solving—a cork has to be extracted from a tall tube—a result which can only be achieved by the planned use of various other materials provided
- Key search: Tests strategy formation as an analogy to a common problem of searching a field for a set of lost keys
- Zoo map: Tests planning, provides information relating to the examinee's ability to plan a route to visit 6 of a possible 12 zoo locations

Other information: The battery also includes a 20-item Dysexecutive Questionnaire (DEX) that is designed to sample the range of problems, emotional or personality, motivational, behavioral, and cognitive changes.

RECOMMENDED
Behavioural Assessment of the Dysexecutive Syndrome for Children (BADS-C)

Intended ages: 8 – 16 years
Testing time: 35 – 45 minutes
Administration: Individual

Intended to be administered by: Trained professionals

<u>Purpose</u>: To assist in the early identification of dysexecutive (DES) functioning deficits in children.

<u>Consists of</u>: A series of brief, varied, and engaging subtests that examine:
- inflexibility
- perseveration
- novel problem solving
- impulsivity
- planning
- ability to utilize feedback and moderate one's behavior accordingly

<u>Other information</u>: The subtests are described as aimed at appealing to both male and female children and emphasizing a sense of success upon completion as well as not being influenced by practiced sub-skills or motor control. Observational data is also emphasized as the examiner is encouraged to observe both the level of competence and the manner in which tasks are completed.

<u>Research Gems: Recommended Executive Function Criterion Measures</u>

Wisconsin Card Sorting Test (WCST)
Comprehension Subtest from the WAIS III
Porteus Maze
Trail B of the Trail Making Test (TMT)
Multilingual Aphasia Examination (MAE)
Semantic Fluency score from the
Repeatable Battery of Neuropsychological Status (RBANS)

NAB Executive Functions Module Kit

<u>Purpose</u>: To provide a marker of planning, engaging with others effectively, problem solving, successfully interacting with the environment to get one's needs met, judgment, conceptualization, cognitive response set, mental flexibility, verbal fluency, and generativity.

Designed for patients with traumatic brain injury, stroke, tumor, hypoxia/anoxia, degenerative disease (Parkinson's disease, Pick's disease, Frontotemporal dementia, Huntington's disease, advanced Alzheimer's disease); attention-deficit/hyperactivity disorder, depression, schizophrenia, obsessive-compulsive disorder, metabolic disorders (Graves' hyper-thyroidism, hypothyroidism), and other lesions.

Chapter 19

Self-Esteem Assessment

"Self-esteem affects virtually every facet of our life….It comes from collective thoughts, feelings, and experiences we have had and continue to have about ourselves throughout our life. Self-esteem has been defined by the National Association for Self-Esteem as: 'the experience of being capable of managing life's challenges and being worthy of happiness.' People who feel good about themselves usually express their feelings in their behavior as well as in an openness to learn and grow from life's lessons. They are more able to meet and solve the problems, stresses, and responsibilities of life with confidence." (Khalsa, 1996, p. xii)

Research Gems: Self-Esteem and NLD

"Self-esteem is the feelings and thoughts we have about ourselves developed through experiences of relating to others, completing tasks competently, and self-direction. It includes our optimism about success. Self-esteem has been compared to the immune system of the mind, soul, and heart. It protects and buffers our inner self from potential damage brought on by failure or blocked attempts at success. Self-esteem allows us to continue taking risks in our lives. The social difficulties, academic difficulties, and experiences of failure experienced by individuals with NVLD have the potential to affect their self-esteem negatively." (Stoddart, 2005, p. 67)

Introduction

In psychological terms, the notion of self-esteem, regarded as an enduring personality trait, typically refers to a person's perception of self-worth or self-respect, and directly relates to one's sense of self-confidence. In his highly respected personality theories, Abraham Maslow cited two primary "esteem" needs, a "lower" need for respect from others, which included needs for status, fame, glory, recognition, attention, and dignity. The "higher" need was that for self-respect, involved a sense of achievement, independence, freedom, competence, confidence, and mastery. (Maslow, 1908-1970)

Although the quest for a solid sense of positive self-esteem is a challenge for all of us the core deficits and challenges that add up to autism, AS, and NLD typically make the achievement of self-worth or attainment of self-confidence a steeper and more laborious climb. Particularly around the middle school years, when children with autism, AS, and NLD join their peers on their initial forays of individuation and establishing their own, self-defining identities, the issue of self-esteem becomes increasingly problematic. Deficits or delays in social skills, pragmatic communication abilities, the capacity to read others, and the ability to "see the big picture," mix together with motor skill deficits (lack of athletic ability), quirky and eccentric habits, topic perseveration, and comorbid issues (gastrointestinal problems, tics, depression, anxiety, obsessive compulsive tendencies and others) to make the already difficult early adolescent years quite trying for most children across the autism, AS, and NLD spectrums. Because of this, the importance of properly assessing the level of self-esteem with which children, adolescents and adults with these conditions present—whether one ascribes to the classic idea of self-esteem as defined by one's ratio of success vs. failure, to the social-learning view that it reflects a stable sense of personal worth, or to the notion that one's self-esteem depends on our competency to deal with life's challenges—takes a very high level of importance.

Assessment Instruments Designed to Assess Self-Esteem

Culture Free Self-Esteem Inventories- Third Edition (CFSEI-3)

Intended ages: 6.0 – 18.11 years of age.
Testing time: 15 – 20 minutes
Administration: Individual or groups
Intended to be administered by: Trained professionals

Purpose: To determine the level of self-esteem in students between the ages of 6 and 19.

Consists of: Three age-appropriate forms: Primary, Intermediate, and Adolescent. Each provides self-esteem scores in four areas: Academic, General, Parental/Home, and Social. The Adolescent Form provides an additional self-esteem score: Personal Self-Esteem.

Other information: Easy to administer and score consisting of "yes/no" answers that can be either written or spoken. Conversion tables provide subscale standard scores based on a mean of 10 and standard deviation of 3, with quotient scores based on a mean of 100 and standard deviation of 15. Standardized on a sample of 1,727 persons from 17 states. Cultural fairness of the CFSEI-3 has been demonstrated in various studies, including differential item functioning analyses and separate reliability for seven subgroups, including male, female, European American, African American, Hispanic American, gifted and talented, and learning disabled.

> "I feel that it is impossible for the human infant to develop a true sense of self without first incorporating others' reactions into his or her basic tapestry of instinctive reactions—this combined process thus creating our social individual selves. Self-esteem, meaning a sense of self-worth, comes later and for some children it is their fundamental lack of a cohesive sense of self, as in autism, which is often misinterpreted as a lack of self-esteem." (Blakemore-Brown, 2002, p. 24)

Research Gems: Self-Esteem Sensitivities

"Despite their apparent self-assurance and indifference to authority, most more-able children with autistic disorders have a very low self-esteem even if they are of high ability. They have all experienced many failures in social interaction and are sensitive to the laughter and scorn of their age peers when they behave in a naïve way. Some develop a paranoid attitude as a result. These sensitivities should be kept in mind when teaching or caring for the children." (Wing, 2001, pp. 151-152)

Self-Esteem Index (SEI)

Intended ages: 8.0 – 18-11.
Testing time: 30 minutes
Administration: Individual or group

Intended to be administered by: Trained professionals

Purpose: A multi-dimensional, norm-referenced measure that helps to assess the way in which persons aged 8 through 19 perceive and value themselves.

Consists of: Four scales including Academic Competence, Family Acceptance, Peer Popularity, and Personal Security. Overall self-esteem is measured by the Self-Esteem Quotient.

Other information: A self-report format requires participants to read the SEI items and then classify each item on a Likert-type scale including: "always true, usually true, usually false, or always false." Evidence of the reliability of the SEI is provided in the form of coefficients alpha computed of each 1-year interval, all of which approach or exceed accepted standards.

Research Gems: The Guises of Self-Esteem

"Clinical data support the view that many children with NLD have negative feelings about themselves that are the product of low self-esteem. Some respond defensively, believing themselves to be special or superior to others, demeaning or denigrating others. Some appear oblivious to these issues, displaying a curious lack of awareness of their status, and apparently taking no ownership of their condition." (Palombo, 2006, p. 113)

Multidimensional Self Concept Scale (MSCS)

Intended ages: 9 – 19 years of age.
Testing time: 20 minutes
Administration: Individual or group

Intended to be administered by: Trained professionals
Purpose: To assess global self-concept and six context-dependent self-concept domains that are functionally and theoretically important in the social-emotional adjustment of youth and adolescents.

Consists of: Six domains each of which evaluates a specific area of psychosocial functioning for youth and adolescents: Social, Competence, Affect, Academic, Family, and Physical.

Other information: Each MSCS subscale yields high reliability with a Total Scale Score reliability exceeding .97 for the total sample. It correlates very strongly with other measures of self-concept and self-esteem and has been shown empirically to identify clients previously identified as being low in self-concept.

Pier-Harris Children's Self-Concept Scale-Second Edition (PHCSCS-2)

Intended ages: 7 – 18 years of age
Testing time: 10 – 15 minutes
Administration: Individual

Intended to be administered by: Trained professionals

Purpose: To assess self-concept and help identify children and adolescents' perceptions of themselves as well as the necessity for further testing or treatment with regard to self-concept issues.

Consists of: Sixty items cover six subscales including:
- Physical Appearance and Attributes
- Freedom from Anxiety
- Intellectual and School Status
- Behavioral Adjustment
- Happiness and Satisfaction
- Popularity

Other information: Considered one of the most widely used measures of psychological health in children and teens. The second edition offers an expanded age range, reduced length, improved interpretive guidelines, a larger and more diverse standardization sample, and updated computer assessment. Test items are simple descriptive statements, written at a third-grade reading level while requesting "yes/no" responses. Useful in both academic and clinical settings to help identify specific areas of conflict, typical coping and defense mechanisms, and appropriate intervention techniques.

Chapter 20

Assessment of Speech and Language

Research Gems: The Role of SLPs in the Assessment of autism

"The SLP plays a critical role in referring children suspected of possible ASD to an audiologist to confirm or rule out a hearing loss. Furthermore, the SLP should play a primary role in the diagnosis of speech and language impairments that can co-occur with ASD, including, but not limited to, features of specific language impairment, apraxia, and dysarthria." (Ad Hoc Committee on Autism Spectrum Disorders, 2006, p. 7)

Introduction: The Integral Role of Speech Language Pathologists

With the abilities to socialize and communicate being paramount for the diagnosis of autism, AS, and NLD conditions the role of Speech Language Pathologists (SLPs) in the identifying, screening, assessing and diagnosing children with these conditions cannot be overemphasized. In essence, SLPs are both essential and indispensable in our work with children who fall across the spectrums of these three conditions. Although the ideal diagnostic role for SLPs would be as one among several other well trained, experienced members of an interdisciplinary team the luxury of such comprehensive networks do not always translate into realities. Additionally, since a large majority of children with these conditions are initially referred directly to SLPs (because of social and/or language problems), or Occupational and Physical therapists (due to their sensory and/or motor related delays) it is imperative for these professionals to be well versed in the early screening of these populations.

"Language pathologists are independent health care providers who have responsibilities at the levels of screening (Level 1), diagnosis and evaluation (Level 2) of autism" (Filipek, et al., 1999, p. 461)."

Speech-language pathologists, also commonly referred to as speech therapists, are trained in assessment, diagnosis, and intervention of speech, language, cognitive-communication, voice, swallowing, fluency, and other related disorders. In general, Speech-language pathologists serve individuals challenged by; the production of speech based sounds; producing these sounds in a clear manner; swallowing difficulties; problems in speech fluency or rhythm (stuttering); voice disorders, (unseemly pitch, harsh voice tone); understanding and producing language; general verbal and nonverbal communication skills; and cognitive communication impairments (attention, memory, and problem solving disorders).

When dealing with autism, AS, and NLD spectrum conditions, SLPs can provide services that typically revolve around addressing communication problems such as the absence of speech, frequent repeating of words or phrases (echolalia) and improper intonation and rhythm. Other areas of assistance offered by SLPs include:

- Instruction on phonological and sound awareness.

- Time related responses reflecting social exchanges.

- Proper manner by which to switch topics during a conversation, and picking up on these signals from others.

- Environmental observations to facilitate functional assessment information about social, interaction, and communicative skills.

- Assessment of vocabulary comprehension.

- Voice control instruction (lowering or raising one's volume level according to appropriate social and situational factors).

- Proper manner in which to engage another or request social or interpersonal attention.

- Classroom observations to monitor skill generalization.

- Instruction on the operation of communication devices.

According to the Individuals with Disabilities Education Improvement Act of 2004 (Pub. L. 108-446), "Individuals with ASD should be eligible for speech-language pathology services due to the pervasive nature of the social communication impairment, regardless of age, cognitive abilities, or performance on standardized testing of formal language skills., speech-language pathologists should avoid applying a priori criteria (e.g., discrepancies between cognitive abilities and communication functioning, chronological age, or diagnosis) and make individualized decisions on eligibility for services. Because formal assessment tools may not accurately detect problems in the social use of language and communication, eligibility may need to be based on clinical judgment and more informal, observational measures." (Ad Hoc Committee on Autism Spectrum Disorders, February, 2006, p. 1)

Assessment Instruments Designed to Evaluate Speech, Language and Communication Skills

Evaluating Acquired Skills in Communication-Revised (EASIC-R)

Intended ages: 3 months through 6 years
Testing time: 15 – 30 minutes
Administration: Individual

Intended to be administered by: Speech pathologists

Purpose: An inventory developed to measure the spoken receptive and expressive spoken language of children with autism.

Consists of: An assessment of semantics, syntax, morphology, and pragmatics communication skills at five levels:

- Pre-language – before meaningful speech
- Receptive I – understanding simple noun labels, action verbs, and basic concepts
- Expressive I – emerging modes of communication
- Receptive II – understanding more complex language functions
- Expressive II – using a more complex level of communication

Other information: Also effective with children who exhibit developmental language delays outside of the autism spectrum.

Research Gems: Early Warning Signs

"The first signs that raise concerns among parents and professionals are typically delays in speech and communication skills, limited social responsiveness, and slow development." (Akshoomoff et al., 2007, p. 887)

Clinical Evaluation of Language Fundamentals – Fourth Edition UK (CELF-4UK)

Intended ages: Ages 5 years to 16 years, 11 months
Testing time: 30 – 60 minutes
Administration: Individual

Intended for: Trained professionals – Speech Language Pathologists

Purpose: To help assess a child's language difficulties and skills, as well as receptive and expressive language scores.

Consists of: An individually administered language test that helps to assess a child's general language ability and determines if a language disorder may be present. If one is determined to be in evidence, more extensive testing provides information about the nature of the disorder, language strengths and weaknesses, language content, and language modalities. Testing with a number of supplementary subtests enables the evaluator to pinpoint critical skills and behavior that underlie the language disorder.

These include:
- Phonological Awareness
- Rapid Automatic Naming
- Digit Span
- Sequences
- Word Associations
- Memory Composites

New subtests include:
- Expressive Vocabulary
- Word Definitions
- Understanding Spoken Paragraphs
- Number Repetitions 1 & 2
- Familiar Sequences Level 2
- Phonological Awareness
- Pragmatics Profile
- Observational Rating Scales

Other information: Features include a multi-step assessment process to assist in developing classroom solutions for each student's language problems. The battery is culturally diverse and includes a rich supplement of visual stimuli.

The new CELF-4UK version contains additional composite scores in:
- Language Structure•
- Language Content
- Language Content and Memory
- Working Memory Scores

Research Gems: Effectiveness of the CCC

"Children with ASD can be adequately differentiated from normal control children in terms of their language deficits, based on the CCC. The present results show that parents and teachers agree reasonably well in the kind of information they give. There was a very low false positive rate, but a relatively high false negative rate. Hence, the CCC is a useful instrument to obtain a global inventory of deficits in the domain of language and to assess language deficits in ASD, but a number of children with ASD would not be detected if the CCC was used as a diagnostic instrument." (Vertè et al., 2006, pp. 283-284)

The Children's Communication Checklist (CCC)

Intended ages: 4.0 – 16.11
Testing time: 5 – 10 minutes
Administration: Individual

Intended for: Parents and teachers

Purpose: A questionnaire designed to measure pragmatic language use and assess language impairment, especially pragmatic difficulties, in everyday situations. It is also useful for children with autism spectrum disorders.
Consists of: A 70-item questionnaire containing nine scales, two of which assess aspects of formal language (fluency of speech output and complexity of syntax), five of which are combined to assess pragmatic language use (inappropriate initiation, coherence, stereotyped conversation, use of context, and conversational rapport), and two of which assess non-language domains (social relationships and unusual or restricted interests).

Research Gems: The CCC and Standardized Language Tests

"The (CCC) checklist does provide a simple and cost-effective method for obtaining systematic information about pragmatic difficulties from parents and professionals. It allows one to quantify severity of impairments in aspects of communication that are not easy to assess using conventional tests. Furthermore, it may highlight the presence of communicative problems in children for whom language has not been a major concern….In its current form, the CCC offers a useful supplement to an assessment battery, complementing the information that can be obtained from standardized language tests." (Bishop & Baird, 2001, p. 816)

CCC Domains: Language:
- Speech
- Syntax
- Semantics
- Coherence

Pragmatics:
- Initiation
- Scripted Language
- Context
- Nonverbal Communication

Other information: The CCC effectively measures aspects of communication, including speech, vocabulary, sentence structure, and social language skills of children and adolescents who speak in sentences. It also screens for general language impairments, identifies children with pragmatic language impairments, and determines if children may benefit from further assessment for autism spectrum disorder.

Research Gems: Use of the CCC with HFA and ADHD

"Compared to NC (normal controls), children with HFA showed pragmatic deficits on all CCC scales. Children with ADHD demonstrated deficits compared to NC as well. Moreover, the ADHD and HFA groups differed from each other on most of the scales….Pragmatic difficulties do occur in both HFA and ADHD. The present studies indicate that the CCC is a useful instrument to obtain information concerning pragmatic language use in both a clinical and a research setting. Although the information of parents is more tightly linked to the diagnosis, combining the information of both parent and teacher slightly improves case identification." (Geurts et al., 2004, p. 1437)

Table: General Assessment Tools for Language

Assessment Tool	Age range	Purpose
Analysis of the Language of Learning	5 – 9 years	To assess metalinguistic language areas
Assessing Semantic Skills through Everyday Themes (ASSET)	3 – 9 years	Receptive and expressive tasks that focus on labels, categories, attributes, functions and definitions
Bankson Language Test (BLT-2)	3 – 7 years	Focuses on semantic knowledge, morphological & syntactical rules, and pragmatics
Boehm Test of Basic Concepts – Preschool Version	3 – 5 years	Screens 26 concepts over two response opportunities each.
Bracken Basic Concept Inventory-Revised (BBCS-R)	2 – 11 years	Measures basic concept knowledge related to color, comparisons, shapes, self/social awareness, direction/position, numbers/counting, letter identification, size, texture/material, and time/sequence
CELF-3 Observational Rating Scales	6 – 21 years	Obtains information from home and school on listening, speaking, reading and writing
Clinical Evaluation of Language Fundamentals-3 (CELF-3)	6 – 21 years	Language skills including linguistic concepts, formulating sentences, following directions, and listening skills
Clinical Evaluation of Language Fundamentals-Preschool (CELF-P)	3 – 9 years	Basic concepts, sentence & word structure, formulating labels, recalling meaning, & linguistic concepts
Communication Abilities Diagnostic Test (CADeT)	3 – 9 years	Language performance in syntax, semantics and pragmatics during story, game, and conversations
Comprehensive Receptive & Expressive Vocabulary Test (CREVT)	4 – 18 years	Receptive and expressive vocabulary

ECO Program	18 months – 8 years	Social play, turn taking, preverbal communication, language, & conversation
Evaluating Acquired Skills in Communication, Revised (EASIC-R)	3 months – 8 years	5-Level inventory to assess pre-language and receptive/ expressive skills
Expressive Vocabulary Test (EVT)	2 – 90 years	Expressive vocabulary and word retrieval
Functional Communication Profile	3 years - adult	Information on skill level re: attentiveness, sensory/ motor issues, speech, fluency, voice, & pragmatic/ social skills
The Listening Test (Includes teacher survey)	6 – 11 years	Listening to/understanding main idea, details, concepts, engaging, reasoning.
Oral & Written Language Scales (OWLS)	3 – 21 years (oral scale) 5 – 21 years (written scale)	Listening comprehension, oral & written expression
Peabody Picture Vocabulary Test III (PPVT-III)	2 – 90+ years	Listening comprehension of vocabulary
Preschool Language Assessment Instrument (PLAI)	3 – 6 years (or older children)	Labeling objects and actions, role-playing, responding to conversations and directions, defining words, solving problems
Test for Auditory Comprehension-3 (TACL-3)	3 – 10 years	Receptive spoken vocabulary, grammar, and syntax
Test of Early Language Development-3 (TELD-3)	2 – 8 years	Receptive and expressive language skills

Test of Language Competence- Level 1	1 – 10 years (Level 1) 9 – 19 years (Level 2)	Metalinguistic performance in the areas of semantics, syntax and pragmatics
Test of Pragmatic Language	5 – 14 years	Measures six pragmatic language subcomponents: physical setting, audience, topic, purpose, visual-gestural cues & abstraction
Test of Problem Solving Adolescent (TOPS)	12 – 17 years	Thinking skills related to fair-mindedness, affect, oversimplication, clarifying, analyzing, generating solutions, evaluating, and thinking independently
Test of Word Knowledge	5 – 17 years	Semantic and lexical knowledge through evaluating word definitions, multiple contexts, opposites, synonyms.
The Word Test-Adolescence	12 – 17 years	Associations, synonyms, semantic absurdities, antonyms, definitions, and multiple definitions

---

Research Gems: Hearing Loss Among Children with Autism

"The audiology clinic may be the first place that children with autism present. Hearing loss may be more common in children with autism than in typical children. It is important to detect any hearing loss at an early stage for the prevention of a possible failure to respond to the education of autism. TEOAE (transient evoked otoacoustic emission) and ABR (auditory brainstem response) measurements may be useful in the differential diagnosis of autism as well as in the measurement of hearing in those children....Although the diagnosis is strengthened when hearing is normal, hearing impairment should not eliminate autism." (Tas et al., 2007, p. 78)

Chapter 21

Assessment of Motor and Visual Skills

Research Gems: Motor Impairments in HFA/AS

"HFA/AS were most impaired with regard to dynamic balance skills and diadochokinesis compared to controls....The problems in dynamics balance skills in this study as well as the postural control findings point towards complex problems in the interaction and integration of different sensory and motor functions in HFA/AS....The difficulties in the dynamic balance and peg board task might further be due to executive function deficits caused by frontal or frontostriatal dysfunction in HFA/AS." (Freitag et al., 2007,pp. 956-957)

Introduction: Introduction: The Integral Role of Occupational Therapists

The American Occupational Therapy Association describes occupational therapy as a skilled treatment that helps individuals to achieve independence in all aspects of their lives. Occupational therapists specialize in assisting individuals to develop skills that are necessary to lead independent and satisfying lives. When working with persons across the autism, AS, and NLD spectrums, occupational therapists (OT's) can assist in the development of basic, motor related skills such as using utensils, handwriting, manipulating tools, buttoning shirts, tying their shoes, developing the ability to catch a ball, open jars, assembling toys, and essentially anything thing else that requires gross and fine motor skills and finger dexterity. Furthermore, however, occupational therapists also specialize in serving the challenges posed by sensory integration dysfunction and sensory processing. Since the manner through which different stimuli are received and interpreted by the senses can be gravely affected by sensory integration dysfunction these challenges can significantly interfere with basic social, personal, and professional skills required to undertake daily responsibilities or engage in play.

Most play related activities, such as catching a ball, swinging on a swing, jumping on a trampoline, skipping rope, and endless others require fine assortments and combinations of motor skills, rhythm and coordination. Vocational skills, as well, also require that our gross and/or fine motor skills be organized, rhythmic and motorically coherent. Assembling components, mowing lawns, typing, working a protractor, taking notes, holding up a book, sorting papers, firing a weapon, using mechanical tools, and most other work related activities, whether blue or white collar, require distinct amounts and combinations of dexterity and the coordination of our sensory fields and motor skills. At home, cooking, cleaning, vacuuming, writing out monthly bills, going up and down the stairs, and other constant necessities all require complex movements that most persons who are not challenged by motor or sensory related disorders take for granted.

Sensory Integration Issues

Symptoms that may serve as red flags for sensory related challenges can occur in any of the many sensory related areas including auditory, gustatory, olfactory, tactile, and visual, as well as vestibular and propioceptive. Auditory related challenges, can affect the way by which one perceived sounds and can result in being either over- or –under sensitive to auditory stimuli. Further, some people with these disturbances may be hypersensitive to some sounds while, at the same time, be hyposensitive to others making an evaluation very difficult and necessitating a trained, experienced professional. Tactile related challenges, likewise, can affect a person's perception of touch leading to the aversion (hypersensitivity) of certain fabrics (such as wool), to hygienic practices (shampooing one's hair, hair cut, trimming one's nails, brushing one's teeth), and avoiding certain objects (wood, metal, rubber), or surfaces (sand, grass, cement) Hyposensitivity to touch, on the other hand, can lead the person to seek certain tactile stimuli, or to repeatedly touch objects or parts of one's body, or the body or belongings of others. Problems with balance and motor regulation can also lead to characteristic autism related movements such as restless movements, flapping of the hands, snapping of the fingers, clumsiness, bumping into furniture and objects, awkward gait, and difficulties with social related activities. Problems with noticing various degrees of pain, temperature, and pressure are also all associated with our sensory system's ability to act and react to these stimuli accordingly.

Our vestibular system involves the structures within the inner ear and helps us in balancing and being aware of changes when we position our heads. Hypersensitive problems with our vestibular system can result in difficulties, or fear, with climbing, sliding, walking on uneven or unstable surfaces, riding a bicycle, or balancing. A hyposensitive vestibular system, on the other hand, may lead to one to seek intense sensory experiences seen in children with autism as body whirling, jumping up and down, spinning, running in "figure eights," and, at times, engaging in activities that can result in injury to themselves or others.

The proprioceptive system involves our muscles, joints, and tendons and the extent to which they provide us with a general awareness of our body position and its relation to our environment. This system is responsible for regulating our sitting positions, balancing our extremities when we climb a set of stairs, and execute both fine and gross motor movements. As with the other areas involved in sensory integration, persons with irregular or sensory deficient proprioceptive systems can either engage in avoidance of the above type behaviors, or seek extra stimulation such as by moving continuously without tiring, or tiring easily after exerting minimal amounts of energy.

An occupational therapy assessment may typically include
evaluation of the following areas:

Visual Perception
Visual Tracking
Handwriting
Physical Strength
Balance and coordination
Range of motion
Bimanual functions
Activities of daily living capabiltites
Fine finger dexterity
Fine and gross motor skills
Self-caring skills
Sensory-motor developmental abilities
Task related skills
Body image
Cognitive-Organization abilities
Neuro-motor abilities
Approaching and executing of developmental tasks
Play skills
Integration and coordination of motor and perceptual skills
Organization skills
Visual-motor integration
Visual-spatial skills
Copy skills, number and letter writing

Assessment Instruments Designed to Evaluate Motor and Visual Skills

The Zurich Neuromotor Assessment (ZNA)

Intended ages: 5 – 18 years of age
Testing time: Approximately one hour
Administration: Individual
Intended to be administered by: Trained professionals

Purpose: To help differentiate pure motor function from adaptive function. Capable of differentiating between performance speed of:
- simple and complex non-adaptive motor movements
- adaptive motor movements and associated movements as a measure of movement quality

Consists of: Eleven subtests administered in sitting or standing position. These include:

- repetitive toe tapping
- heel-toe-alternation
- repetitive hand patting
- pro and supination of the hands (alternative hand movements)
- repetitive and sequential finger tapping
- peg board
- static and dynamic balance
- diadochokinesis
- stress gaits (walking on toes, heels, inner and outer sole of foot)

Other information: In addition to the above subtests, five "block components," summary measures of obtained single measures, are calculated, including: motor performance/adaptive performance, peg board, dynamic balance, static balance, and associated movements. Nine "differential components" are further calculated, comprising summary measures of the ratio of simple versus complex motor movements, speed of upper versus lower extremities, laterality of motor, and adaptive movements, in addition to five differential components of movement quality.

Research Gems: Macrographia in Persons Across the Autistic Spectrum

"Macrographia was observed among subjects with autism spectrum disorder which remained statistically significant when covaried with education level. This finding may correlate with the anatomical abnormalities present in the cerebellum of individuals with autism spectrum disorder." (Beversdorg et al., 2001, p. 97)

Wide Range Assessment of Visual Motor Abilities (WRAVMA)

Intended ages: 3 – 17 years
Testing time: 4 – 10 minutes per subtest
Administration: Individual or groups

Intended to be administered by: Trained professionals

Purpose: To evaluate visuomotor, visuospatial, and fine-motor skills

Consists of: Three separate tests each designed to assess visuomotor, visuospatial, and fine-motor skills of children and adolescents.

Other information: Described as the first test battery that allows the examiner to evaluate and compare the above skills using norms gathered from the same standardization sample.

Research Gems: Motor Impairments and Brain Function in HFA/AS

"The association of autistic symptoms with neuromotor performance in the full sample as well as in the HFA/AS group points towards an essential role of motor impairment in autism spectrum disorders. The association of adaptive motor abilities and diadochokinesis with the three core symptom domains and social withdrawal are in support of the view that autism pathology comprises widespread altered brain function, not only resulting in the triad of diagnostic symptoms in this disorder but also in problems with adaptive motor abilities and other complex cognitive abilities, like difficulties in executive functions, complex language abilities, theory of mind or emotion processing." (Freitag et al., 2007, p. 957)

Mullen Scales of Early Learning

Intended ages: Birth to 5 years, 8 months.
Testing time: 1 –year old: 15 minutes; 3 –year old: 30 minutes; 5 –year old: 40-60 minutes
Administration: Individual

Intended to be administered by: Trained professionals

Purpose: Measurement of:
- Gross motor
- Visual Reception
- Fine Motor
- Expressive Language
- Receptive Language

Consists of: A series of colorful manipulatives and artwork designed to attract young children for the evaluation of strengths and weaknesses in the above areas.

Other information: The Mullen Scales are designed to help professionals to establish a foundation for effective intervention and to formulate a baseline from which to determine
appropriate teaching strategies. Computer-generated intervention reports list developmentally appropriate tasks that parents can help their children learn at home.

Research Gems: "Measuring Visuospatial Tasks in Autism and Asperger's"

Using the Rey Complex Figure Test as part of a battery of visuospatial tasks thought to measure central coherence (embedded figures, block design) "participants with autism were distinguished by relatively good performance on visuospatial tasks, though there was no superiority effect in those with Asperger's syndrome. Performance on the visuospatial battery did not significantly predict susceptibility to illusions in various participant groups, including those with autism and Asperger's syndrome. This suggests that perception of illusions and performance on visuospatial tasks may rely on different mechanisms." (Ropar & Mitchell, 2001, p. 539)

Rey Complex Figure Test and Recognition Trial

<u>Intended ages</u>: 6 – 89 years
<u>Testing time</u>: 45 minutes (including a 30-minute delay interval)
<u>Administration</u>: Individual

<u>Intended for</u>: Trained professionals

<u>Purpose</u>: To measure visuospatial constructional ability and visuospatial memory.

<u>Consists of</u>: Three drawing trials designed to assess recognition memory using the elements of the Rey Complex Figure, and assess the respondent's ability to use cues to retrieve information with a Recognition Trial.

<u>Captures five domains of neuropsychological functioning</u>:
- visuospatial recall memory
- visuospatial recognition memory
- response bias
- processing speed
- visuospatial constructional ability

<u>Other information</u>: This form of the test standardizes the materials and procedures for scoring drawings. The same scoring criteria apply to all three drawing trials. Based on a 36-point scoring system scores range from 2 (accurately drawn, correctly placed) to 0 (inaccurately drawn and incorrectly placed, unrecognizable, or omitted).

Research Gems: "Repetitive Sensorimotor Behaviors"

"A factor analysis found evidence for a repetitive sensorimotor (RSM) factor and an insistence on sameness (IS) factor. Behaviors that loaded on the RSM factor were prevalent in children with ASD and significantly more common and severe than in children with DD (non-spectrum developmental disorder), or TD (typical development). On average, children with ASD had more RSM behaviors. Behaviors that loaded on the IS factor were relatively uncommon and did not differ in prevalence or severity across groups." (Richler et al., 2007, p. 73)

Research Gems: "Girls vs. Boys"

"All children (22 girls and 68 boys with autism spectrum disorders, mean age = 28 months) achieved strongest performance in visual reception and fine motor followed by gross motor and language functioning. Sex differences emerged in developmental profiles. Controlling for language, girls achieved higher visual reception scores than boys; boys attained higher language and motor scores and higher social-competence ratings than girls, particularly when controlling for visual reception." (Carter et al., 2007, p. 86)

Chapter 22

Red Flags

"Red Flags" are, in essence, practical "shout outs," or warning signs, that help to alert us, whether parents/caregivers, educators, therapists, or diagnosticians, to the possibility that a person may be presenting with autism, AS, or NLD. Sometimes subtle, other times blatant; sometimes early during the course of development, other times late; sometimes formal, other times informal, awareness of these signs can be quite helpful in helping to identify and screen these potential conditions so that proper referrals to qualified persons can be made during the early stages of the course of the particular disorder. The purpose of this chapter, and its many checklists, is to facilitate this process.

Screening instruments designed for early identification of potential early symptoms in autism, AD, and NLD populations

Early Parental Concern Red Flags

- First words late (23 months)
- Horrendous tantrums
- Late to walk (20 months)
- Withdrew from other children
- Loss of spoken language at 28 months
- Slow progress to phrase speech
- Repetitive play
- No fear of danger
- Constant crying
- Not interested in infant toys
- Loss of spoken language at 14 months

(McConachie, Le Couteur, & Honey, 2005, p. 171)
(See Autism "Red Flags" Checklist© in Appendix C.)

"Red Flag" Checklist for Parents and Caregivers

Early Development Patterns that May Indicate Autism

(The greater number of checked "markers" indicates the greater the probability that the child may fall within the profile of the "broad autistic phenotype," or within the spectrum of autism or pervasive developmental distinction.)

Early Markers:

___ any type of regression (loss of language, gesturing, or social skills)
___ no response to being called by name
___ apparent problems with understanding language
___ a pattern of mutism accompanied with rare, spontaneous speech
___ failure to point by age 1
___ lack of production of single words by age 6 months
___ lack of production of babbling, pointing, or other nonverbal gestures by age 12 months
___ failure to speak words by age 14 months
___ ability to speak only 12 words or less by age 18 months
___ lack of production of spontaneous or two-word phrases by age 24 months
___ lack of production of complete sentences by age 36 months
___ absence of nonverbal signs (nodding or shaking head) to indicate yes/no answers by 36 months
___ impaired age-appropriate social skills
___ general inflexibility
___ a pattern of tantrums or meltdowns when routines are broken
___ a pattern of concrete, repetitive play
___ over- or under-sensitivity to sensory triggers (visual, auditory, olfactory, gustatory, tactile)
___ lack of direct eye contact
___ "empty gazing," or "appearing to stare right though you"
___ motorically clumsy and uncoordinated in comparison to peers
___ repetitive movements that appear to lack purpose or intention, such as rocking or pacing back and forth, flapping of hands or arms, wringing or twisting fingers
___ failure to answer questions by preschool age
___ random speech lacking practical communication by preschool age
___ echolalia persisting into preschool age
___ pronoun confusion persisting into preschool age
___ a pattern of referring to self by own name into preschool age
___ "video-speak" or the repetition of scripted or memorized expressions into preschool age
___ a pattern of perseveration on special topics or preferred themes into preschool age
___ inability to tell a coherent story into preschool age
___ a pattern of speaking in a monotone into preschool age
___ a pattern of speaking in high-pitched tones into preschool age
___ a pattern of speaking in "sing-songy" voice into preschool age
___ a pattern of flat, apparently emotionally detached vocalizing into preschool age
___ difficulties with participating in peer relevant athletic activities
___ apparent clumsy gait when walking or running
___ difficulties climbing, jumping, or hopping on one foot
___ problems with buttons, zippers, or tying shoes

__ difficulties with arts and crafts projects
__ inability to hold crayons, pencils, or markers
__ poor penmanship or handwriting skills in relation to peers
__ unusually hasty alternating body movements
__ problems with coordination and/or balance

Additional Markers

The following sections expand on the preliminary, potential early markers listed above.

General Pattern Red Flags

<u>My child could be described as one who</u>:

__ appears not to like being hugged unless it is very tightly
__ appears not to like being caressed, stroked, or fondled
__ tends to relax in response to deep pressure or massage
__ does not typically respond to his/her name being called
__ tends to look at objects, or things, around the room rather than making eye contact
__ appears to ignore, or not respond to, attempts at redirection
__ tends to focus on particular trinkets (earrings, eyeglasses, bracelet) or details (wrinkles, beauty marks, freckles, small scar) rather than looking into one's eyes when attempting face-to-face contact
__ appears to use a sideways, lateral, or peripheral rather than direct eye gaze
__ tends to make eye contact that could be described as both intense and distant at the same time
__ tends to use toys in concrete (lining them up) rather than imaginative (giving them names and/or social roles) play
__ appears to lack gesturing during social interactions
__ appears to lack flexibility
__ has a strong preference for routine activities and becomes quickly annoyed or upset when changes are introduced
__ has extreme difficulties making transitions to a greater degree than his/her same age peers
__ seems to lack the awareness that things (toys), thoughts, or emotions can be shared
__ has a pattern of imitating physical behaviors and body movements
__ has an uncanny ability to recreate scenes to the letter without use of creative license
__ has above average to remarkable rote memory
__ has significant problems adapting to new, or changing, situations
__ appears not to imitate facial expressions but can mimic vocalizations (accents, prosody, inflections, intonation, voice tone) verbatim
__ will at times use words or expressions out of context and adamantly resist correction
__ at times uses "sing-songy" inflections when speaking with others
__ tends to speak with a monotone
__ will often copy the inflections, accents, or voice characteristics of adults or other children at times, also inserting memorized phrases as part of a conversation
__ has a pattern of using scripted language
__ has an uncanny ability to rhyme words
__ tends to engage in "streams" of conversation without appropriate pauses

__ has an uncanny ability to follow directions explicitly but becomes quickly annoyed or exasperated at any interruption or deviation

__ keeps toys and belongings in specific areas and becomes quickly annoyed or upset if they are moved or re-arranged

__ obsessively rewinds videos to the very beginning each time they are watched and cannot tolerate starting them "halfway in," pausing them, or turning them off until they are watched to the end.

__ insists on having the text captions on whenever watching videos or television programs

__ becomes obsessed with certain videos or television programs and insists on watching them repeatedly

__ seems to lack age-appropriate awareness regarding personal belongings, both his/her own and those of others

Social – Interactive Pattern Red Flags

<u>My child could be described as one who</u>:

__ prefers to play on his/her own

__ seems to relate better to adults than his/her same age peers

__ is not good at playing socially interactive games

__ prefers to play with the same, rather than a variety, of toys

__ prefers games that do not require much creativity

__ seems to be much more "on the go" than his/her same age peers

__ seems to be much quieter and isolated than his/her same age peers

__ prefers games that involve repetition and predictability

__ prefers to make his/her own rules when playing games

__ appears more preoccupied with following rules "to the letter" than enjoying a game for its own sake

__ becomes easily annoyed with any changes to a set routine

__ has extreme difficulties with making transitions

__ seems to lack the curiosity shared by his/her same age peers

__ tends to perseverate on unusual fears or worries

__ has unusual interests

Sensory Challenge Red Flags

<u>My child tends to</u>:

__ over- or under-react to certain visual stimuli

__ have an extraordinary sense of smell and become intolerant over mildly noxious or unpleasant scents

__ be easily startled by certain mild sounds

__ be completely unaware of noises

__ have a strong, negative reaction to certain types of touch

__ have a strong preference for deep pressure

__ have a strong preference for certain types of fabric and a complete aversion to others

__ have a strong aversion for certain foods, restricting his/her food intake to very limited choices

__ engage in self-stimulatory behaviors such as rocking back and forth, flicking his/her fingers, shaking his fingers over his eyes, wringing his/her hands, or "flapping" his hands or arms

__ walk on his/her toes

__ react to certain things very slowly

___ engage in daydreaming or "zoning out" behaviors
___ at times become entranced with details or "something out there"
___ struggle with gross motor skills, such as catching a ball
___ have a very high pain threshold
___ be overtly sensitive to relatively mild painful experiences such as casual scrapes, bumps, and bruises
___ have very unusual tolerance, or lack of, for thermal fluctuations
___ have above average to remarkable mechanical abilities when assembling objects but struggles with practical application skills such as lacing shoes, using a can opener, or opening a lid
___ have an unusual way of walking and/or running
___ have problems with balance (such as riding a bicycle, or walking a beam)
___ clumsily bump into objects in a "bull in a china shop" manner
___ have problems physically beginning and/or ending physical activities
___ adapt to pace fluctuations when working or playing
___ engage in play that involves fine dexterity or motor coordination
___ have problems judging distance
___ have sleep problems
___ engage in impulsive activities
___ shy away from certain materials such as paint, clay, or chalk
___ have no interest in playing games unless he/she is in complete charge
___ have very poor body posture
___ lack general coordination
___ lack physical stamina
___ not complain when sick or tired
___ have laser-like focus for special interest subjects while lacking the ability to concentrate on subjects or topics of little to no interest regardless of reward contingencies, behavioral or social implications (getting a passing grade, being liked)

Communication Pattern Red Flags

<u>My child could be described as one who</u>:

___ has problems using, or understanding, body language or posture
___ has problems using, or understanding, facial expressions
___ has problems picking up on, or demonstrating, different emotions
___ has problems using, or understanding, slang terms
___ has problems using, or understanding, metaphors and analogies
___ has problems using, or understanding, social situations
___ has problems using, or understanding, unwritten social rules
___ tends to use sophisticated language or obscure words
___ has a sophisticated vocabulary but seems to struggle with practical conversation
___ appears to prefer communicating by using self-invented signing rather than spoken language
___ appears to have problems communicating or describing his/her feelings
___ appears much more comfortable interacting with older children or adults than with children of his/her same age
___ seems to talk to him-/herself much more often than his/her same age peers
___ appears to lack enthusiasm or "sparkle"
___ tends to over-dramatize situations much more often than his/her same age peers

___ seems to talk "at you" rather than engage in reciprocal conversations

___ at times will use snippets from television commercials or programs, movies, or books in response to general questions

___ tends to use echolalia (repeating what someone else has just said) as a form of responding

___ has a pattern of perseverating on particular topics or interest areas to the point of exhaustion or exasperation

___ has a pattern of misunderstanding simple instructions

___ appears to have the ability to memorize complex patterns or details but misunderstands simple instructions

___ appears to learn much more effectively by watching things being done (visual learning) or doing things him/herself (kinesthetic learning)

___ appears to struggle when answering practical questions—even though he may be well aware of the answer—and will typically respond with rote or memorized answer sets

___ appears much more comfortable in one-to-one situations than when among groups of three or more persons

___ when interacting with others will tend to share information rather than engage in give-and-take discourse

___ appears to have very little interest in hearing other's opinions or ideas

___ tends to dominate conversations typically by speaking in a lecture-type manner about his/her special interest topics

___ appears to need being in charge with little to no room for compromise

___ appears to be insecure

___ tends to be become easily frustrated

(See Positive Characteristics Checklist© for persons with AS, HFA, and NLD in Appendix D.)

Sensory Integration "Red Flag" Checklist

Potential Red Flags:

- Poor self-esteem or self-concept
- Apparent clumsiness, carelessness, or disinterest in others
- Heightened awareness of background noises or sounds
- Startled reactions to sudden or unexpected sounds (noisy environments may trigger low tolerance, shutting down or tantrum)
- Fascination or preoccupation with lights, fans, running water, spinning or rotating objects (wheels or clock pendulums)
- Preference for dark, or low-lit rooms and avoidance of bright lights (low tolerance for fluorescent lights)
- Avoidance of direct eye contact or intense stares at some people or objects
- High sensitivity to certain lights, sounds, or smells
- Delays in speech, language, or motor skills that may be misdiagnosed as other problems such as apraxia, dyspraxia, or other disorders
- Delays in academic achievement that may be misdiagnosed as poor cognitive skills or low intelligence
- May lack reaction to strong odors while exhibiting low to no tolerance for some mild scents (after shave, toothpaste, cologne, perfume)
- Certain foods may be avoided or not tolerated due to their taste, look, smell, or texture
- Low tolerance for certain textures such as sand, glue, finger paint, sticky papers, grain, clay, "slimy" feeling toys, or other substances typically enjoyed by same-age peers

- Concentration may be impeded or interrupted by seemingly innocuous things such as deformities on a pencil, a hard chair, a mildly wrinkled paper, circulating air, the murmur of a heating system, an unintended brush or harmless nudge from a peer
- Objects may be smelled or explored (touched, caressed, massaged, spun) extensively
- Repetitive movements such as hand flapping; may be misdiagnosed as autistic.
- An apparent constant seeking of movement or hypermotoric activity
- Muscles may be weak, with poor endurance for physical activities
- Taking things apart, spinning objects
- Toe walking, bouncing, or spinning
- High tolerance or low awareness of pain, pressure, or temperature
- Problems with coordination (gross and/or fine motor) and balance
- Climbing or playing on playground equipment may be avoided or instill fear or apprehension
- Accident prone and seemingly dare-devilish at times while unduly cautious and apprehensive at other times
- Activity levels that are unusually high or low (sometimes appearing as manic-depressive swings); may be misdiagnosed with bipolar disorder.
- Problems transitioning from one situation to the next or generalizing across situations, even if these are familiar; may be misdiagnosed as conduct disordered or oppositional defiant
- Problems with flexibility and change and a strong preference for structure and repetition
- May be incredibly organized in some areas while completely disorganized in others
- May be either overly or under affectionate with others whether closely familiar or complete strangers
- May avoid games involving physical contact, and repel attempts to hold hands, hug, or reciprocate physical affection
- Appearance of anxiety, worry, fear, or panic at times when all around is calm and secure, while completely fearless, or unaware, at other times of stress or when confronted with typically anxiety-provoking events
- Aggression or striking out with minimal or no (apparent) provocation
- Hyperactive or hypo- (under) active levels of activity sometimes to the point of taking excessive risks and engaging in dangerous activities; may be misdiagnosed with attention deficit hyperactivity disorder
- May seek excessive amounts of sensory stimulation (hypersensitive) at times, while needing extended periods of calm and quiet at others. May also need inordinate amounts of time to calm down after physical activity or to become stimulated after periods of rest
- Intolerance of certain textures and strong preference for others (may refuse to wear certain clothes, or fabrics, or insist on wearing certain others)
- Strong or absent reactions to stimulation of the face, hands, or feet
- Avoidance of grooming related activities such as hair combing or brushing, teeth brushing, face washing, hair cuts
- Extremely short attention spans or highly distracted in some areas while "laser-focused" in others
- May work on, or play, with an object or engage in a solitary pursuit for extended periods of time of intense, all consuming focus, while restlessly jumping from one activity to the next at other times

Frequently Reported Red Flag Behaviors

The following list includes frequently reported behaviors from a sample of children with high-functioning autism and Asperger's syndrome, as reported on a sample population obtained via the Repetitive Behavior Interview:

Demonstrated Behavior	% HFA	% AS
• Repetitive talk about one topic	85	79
• Difficulty trying new activity	85	68
• Abnormally obsessional interest	76	63
• Watch same video continuously	76	52
• Insistence on certain routines/rituals	67	37
• Lining things up in rows/patterns	67	32
• Spinning/banging/twiddling	67	26
• Pacing/stereotyped walking	62	58
• Compulsion (contamination, order)	62	37
• Hand & finger mannerisms	48	48
• Vocal or motor tics	48	42
• Sucking objects	43	53
• Rocking or spinning	43	48
• Self-injurious behavior	43	42

(South, Ozonoff, & McMahon, 2005, p. 151)

Asperger's Syndrome: JMO-6 Red Flags Checklist©

Extended Text Version
John M. Ortiz, Ph.D.

Topic Area 1: Social Interaction Differences

1. __ Limited social group interactions
2. __ Difficulties reading, interpreting, or deciphering the intent behind facial expressions
3. __ Limited ability to describe emotions intended during personal interactions
4. __ Difficulties interpreting emotions displayed in photographs, caricatures, or artistic renderings
5. __ A focus on detail (eyebrows, facial wrinkles, or markings, skin blemishes, disproportionate facial characteristics) vs. gestalt (the face as one, cohesive entity) during social interactions
6. __ Difficulties interpreting or recognizing social rules or taboos
7. __ Difficulties interpreting or understanding metaphors, analogies, slang, cultural expressions, or cultural idioms
8. __ A tendency toward making impulsive statements during public interactions (saying what most persons would either keep to themselves or say in private)
9. __ A pattern of expressing self as someone younger (about 2/3 of his or her age)
10. __ An apparent inability to filter some personal thoughts or expressed feelings that may be considered inappropriate or questionable in a particular context

11. ___ An apparent use of scripted or memorized responses that may be used in repeated situations sometimes resulting in out-of-context or faux pas verbalizations

12. ___ Displaying "out-of-sync" (either over- or under-excitability) reactions to a scene in a movie, television show, or advertisement that could be misinterpreted as exaggerated, dramatic, or out-of-context

13. ___ Displaying "out-of-sync" (either over- or under-excitability) reactions to a social event, personal story, or humorous anecdote that could be misinterpreted as purposely exaggerated, dramatic, insensitive, sarcastic, ingratiating, rude, disrespectful, or hurtful

14. ___ Demonstrating social reactions that are emotionally "out-of-sync" to the situation at hand (laughing at telling of a sad event, appearing sad at a happy event, intense anger in reaction to a minor social infraction)

15. ___ Ritualistic politeness that may come across as superficial or sycophantic

16. ___ Ascribing to social responses that may, although sincere and honest, may be described as shallow, phony, insincere, or artificial

17. ___ Displaying behaviors that may, although attempted in earnest, may be perceived as deceitful, condescending, or rude

18. ___ Difficulties when attempting to deceive or impress others during social interactions

19. ___ Described as childlike, gullible, candid, direct, law-abiding, reliable, guileless, naïve, immature, or socially unsophisticated

20. ___ May use certain analogies, memorized scripts or phrases, or metaphors in out-of-context situations when the intended meaning will come across nonsensical

21. ___ A pattern of foiled, or unsophisticated attempts at manipulation, deceit or social gossip

22. ___ Lack of attachment for some prized possessions in combination with ardent attachment to comparatively trivial or marginally valuable items of special interest or obsessive collections

23. ___ Apparent lack of empathy toward others

24. ___ Emotional displays of righteous indignation in reaction to a minimal slight or understated emotional response to a significant social slur

25. ___ Apparent inability to read, or interpret, nonverbal or underlying social messages

26. ___ An inclination to describe feelings or emotions, either in self or others, through detached, logic-based statements that may appear as rationalizations or intellectualizing

27. ___ Difficulties deciphering thinly veiled social messages (Following an interview: "We're probably going in a different direction" may be taken literally as meaning that the interviewer will be traveling in an opposite geographical direction rather than connecting the response to the interview itself.)

28. ___ A pattern of expressing emotions in a manner that would be typically considered either overtly inappropriate or uncaring to the point of insensitivity

29. ___ Eye-to-eye contact may range from what could be described as "gaze avoidance" in some individuals or in certain situations, through "awkward" or "dys-rhythmic" in different social situations, to "intense" or "penetrating" in other individuals or during particular circumstances

30. ___ Attempted sincere displays of nonverbal social messages may range from mildly confusing (appearing surprised when attempting excitement) or mixed (relieved while annoyed at the same time), to being in total contrast to what is being said (stating "I'm sorry about your loss" while smiling) or being misinterpreted as mockery

31. ___ A pattern whereas verbal inflections or tonal emphasis may be placed at the wrong sentence juncture so as to come across as confusing or in opposition to what is meant (a comment such as: "I never said I liked you," for example, can be interpreted in various different ways depending where the emphasis is placed: "I…never said I liked you," conveys a different meaning than "I never said I liked you," which would typically be interpreted differently from "I never said I liked you…" etc.)

32. ___ A pattern whereas voice tone or prosody may be incorrectly emphasized so as to come across as

confusing, condescending, or misinterpreted as opposite from its intended meaning (an attempt at sounding animated, for example, may come across as sarcastic, or an attempt to provide support may be unintentionally perceived as seductive)

33. __ A pattern whereas verbalized comments may be out-of-sync with the accompanying facial expression (for example, the comment; "wow, that sounds really interesting," if said while rolling one's eyes will likely be interpreted as sarcastic, whereas if spoken as one walks or looks away from the person would likely be perceived as insincere or as mockery

34. __ A tendency to dominate conversations by maintaining one-way communication centering around special interest topics and/or failing to engage or reciprocate in two-way dialogues

35. __ Apparent inability forming typical affective contacts with others

36. __ Atypical reactions or relating to day-to-day social situations

37. __ An apparent preference for isolation or disengaging from others or the surrounding social environment

38. __ An apparent pattern of disregarding typically expected social conventions, particularly when these are unwritten or nonverbally expressed

39. __ An apparent pattern of disconnecting from others or the surrounding social environment particularly during emotionally dictated events

40. __ An apparent preference for "things" or "objects" rather than people

41. __ A pattern of isolating self, rather than seeking social support in times of distress, illness, or injury

42. __ A pattern of focusing describing emotional events in a detached, logical, and/or analytical manner

43. __ A pattern of not complaining about significant wrongdoings, physical maladies (stomach virus), or events (a concussion), while perseverating in depth and detail about seemingly minor slights or minimal discomfort (a head cold) or injuries (a scratch)

44. __ Extremely dependent, at times to the level of appearing obsessive compulsive, regarding timeliness, paying bills, keeping deadlines, and following strict routines

45. __ A lack of tolerance toward others who do not maintain adherence to keeping appointments, following schedules, or breaking rules

46. __ A pattern of either exquisite orderliness in some areas and complete lack of organization in others

47. __ A pattern of either unkempt grooming and poor hygiene or ritualistic—at times bordering on obsessive compulsive—adherence to personal appearance

48. __ Appearance or perception by others as "narcissistic," selfish," or "conceited," may in fact be a social mask or reflection of low self-esteem, poor social awareness, or pattern of arrhythmic social interaction

49. __ A pattern of either "helping self" to things such as food or drink at private social or professional functions (walking in, uninvited, into a private business meeting) may be perceived as "a sense of entitlement," in contrast to alternate situations where she may shy away (an open buffet event where she is a guest)

50. __ A pattern of appearing "controlling" in certain situations (planning the itinerary for a neighbor's house party) while appearing uncaring or uninvolved in other situations where social mores or expectations may dictate that he take greater responsibility (family outing)

51. __ May make social faux pas during sensitive social gatherings (funeral, wedding), or extremely sensitive, often scripted comments in other, similar situations

52. __ May not assist with "problem solving" or "brainstorming" in situations where expertise may provide significant advantage while appearing to "take over" or "attempt to control" meetings or discussions with an air of obstinacy in others

53. __ May be described in some situations as "stubborn, inflexible, or tenacious," vs. "easy to get along with, compliant, or accommodating" in others

54. __ Although will likely defend self with dogged determination in most situations will rarely react with violence
55. __ A history of being bullied
56. __ May have a history of "physical violence" as a result of years of being bullied without receiving the support needed to counter such attacks in socially acceptable ways
57. __ Instances of social manipulation, coercion, or intimidation toward others are rare if not non-existent
58. __ May easily be coerced or manipulated by others in social situations
59. __ Naïvette, social awkwardness, or lack of social sophistication may result in attempts at flirting, or engaging the opposite sex, coming across as embarrassing, degrading, inappropriate, or harassment
60. __ Patterns of isolating, or alienating self, from others when attending social events or in the presence of large (at times simply more than two people) groups

Topic Area 2: Adherence to Routines and Consistency

1. __ A strong preference for, and adherence to, daily routines
2. __ A pattern of following ritual-like routines in both personal and professional situations
3. __ Small, random changes in schedules or routines may lead to distress and, at times, effect ability to return to, or stay on, the task at hand
4. __ Small change in schedule or daily routine (moving a meeting up by five minutes) may present greater inability to accommodate, or emotionally recuperate, than major change (cancelling the meeting)
5. __ A pattern of producing stereotyped behaviors, repetitive movements, verbal sounds (grunts, mumbling, humming), or remarks
6. __ Limited spontaneity and an apparent lack of flexibility
7. __ Maintaining uniformity will typically provide comfort while obstructions to same will likely result in high levels of anxiety and distress
8. __ External appearance of cluttered environment or disorder may in fact be a complex system of precise organization
9. __ Typically described as: single-minded, pedantic, efficient, or painstaking by some vs. nitpicky, fastidious, rigid, or unbending by others
10. __ Problems with "theory of mind" (ability to "read or interpret" subtle social nuances or underlying messages during interpersonal communications) may veer toward following strict routines or adhering to inflexible standards
11. __ Adherence to repetition in terms of movements, verbal utterances, interpersonal scripts, and special topics of interest (typically provide a sense of order and stability thereby minimizing stress and anxiety)
12. __ Pattern of elaborate routines, of no seemingly apparent purpose to the casual onlooker (again, may typically provide a sense of order and stability thereby minimizing stress and anxiety)
13. __ Preoccupation with special interest topics, themes, or activities that typically involve obscure, limited, and at times archaic subjects
14. __ Perceived "lack of imagination" (may in fact be adherence to factual details or resistance from veering away from concrete, observable features. Example: "Imagine this cardboard box is a sailboat…" may yield, "But it's not a sailboat, it's just a cardboard box.")
15. __ Perceived "lack of imagination" when playing with toys, such as lining up a collection of trucks, blocks, or figurines (may in fact be a preference to arrange via peculiar identifying features resulting from a keen eye for detail or adherence to structure based on a complex system of organization unperceived by the onlooker)

16. __ Special topic interests may yield obsessive-like infatuation for periods of days, weeks, months, or years whereas all available factual data on the topic is collected, memorized, and discussed at times incessantly and to the negligence of other, more immediate or relevant topics. Interests in these topics may make a smooth, almost seamless transition into other related or unrelated topic areas; end abruptly with the interest being channeled into a completely different topic or theme; or, at times, lead into a lifelong hobby or career

Topic Area 3: Aptitudes, Skills, and Talents

1. __ Intelligence (IQ) testing pattern of high scores in tests and subtests that measure eye for detail, sequencing, deciphering patterns, block design, puzzles, logic, localization of embedded figures, decoding
2. __ An increase in ability to adapt to changing situations and compensate for deficiencies with increased support and maturity
3. __ Sophisticated ("professor-like") and extensive vocabulary at a young age
4. __ Early speaking although speech may be scripted or memorized dialogues
5. __ Early ability to read (sometimes Hyperlexic, or an early ability to phonetically decode written text without full comprehension of material)
6. __ Pattern of describing experiences or conversing using atypical phrases or uncharacteristically sophisticated language
7. __ Astounding memory for distant events, with particular emphasis on facts and details, often mixed with poor current events or moment-to-moment recollections
8. __ Poor recall of names or recognition of faces of family members, close relatives, or local places often balanced with exquisite recall of unknown persons (historical characters), faint acquaintances (names of every pupil throughout their grammar school years), and exotic locales
9. __ Poor ability to memorize useful or currently necessary information (details for a school quiz) often balanced with phenomenal memory for seemingly useless data such as sport statistics dating back to previous centuries. , types of dinosaurs stretching over myriad prehistoric stages, or bus schedules covering extensive geographical areas
10. __ Patterns of logic and meticulous attention to detail may result in unusual perspectives or atypical ways of approaching problems that lead to, at times, extraordinary solutions to problems
11. __ Patterns of self-learning, often by focusing on non-traditional approaches or following unexpected paths
12. __ Topic interest areas may be often described as unique, restricted, or constrained
13. __ Remarkable patterns of logical, deductive reasoning is typical, whereas patterns of poor inductive and abductive reasoning are common
14. __ At times, outstanding patterns of abstract thinking that cannot be described as either "in the box," or "out of the box," but, rather "no-box," or beyond any "boxed (typical)" concept of emblematic reasoning
15. __ Noteworthy ability to notice detail or "see the trees rather than the forest," balanced with poor ability to generalize or "see the big picture"
16. __ Pattern of intellectualizing to describe emotions or personal experiences that may appear as affective detachment
17. __ May invent original words or phrases, or create exotic phrase or word composites from standard vocabulary, to describe situations or insert into formal or informal conversations
18. __ Often demonstrates rich, extensive prowess in vast—although often limited—areas of knowledge such as social stories, history, geography, music, art, sports, and other areas where large fields of data can be collected and systematized

19. __ High levels of intellect often restricted to selective, or "splinter" areas, although these can grow exponentially with age and education

20. __ Although a keen interest in fiction may exist, more typically intellectual pursuits involve formal texts and often includes product manuals, dictionaries, telephone directories, and encyclopedias

21. __ Personal reading preferences seldom involve novels or short stories but instead veer toward autobiographies, often of historical characters

22. __ Pattern of systemizing ("if – then" system correlations, exploring and constructing systems, analyzing and exploring) rather than empathizing (focusing on thoughts and emotions, predicting behaviors, connecting and resonating with others)

23. __ Typical careers tend to emphasize systems operations such as physics, electronics, computer science, laboratory work, math, engineering, material sciences, technology, economics, business, and the military. Other common careers emphasize attention to detail such as research, accounting, laboratory work, archeology, anthropology, meteorology, editing, horticulture, product design and analysis, graphic design, writing university texts and product manuals. Careers emphasizing routine, repetition, and structure also present areas of interest and potential success (assembly line work, landscaping, packaging, sorting, organizing, listing, collecting and assembling data, creating catalog systems)

24. __ Seldom interested in empathizing-type careers that focus on social systems such as health care, liberal arts, social sciences, politics, poetry, creative writing, politics, psychology, social work, nursing

25. __ Ability to succeed in sports that require fine motor skills or team work (baseball, basketball, football, soccer, volleyball) typically poor but ability to do well in sports that emphasize endurance (swimming, long-distance running, cycling, rowing, marathon, skiing) or focusing on detail (martial arts, archery, billiards, horseshoes, shooting, laser tag, paintball), or repetition (yoga, table tennis, handball, trampolines, gymnastics, body-building, weight-lifting, kayaking, sailing)

26. __ Typical interest and excellence in playing computer games, board games and video, or virtual-reality type games.

27. __ Typically proficient in table games, particularly those that require attention to detail, memorization, and pattern recognition such as Scrabble, checkers, chess, dominoes, Monopoly, card games, Sudoku

28. __ In school, will typically perform best in structured, well-organized environments and subjects that require an orientation to detail and/or memorization (spelling, history, math, science, computers), but perform poorly in subjects that require insight into the human condition (psychology, social sciences, health)

29. __ Pattern of skills will typically not reflect standard patterns of expectation with areas of strength, or even giftedness, typically accompanied by severe educational areas of drought, valleys or deficiencies that will seem inexplicable to the untrained—and often trained—observers. An excellent reader, for example, may be a poor speller, or the opposite. Sensational mathematical calculation skills may be accompanied by an inability to demonstrate the work on simple calculations

30. __ Keyboarding and typewriting skills will typically be vastly superior to handwriting and penmanship skills, which may often be misinterpreted as the work of someone with severe intellectual deficiencies, unrelated physical challenges (stroke, cerebral palsy, tremors, brain damage), or as the writing of someone of much younger years

Topic Area 4: Communication Skills and Eccentric Language Characteristics

1. __ Communication patterns may be marked by naivettè or a sense of immaturity
2. __ Physical boundaries typically expressed by over-sensitivity to being touched, hugged, or lightly caressed (deep pressure, such as acupressure and/or massage, however, often perceived as pleasurable and calming)
3. __ Two-way interpersonal communication is typically difficult or awkward with a preference for one-sided expressive communicative style (typically talking about special topics often in didactive style)
4. __ Often described as "out-of-sync," "in own world," or "in different wave-length" from others
5. __ May often appear emotionally "distant" or mentally preoccupied or "in a zone"
6. __ One-to-one communication is typically one-sided with persistence of circumscribed interest topics
7. __ Often relate much better socially and interpersonally to those with "listening" or "receptive" communication styles
8. __ As children, typically more comfortable interacting with older children or adults than with same-age peers
9. __ May excel in communicating to captive audience, such while conducting an educational lecture or seminar, entertaining, or giving a class report
10. __ Typically more comfortable with literal, exact, and unembellished, rather than figurative, abstract or symbolic aspects of communication
11. __ Nonverbal (paralinguistic) aspects of communication both physical—such as body gestures, facial expressions, posture, body proximity—and expressive—deep sighs, fluctuating tones, voice prosody and volume, eye gaze, speech modulation—are typically missed or misinterpreted
12. __ Subtle messages, particularly those of a nonverbal nature, are typically misread or ignored (example: May speak about special topic area for extended period of time in spite of repeated nonverbal messages, such as eye rolling, deep sighs, and starring at a clock, exhibited by the listener)
13. __ Will typically tolerate conversations on non-interest topics for limited time before abruptly veering into a dominating discussion of favorite topic usually without regard to the listener's lack of interest
14. __ Pattern of giving unelaborated abrupt, direct, and succinct answers during conversation seeking open-ended discussion
15. __ Honest, to the point, concise, matter-of-fact answers given in earnest may be perceived as terse, unfriendly, and condescending
16. __ Interpersonal style that at times comes across as if assuming large breath and depth of knowledge on the part of the listener, while at other times appearing as if talking down in almost patronizing manner
17. __ Use of language may be inappropriately sophisticated, formal, or technical for the situation at hand
18. __ Eye contact during social interactions, when a result of training rather than natural conditioning, may come across as awkward or strained and misinterpreted as suspicious or showing lack of interest
19. __ Physical gestures and facial expressions, when a result of training rather than developed through natural, life-long social interactions, may come across as forced or phony, or misinterpreted as coming from a sense of discomfort, shyness, or deception
20. __ Physical gestures and facial expressions may also come across as arrhythmic—or not "in sync" or complimentary to the verbal message—or "alien," such as patterns that may be expected from someone from a foreign culture on a non-native speaker
21. __ A pattern of struggling to understand and interpret intentions and distinguish between those that are genuine or well-intended from those that are deceptive or malicious
22. __ A pattern of insecurity, lack of trust, and high sensitivity to being "on-guard," typically as a result of inability to decipher intentions
23. __ Problems with command of Instrumental Gestures, such as silent, nonverbal signs of attracting attention ("come here"), pointing ("look at that!"), or producing a symbolic message ("lower your voice")

24. ___ Problems with interpreting Expressive Gestures, struggling to distinguish between nonverbal threats (a finger being waved in admonishment) and harmless gesturing (a finger pointing at a spot on one's shirt), or a condescending vs. a supportive smile

25. ___ While sequential (those that follow a pattern or order) and systemizing (mechanical, behavioral, or rule-based) stories are typically well understood, abstract (those that require personal detachment or objectivity, insight, or fantasy) stories are typically misinterpreted or require detailed explanation or translation into concrete, logical terms

26. ___ Pattern of beginning conversations abruptly, curtly jumping to the main point without explanation, and/or ending them in the same manner

27. ___ A pattern of interpersonal conversations that emphasize the imparting of information, or take on a descriptive, rather than personal or emotional resonance

28. ___ A pattern of social communication that can typically accommodate complex technological associations, but avoids such parallels to social relationships, personal matters, or social dynamics

29. ___ An adherence to detail, combined with a sense of social naivettè (or immaturity) and poor "theory of mind" (being able to put oneself in another's shoes) may result in many social faux pas situations

30. ___ Above issues will also often result in being perceived as "bossy," or controlling; boorish, or impolite

31. ___ Above issues, coupled with a sense of impulsivity (inability to filter messages) may also result in a pattern of offensive ("you sure have gained a lot of weight!"), disrespectful ("for an old person you are really stupid"), or sexually inappropriate ("you are beautiful I would like to have sex with you") comments

32. ___ A pattern of responding to questions literally, even when they may be presented figuratively, or formally when presented in informal settings or situations. (a request of "*could* you hand me that file?" for example, could elicit a response of "yes," implying that, yes, the file *could* be handed, however, without further action being taken. In effect, the request should be reworded more explicitly such as: "*will* you please bring me that file." Likewise a general question such as, "what did you do yesterday," could be followed by a detail, minute by minute discourse of the previous day's events, or even a question asking for clarification such as: "do you mean starting from the moment I woke up until I went to sleep?" which could be taken as sarcastic or an attempt at juvenile humor)

33. ___ A pattern of being perceived as aloof, unfriendly, or distant (this is often evidenced even when attempting to come across as friendly, approachable, or "not too pushy," and can result from an extension of failed interpersonal attempts, or fear of rejection)

34. ___ A pattern of being perceived as superior, standoffish, or "entitled" (often a result of being perceived of as inferior, "retarded," "slow," an attempt of bolstering damaged self-esteem, or having been abused or taken advantage of over the years)

35. ___ A pattern of responding that is perceived as submissive and accommodating in some, or aggressive and rebellious in others. The former pattern can be misinterpreted by outsiders as "weak or inactive," while the latter often results in judgments of "oppositional" or "conduct disorders"

36. ___ A pattern of responding that shows lack of common sense, immaturity or general awareness of social mores. These behaviors are generally misinterpreted as defiance, "spoiled-child" syndrome, or an uncaring attitude toward others.

37. ___ A pattern of responding to simple questions with detailed elaboration or embellishment

38. ___ A pattern of responding to simple questions with uncharacteristically formal language, at times using obscure or arcane terms no longer in use

39. ___ A pattern of responding using monotone or colorful speech inflections, exotic accentuation, or foreign pronunciations (adapting French, German, British, Spanish, Russian, etc., accents) that change depending on mood and situation but typically without any discernible pattern or apparent* reason

* The notion of something being "apparent" is one that is often difficult for the inexperienced outsider to detach from or abandon as the notion of "why" (a quest for an underlying "reason" is always desirable). When dealing with spectrum populations, however, it is often best to abandon the quest for "the underlying reason," or "why," and simply accept the mode of presentation and move on. First, an actual, concrete "reason" for "why" something is being done, or how it's being said (such as a faux inflection or accent) may not exist. Second, the "reasons" are likely to change depending on the mood of the (autistic) speaker. Third, the speaker may simply not know "why" this faux inflection is being adapted or not be aware of it. Fourth, asking for an explanation could send the (autistic) speaker into a reclusive shell, terminating all hope of further discussion or exploration. Fifth, the (autistic) speaker could misinterpret the questioning of the faux inflection as threatening, or a discovery of "being found out," therefore also retreating into a silent shell, or taking a defensive, or aggressive stand. The "reasons," then, are multitudinal and multidimensional, and the bottom line is that it really does not matter, and that the best course is to simply accept this as yet another thread that constitutes "the autistic difference," and makes it unique, and take advantage of the fact that an actual conversation is taking place

40. __ A pattern of casually inserting uncommon words of arcane phrases in causal conversation (using words such as "caustic," or "mordant," for instance, rather than the more common "biting," or "sarcastic." Using phrases such as "be gone with you!" all of which may cause the listener to misjudge them as pompous, patronizing, or just plain strange)

41. __ An incorrect use of language combined with sophisticated language that can make the listener think that, since the (autistic) speaker's language is of such a high level, it is perhaps oneself who is mistaken about the incorrect word usage. (A statement such as: "The 1939 Chevrolet Roadster automobile which struck her, rendering her unconscious, created a chaotic aura of inexplicable havoc among the pedestrians" would likely veer the listener away from the fact that the phrase "*which* struck her," should grammatically be: "*that* struck her," among other things.)

42. __ A pattern of incorrect pronoun usage that leads to confusing interpretations of the message. (Leaving out the pronoun's antecedent, for example, seems to be a common problem, particularly when the pronoun reference exists only in the (autistic) speaker's mind. Due to theory of mind (inferring that the listener knows who or what one is talking about) problems with this issue can become further complicated during two-way communications. For example, the sentence: "I told Clark, Davie, and Kaimen, which made the teacher mad," leaves it unclear as to telling which, all, or any combination of the boys exactly made the teacher mad. Was it that Clark was told? That Clark and Davie were told? Davie and Kaimen? The antecedent, therefore, is not clear as it only exists in the speaker's mind.)

43. __ A pattern of highly sophisticated speech, or idiosyncratic language, in very young children, that attracts a sense of awe in public. This thread of the spectrum difference, typically heard among children with Asperger's, often leads the casual—or even the educated—listener to infer that the child's cognitive ability, and comprehension, is vastly superior to what it might actually be.

44. __ A pattern of speech, particularly among young children with Asperger's, that is, upon initial encounters, perceived as humorous, highly advanced, or even of a gifted level, but which actually serves as an unintentional mask that diverts the listener away from the child's social ineptitudes or liabilities

45. __ Odd use of language may also extend into the following forms, some of which may be produced intentionally at times, but intentionally, or even habitually, at others during various periods of development:

46. __ malapropisms (absurd word use): "Line up in a straight curve."

47. __ spoonerisms (unintentional transpositions of letters or syllables): "I like her sin twister"

48. __ advertising slogans: "No interest rate if purchased by May 31st!" (in response to the question "what are some of your interests?"

49. __ homophones (words that sound the same but which have different spellings): "He doesn't have any come passion" (vs. compassion), "Be forewarned!" (implies he needs to be warned four times, "FOUR-warned")

50. __ homonymous contranyms (words or expressions with contrary meanings): "They're going to raise (put up) the building then raise (rather than "raze," or tearing it down) it back to the ground."

51. __ homographs (words with different meanings that are spelled the same):
"He bought a new bat to play with" (the child may not know whether a baseball bat, or flying bat are meant)

52. __ rhyming: "What are you thinking?" may trigger, "What are you thinking, what are you linking, what are you drinking, what are you tinkling…" for several minutes.

53. __ palindromes (words or phrases that run the same frontward and backward): "Pull up if I pull up!"

Cliches, metaphors, slang and analogies

54. __ Cliches – these are often misunderstood as literal, such as a phrase like: "He led a hand-to-mouth existence" might be inferred as meaning the individual needed to eat his own hands to survive.

One of the biggest mistakes we can make
is to start off with expectations.

Topic Area 5: Outward Appearance

Typical descriptive words: "odd, atypical, uncommon, different, unusual. At the extreme: strange, bizarre."

1. __ Outward appearance that is either unkempt or exquisitely neat or veering on immaculate. Overall appearance can also be partly unkempt (rumpled clothing, scruffy beard, and tousled hair) alongside other aspects that are the mirror opposite (immaculately polished shoes, and elegant, tailored sports jacket).

2. __ A pattern of being quiet, respectful, and mannerly, or highly talkative but with discourse typically involving the imparting of information (data, product descriptions, facts), in depth discussion about a preferred topic, or scripted language.

3. __ A pattern of either mismatched, unusual clothes or ritualistic-like wearing of "uniform-type" outfits (wearing the same, or similar clothing combinations repeatedly)

4. __ Atypical eye-to-eye gaze that can give the appearance of avoidance, distrust, or "mind being elsewhere," in some individuals. Others might have a characteristically intense, almost piercing gaze often described as "looking straight into my mind," while still others' gaze is described as "other worldly," "absent" or as if "looking right through you."

5. __ Peripheral, either in the sense of being "coming from the periphery, or a sideways glance," or seemingly tangential, in the sense of being only marginally important or necessary

6. __ A pattern of "visual scanning," whereas there is an appearance that information is being collected from the environment in short, sweeping lateral glances

7. __ Awkward body language and nonverbal gestures that can give the appearance that the person might be "up to something," "feels uncomfortable," or is uninterested

8. __ Pattern of being described by others as shifty, devious, guarded, anxious, and/or unapproachable.

9. __ Facial expressions that seem to lack affect or emotion although the impression left on different onlookers might be described anywhere from "seemed to have no emotion whatsoever," through "I was a little bit scared," and to "appeared quite happy and to have this deep sense of peace and calm"

10. __ A pattern of facial expressions that tend to either contradict accompanying language (smiling when describing a sad story), or appears over-dramatized, exaggerated, or forced (often as a result of poorly exhibited social skills training)

11. __ Physical gestures and posture that is typically perceived as rigid, stiff, un-animated, gangly, or "robotic"

12. __ Physical gestures accompanied by stereotypic movements that may appear dys-rhythmic, exacting, or uncomfortable

13. __ A pattern of being described as either passive, or "a follower," or stubborn, or someone who "needs to do everything him/herself," or "always be in control"

"No-Box" is a concept, or paradigm, relating to something that cannot be easily described, categorized, or understood by "boxed," or traditional, systems. An attempt at a description might indicate that the person who fits into a "no-box" paradigm does not "march to the beat of a different drummer," but rather, that he/she "makes up his/her own beats as he/she creates his/her own march along the way."

14. __ A pattern of poverty with regard to gross motor skills often accompanied with good to excellent fine motor skills

15. __ A seeming lack of self-aggrandizement or spirit of empty boasting

16. __ Personal achievements, as well as failures, might typically only be described upon request, and then often noted with a sense of detachment and objectivity, and presented in list form that might further include dates and other descriptive information

17. __ A pattern of beginning, and ending, personal and professional conversations abruptly, without preliminary or socially adequate antecedent, starting off by delving directly into the meat of the issue, and/or closing with a terse, scripted line such as "time to go," "all done," or even "period"

18. __ An apparent attitude, or mood, that might be typically perceived as one of either depression, anxiety, worry, suspiciousness, hesitancy, or restrain, or emotionally distant although inquiring about it might yield a simple, often genuine "I feel great!"

19. __ As school-children might be, or have been, described as the "class clown," "teacher's pet," or "weird kid"

20. __ A pattern of attempted socializing that is overtly formal or friendly, textbook scripted, or that contains a rich mix of lines memorized from books and/or movies and television programs

21. __ A pattern of imitating, or mimicking, another person's accent, inflection, speech prosody, habits, gestures, and/or expressions while engaged in social interaction either as a conscious attempt to "bond or connect," or without any conscious awareness of the behaviors

22. __ A pattern of consciously, or unconsciously, adapting the dress, style, habits, or preferences of someone who is found attractive or whose qualities are desirable

23. __ A pattern of either inserting long, often uncomfortable pauses in the midst of a conversation, or short, staccato-type breaks that appear to have an almost metric-like quality as if the sentences are being divided into even compartments to fulfill a comfortable structure

24. __ A pattern of almost loop-like, seemingly endless strands of speech that can either maintain a single, consistent topic focus for remarkable lengths of time, or that can change themes abruptly and often without meaningful connection to the prior theme or subject matter

25. __ Idiosyncratic physical movements, or gestures, that may involve finger twisting, hand flapping, hand wringing, nervous tapping, muscular jerks, or spontaneous tics or movements

Executive Function related problems:

26. A pattern of problems that may include:
    - __ Poor organizing or structuring activities
    - __ Poor planning abilities
    - __ Poor multitasking abilities
    - __ Poor ability to shift attention
    - __ Poor ability to accommodate rapidly changing situations or environments
    - __ Poor ability to switch topics
    - __ Rigid thinking patterns
    - __ Poor processing speed
    - __ Difficulty focusing on intended details
    - __ Delays in "if – then…" type thinking
    - __ Poor ability to tolerate frustration
    - __ Successful integration of work production
    - __ Seeing the big picture
    - __ Seeing the long term goal
    - __ Rigidity or perfectionist-type attitudes that negatively affect work productivity
    - __ Feeling or appearing overwhelmed
    - __ Failing to understand main ideas or long term goals
    - __ Poor time management skills
    - __ Ability to return to, and complete, unfinished tasks
    - __ Propensity to abandon activities in order to embark on new ones
    - __ Wasting time talking and worrying about projects rather than planning and working on them

(See Executive Function Challenges Checklist© in Appendix E.)

Topic Area 6: Sensory Challenges and Differences

Hyper-/Hypo-Sensitivity Patterns

Patterns indicating a hyposensitivity (under-sensitivity or reactivity) or hypersensitivity (over-sensitivity or reactivity)—or a combination of both—to:

1. __ Certain types of touch. An aversion to, or startle response to caressing, stroking, mild hugs, or light physical contact and/or a preference and attraction to deep (accu) pressure, concentrated massage, or "bear" hugs

2. __ Certain odors. An aversion of sometimes even mild, seemingly innocuous scents or unusual attraction to particular smells. May involve either an unusual, keen awareness to mildly noxious odors, or an extraordinary ability to perceive same. May also involve an unusual ability to distinguish between, or identify, very mild scents, and/or a lack of ability to recognize others.

3. __ Certain sounds (easily startled, frightened or pre-occupied by seemingly innocuous sounds and/or apparently unaware of certain loud noises, delayed response or reactions to auditory warning signals). May also involve problems focusing in the midst of surrounding noise or competing auditory signals, speaking in loud voice or whisper, uttering sounds or noises that have no apparent purpose, and apparent problems with auditory processing, such as following directions or understanding instructions. The ability of perfect or absolute pitch is found across larger number of individuals in comparison to the general population while a strong aversion (clamping hands over ears and asking the person to stop singing or playing) to those who sing off key, or to instruments played out of tune, is also common. Accordingly, strong preferences for certain types of music, while disdain for others, is also not unusual.

4. __ Certain tastes. Preference for certain, typically very limited, types of foods and complete rejection of others. Inclination may be either for very hot and spicy or, conversely, very bland, plain food. May claim that certain foods cause gagging, choking, or cannot be swallowed. May include eating the same food(s) repeatedly, sometimes for years. May also involve an unusual ability to distinguish between, or identify, slightly different tastes (such as identifying the difference between two types of cola).

5. __ Certain types of lights and/or colors. Particularly problems with fluorescent and/or sensitivity to bright lights. May include a preference for either dark or dim lighting, difficulty discriminating between certain colors, becoming anxious or overtly stimulated when in the presence of certain lights (random or continuous strobes, flashing, intermittent), squinting and/or rubbing eyes, problems reading text written in certain color surfaces, a strong preference for certain colored lighting.

6. __ Certain types of clothing (a preference/aversion for certain textures). Typically referred to as "tactile defensiveness" this may involve a strong dislike, or outright rejection, of certain fabrics such as wool ("feels scratchy!"), acrylic ("feels clingy!"), silk ("feels slimy!"), etc.

7. __ Thermal environment. May either overdress or underdress regardless of temperature gradient, at times wearing the same thermal covering, or lack of, in spite of climactic variants.

8. __ The surrounding environment. A fear of heights, open or closed spaces, crowds and/or seeking out or preferences for certain types of environments—such as being in tight, closed-in spaces, cubicles, closets, elevators.

9. __ Certain types of movement. Seeking—or shying away from—spinning or fast movement activities

Sensory Challenges during Early Development

Has a concern ever been recorded, or voiced, over potential, early problems involving:

10. __ late developing speech or language skills?
11. __ language or vocabulary prowess during early years?
12. __ vision acuity, discrimination, or perception?
13. __ hearing or auditory processing?
14. __ gross or fine motor skills?
15. __ an over-reactivity (extreme sensitivity) to mildly painful experiences (bumping mildly against a wall) or relatively innocuous touches (brushing or combing hair)?

16. __ under-reactivity (apparent lack of awareness or sensitivity) to mild to moderate (cuts, scrapes, bumps, bruises), and at times even moderate to severe physically painful experiences (broken bones, concussion, moderately deep wound or cut)?

17. __ coordination of parallel physical activities (assembling blocks, playing with LEGOs, using small tools, playing with mechanical toys or games that require fine dexterity, the rhythmic use of both hands, or the hands and feet in concert?

18. __ an awkward gait (dys-rhythmic walking, pacing, or running)?

19. __ balance or movement abilities (vestibular)? These may include problems with stairs or escalators, rocking back and forth, poor overall balance such as riding a bicycle or walking a straight line, holding head up while reading or writing, or engaging in vigorous or spinning-type games or activities.

20. __ body awareness (body percept), or being able to rhythmically manipulate his/her own body or locate his/her own body's spatial relationship within the surrounding environment? This may also involve a pattern of being clumsy or accident prone.

21. __ motor planning (praxis), including knowing when to begin and end an activity, sequencing steps in an activity?

22. __ lateralization (being able to ascertain hand preference)?

23. __ body position (propioceptive)?

24. __ visuo-spatial? Problems may include judging distances (driving, playing ball), recognizing people, shifting attention between modalities, attentive mastery of central vs. lateral stimuli, and a propensity to over-focus on some things while disengaging or losing track of others.

25. __ sleep patterns, sleeplessness, recurrent nightmares?

26. __ allergies?

27. __ sensory seeking ("daredevil" activities, carefree disregard for risk or danger), or sensory avoiding (reluctance to join in games that involve roughhousing, stunts, speed and coordination, or physical contact)?

28. __ an early reluctance to use, work, or play with certain materials (chalk, clay, "gooey" or messy substances, finger paints, metal, wood, grainy objects) or walk on certain surfaces (grass, dirt, sand, sidewalks with cracks, carpet, wooden or marble floors, artificial turfs)?

29. __ age or developmentally-appropriate ADLs ("activities of daily living," such as dressing self, buttoning, tying shoes, combing or washing hair, using zipper)

30. __ a poor attention span for things that are not within the sphere of special topics or personal preferences and/or "laser-like" focus for special interest areas?

31. __ fidgeting, being unfocused, twitchy, or nervous, or having restless behaviors?

32. __ worries or fears about generally insignificant things and/or a lack of worry, fear or concern over potentially dangerous or hazardous situations?

33. __ adapting unusual levels of caution when engaging in certain activities and/or "jumping head first" into potentially hazardous areas or dangerous activities without planning or forethought?

34. __ muscle tone (described as being stiff, rigid, or "robotic-like," or limp, sagging, and droopy Having poor body posture. Problems with loosening jar lids, mechanical assembly, habitually dropping objects, and extending into apparent inability to apply enough pressure to cut or chew a steak, open some doors, or lift mildly heavy objects.

35. __ stamina or sickness Lack of stamina or pattern of tiring easily in some individuals in direct contrast to others who tend to endure thirst, hunger, exhaustion, and ill health without complaint.

Nonverbal Learning Disability

JMO:NLD-6 – Red Flags Checklist©

The following checklist was designed to function as a "red flag" inventory to assess laypersons and professionals in determining the extent to which someone may be displaying the characteristics, behaviors, strengths, and challenges typically expressed by persons with NLD. Although deficits, and strengths, in a number of areas, such as the ones exemplified through the eight sections below, are typically found among many persons with NLD, one should keep in mind that the NLD syndrome is one that has many diverse roots and can be manifested in any number of ways. With that in mind, the sections below highlight the deficiency—and strength—areas typically exhibited by individuals challenged with this condition.

(1) <u>Intellectual Profile</u>
   ___ Average to above average full scale IQ
   ___ Verbal skills significantly superior to performance skills
   ___ Good rote memory skills
   ___ Superior memory for details
   ___ Poor ability to synthesize information
   ___ Slow processing speed
   ___ A superior ability to learn via auditory vs. visual or kinesthetic teaching
   ___ A pattern of doing well in language arts in comparison to math, science, or technology
   ___ A pattern of early language development
   ___ A pattern of early, sophisticated speech and vocabulary
   ___ Rote language skills typically above average to excellent
   ___ Poor insight or abstract ability
   ___ May have unusual articulation patterns

(2) <u>Professional and Academic Related</u>

Typical Areas of Strength:
   ___ Good to above average spelling abilities
   ___ Good to excellent verbal skills
   ___ Good ability to work independently
   ___ Good ability to assimilate information presented through auditory means
   ___ Good auditory comprehension and retention
   ___ Good ability to work in small, quiet, structured, and well-organized environments where rules are clear and goals are clearly spelled out
   ___ Good ability to work and focus on areas of preferred interest
   ___ Good attention to detail
   ___ Good rote memory skills
   ___ Good ability to deal with literal and concrete type problems
   ___ Adept at multi-lingual skills
   ___ Good ability to process words and symbols
   ___ Good creative writing skills
   ___ Good ability at problem solving that involves verbal processing

__ Good ability to think in words (vs. pictures or mechanically)
__ Good ability to deal with repetitive, sequential, stable responsibilities
__ Good ability for step-by-step problem solving
__ Reliable, responsible, trustworthy
__ Motivated and enthusiastic when engaged in area of special interest
__ Methodical, dedicated, and diligent workers
__ Patient, willing to learn
__ Dependable and conscientious

(3) Typical Areas of Weakness
__ Poor fine motor skills
__ Poor mechanical aptitude
__ Problems assimilating new information presented visually or kinesthetically
__ Typical pattern of poor skills in basic math
__ Poor writing skills (penmanship)
__ Poor ability to work in groups, teams, or "people-related" pursuits
__ Poor ability to influence others
__ Inconsistent emotional stability particularly in social situations
__ Typically not inclined to arts and crafts related activities
__ Typically not athletic or physically coordinated
__ Poor multi-tasking or improvising skills
__ Poor ability to deal with novel, complex, or quickly shifting responsibilities
__ Slow processing skills
__ Poor ability to make quick, spur-of-the-moment decisions
__ Poor flexibility
__ Problems following visual diagrams
__ Low tolerance for stressful situations
__ Anxious tendencies
__ Insecure
__ Poor dexterity
__ Directionally challenged
__ Problems with time management

(4) Socio-Emotional Related Problems

__ A pattern of problems picking up on social assumptions
__ A pattern of poor social adeptness or adaptability
__ Limited ability to pick up on other's intentions
__ Limited ability to read nonverbal messages such as facial expressions, body postures, and voice tones
__ Poor ability deciphering unstated expectations or "reading between the lines," leading to problems regulating social interactions
__ Poor ability to decipher hidden curriculums and unspoken social rules
__ Limited ability deciphering metaphors, analogies, and slang
__ A pattern of poor peer relations
__ Difficulties with appropriate emotional reciprocity

__ A pattern of poor practical or communicative language skills
__ A tendency to interpret situations concretely and literally
__ A tendency to interrupt, or speak "out-of-rhythm" during conversations
__ Problems reciprocating during interpersonal discussions
__ Problems with deciphering emotional content and tuning into others' feelings
__ Difficulties taking another person's perspective during conversations
__ A tendency to misread social innuendoes
__ Difficulties shifting attention or making smooth transitions during conversations
__ May have tendencies toward depression and anger outbursts

(5) Outward Appearance
__ Often described by others as "odd," "socially clumsy," or "awkward"
__ Often perceived by others as ill at ease, uncomfortable, or anxious when engaged in social interactions
__ A pattern of social communication often described as inappropriate, tactless, or insensitive.
__ Described as having a rigid, stiff, or ungainly appearance
__ Tendency to "talk too much," or "ask too many questions"
__ Often described as compulsive or ritualistic
__ Perception of being naïve, gullible, or immature
__ Problems making social judgments
__ At times perceived of as guarded, suspect, or shifty
__ Typically poor or undeveloped muscle tone
__ Typically not athletic or physically coordinated
__ Intense, focused determination on topics of particular interest
__ May have the tendency to become rigid, jittery, or antsy when anxious
__ A tendency to be clumsy or accident prone
__ Loyal and dependable
__ Good sense of humor
__ Friendly
__ Enthusiastic
__ Mature

(6) Sensory Related Issues
__ Vestibular—balance- or movement-related activities typically present challenges
__ Body percept—a poor sense of body awareness or of spatially differentiating oneself from the surrounding environment
__ Praxis—ability to motor plan, or sequence motor-related activities typically present challenges
__ Propioceptive—problems with body positioning and coordination
__ Visuo-spatial—spatial skills, such as locating objects in space (catching a ball, juggling, mechanical aptitude, judging distances) are usually poor
__ Lateralization—rhythmic or integrative hand-hand, hand-feet, and/or crossing the body activities typically present problems
__ Poor ability to integrate or coordinate visual-motor skills
__ Poor adaptation to the environment by way of visual manipulation
__ Poor visual memory and visual-related problem solving skills

"I suggested that a useful approach to making diagnostic differentiations was to begin by distinguishing between two sets of processes. The first set involves the simple decoding of nonverbal perceptual information; the second set involves the interpretation of the meaning of that information." (Palombo, 2006, p. 125)

Chapter 23

Theory of Mind Measures

Research Gems: Brain Regions Involved in Theory of Mind

The process that involves our ability to attribute intentions to oneself, or others, Theory of Mind, is commonly also referred to as "mentalizing," or the "intentional stance" is believed to involve automatic—rather than deliberate—processes that involve a number of cortical regions. According to current research, three of the regions that are "most consistently activated during mentalizing are the paracingulate cortex, the temporal poles, and the superior temporal sulcus at the temporoparietal junction. Individuals with autism, who typically fail mentalizing tasks, show reduced activation during mentalizing in these regions, and in the parcingulate region in particular." (Kampe et al., 2003, p. 5258)

What is Theory of Mind?

With regard to autism, AS and NLD, Theory of Mind (TOM) refers to a person's ability to attribute another person's mental, or emotional, state or intentions. In effect, it is one's ability—varying at different levels from person to person—to understand and infer, or "mentalize," someone else's beliefs, intents, desires, level of pretension, degree of interest in what one is saying, amount of actual knowledge about a topic being discussed, and, in general, an overall awareness of another person's mental and/or emotional processes. According to research with autistic, AS, and NLD populations, various processes related to these conditions (one of the most current being Mirror Neuron Dysfunction Theory) tend to obstruct their TOM capabilities making it very difficult for persons with these challenges to "read" others particularly during social situations or when the mode of communication is subtle, emotional, or intentionally deceptive, misleading, or playful. In essence, problems with TOM make it very difficult for persons who experience this deficit to relate to others or to understand the level, nuances, and intent of basic communications (friendly/hostile, formal/informal, serious/playful, superficial/interested, sincere/artificial, angry/excited, anxious/calm, sad/happy). TOM deficits can range from mild, to moderate, to severe. Depending on the extent of the severity one individual might be able to pick up on moderate, but not mild intentions, while another might not be able to fully grasp an intention even when it is abruptly demonstrated. As such, when communicating with persons known, or suspected, to have problems with TOM it is strongly recommended that one be clear, concise, concrete, and direct, stating exactly what one means to communicate without ornamentation or "mind games." The use of metaphors, analogies, slang and the like, for instance, should be eliminated from these communications. The purpose of this chapter is to assist us in identifying the presence, as well as the extent, of TOM deficits when dealing with autistic, AS, and NLD populations.

Assessment instruments designed to assess theory of mind in autism, AS, and NLD populations

Assessment Instruments Designed to Assess Theory of Mind in Autism, AS, and NLD Populations
The Cambridge Mindreading (CAM) Face-Voice Battery

<u>Description:</u>
The CAM was designed to assess recognition of complex emotions and mental states in the face and the voice by examining each emotion via both visual and auditory modalities using motion in a visual task. Based on a newly described taxonomy of emotion, the model "comprises 412 unique emotion concepts, including all the emotion terms in the English language, as well as epistemic mental states with an emotional dimension (e.g., doubting). Mental states that could be a purely bodily state (e.g., hungry) and epistemic states with no emotional dimension (e.g., reasoning) are not included" (Golan, Baron-Cohen & Hill, 2006. p. 171).

For test construction the 412 emotions then are grouped into 24 mutually exclusive emotion groups (happy, thinking, sneaky) and subdivided into 6 separate levels each of which represents an age range from preschool through adulthood. Actors of both sexes, filmed enacting each of the 412 emotions—using video to capture their facial expressions and audio their vocalizations—were then validated.

As described by its authors, "The CAM battery evaluates a selection of 20 emotion concepts, taken from the above mentioned taxonomy, representing 18 of the 24 emotion groups….The battery includes two tasks: emotion recognition in the face and emotion recognition in the voice. Each of these tasks has fifty questions, in which the participant is either watching 3 – 5 second silent clips of actors portraying an emotion (facial task) or listening to short sentences (vocal task). After watching the clip/listening to the voice recording, the participant is presented with four adjectives and is asked to 'choose the word that best describes how the person is feeling'" (Golan, Baron-Cohen, & Hill, 2006. p. 171).

The four different scores that can be derived from the CAM include:
- An overall emotion recognition score: the sum of all the correctly answered questions, ranging from 0 – 100, describing overall emotion and mental state recognition
- Facial emotion recognition score: the sum of all items answered correctly from the facial items (0 – 50).
- Vocal emotion recognition score: the sum of all items answered correctly in the focal items (0 – 50).
- Concepts correctly recognized: Either sum of concepts correctly recognized (0 – 20); or the particular concepts correctly answered, analyzed individually/by subgroups as either positive or negative.

<u>Research Gems: "The CAM as an Improved Theory of Mind Task"</u>

"The Cam battery allowed a test of the recognition of specific emotions and mental states as well as overall performance, and recognition in the two perceptual channels separately. It also tested recognition of complex emotions and mental states using films of faces rather than still pictures…results showed that individuals with Asperger Syndrome (AS) when compared to general population controls, had more difficulties in recognizing mental states from both faces and voices. In addition, participants with AS recognized fewer mental state concepts then controls….The CAM tests recognizing emotions independent of weak central coherence or executive function because there is minimal context or planning, which burden working memory." (Golan, Baron-Cohen, & Hill, 2006, p. 178)

The Awkward Moments Test

Description:
Film excerpts showing characters in social situations are shown to the examinees who are required to answer questions regarding the characters' mental, or "mentalizing," states. For each excerpt the participants are required to answer one question on the character's mental
state during social and non-social related situations. The brief video film excerpts are taken from British television commercials and programs that depict characters experiencing socially awkward or unpleasant moments.

Research Gems: Theory of Mind

"A theory of mind is a mental picture, held in a person's mind, of the feeling states and intentions of other people. A theory of mind enables us to impute attributions to others and to respond empathically to their emotions. It also enables us to suspect deception. A theory of mind may be what enables young children to differentiate between imaginary/pretend thoughts and play and actual events, events for which socially agreed upon meanings resonate as social facts." (Nadesan, 2005, pp. 120-121)

The Empathic Accuracy Paradigm

Description:
A video-based instrument, designed to approximate a naturalistic empathic accuracy task, requires the examinee to interpret the thoughts and feelings of two characters who have been unknowingly filmed. Examinees view the two videotaped interactions, each of which depicts a male and female stranger engaged in personal conversations and are then asked to infer the unexpressed thoughts and feelings of the four characters. The test reportedly uses a standard for correct responses that is more objective than earlier, similar theory of mind tests due to the approach of matching responses to the target character's actual subjective experience. The instrument has also been found sensitive in differentiating high-functioning individuals with pervasive developmental disorders from control subjects (Dziobek et al., 2006, p. 624). The authors suggest that mind-reading deficits of able adults with PDD might only be discernible when a sufficiently complex naturalistic assessment method is used to assess mentalizing states (Roeyers et al., 2001).

Research Gems: Theory of Mind – Innate or Acquired Hard Wiring?

"The theory of mind hypothesis is one account of the 'modalized' specific social deficiencies characterizing the behavior and communication of people with autism, even people who are otherwise 'normal' in their intellectual functioning. Consequently, the idea of a theory of mind and its implications for autism have stimulated much interesting research and considerable debate about whether the phenomenon is innate—hard-wired into the human brain from birth—or acquired (albeit acquired in its acquisition), through social interaction and language development." (Nadesan, 2005, p. 121)

The Strange Situation Test

Description:
Consists of 24 short vignettes, or 12 pairs of stories each of which contains two examples. Subjects are asked to provide an explanation for the ambiguous actions in the short stories. Story types include; Pretend, Persuade, Sarcasm, Double Bluff, Joke, Figure of Speech, Lie, Misunderstanding, and White Lie. The test also includes comprehension and justification questions that involve inferring either a character's mental state or the nature of physical events.

The Faux Pas Task/Test

Description:
The Faux Pas Task is a theory of mind test designed for children ages 7-11 where subjects are asked to identify a faux pas contained within the stories. It is used to examine their ability to recognize "faux pas" and help assess the theory of mind across persons throughout the neurotypical, autistic, and Asperger's spectrums. A "faux pas" is described as "when a speaker says something without considering if it is something that the listener might not want to hear or know, and which typically has negative consequences that the speaker never intended" (Baron-Cohen et al., 1999, p. 5).

The test involves reading 10 stories to a subject. Each story contains a social faux pas and 10 control stories each of which contain a minor conflict without a faux pas. Following each story the subject is asked to identify whether or not that particular story contained a faux pas (contained something that should not have been said). Stories containing faux pas are followed by questions where the subject is asked (a) why the faux pas should not have been said, and (b) why the subject feels it was said. The premise of the test is that understating of a faux pas relies on two mental states: (a) the person making the faux pas does not know it should have been said, and (b) the faux pas would upset or hurt the person hearing it. Regardless of the subject's answer to the first question, all stories are also followed by questions designed to determine whether the subject understood the premise of the story.

Available from *Journal of Autism and Developmental Disorders*, 1999, 29:407-418.

Reading the Mind in the Eyes Task, Revised (Adult Version)

Description: A measure of adult "mentalising" designed to distinguish between adults with Asperger's syndrome or high-functioning autism from controls.

Consists of eye region photographs of 36 male and female faces that present subjects with a choice between words printed at the four corners of the area that frames the photographs. The subject must then choose one of four adjectives or phrases that best describes the mental state of the person in the photograph. In essence, the participant chooses the word that, in her or his opinion, best describes what the individual in the photograph may be thinking or feeling as can be evidenced via the expression in the eyes.

Available from S. Baron-Cohen. (2003). *The essential difference: The truth about the male and female brain*. New York: Basic Books, pp. 187-199.

Stories from Everyday Life

Test Description:

The test, comprised of 26 short stories (or 13 pairs of different types of stories), is described as a "contextually complex theory-of-mind battery aimed to record the participants' ability to make inferences about *physical* as well as *mental* states." The first part of the stories is used to describe a *physical* or *mechanical* event, and a test question then examines a participant's ability to make an inference about a physical state. The latter part of the stories contains two questions aimed at examining the participant's ability to infer a *mental* state from the story's context. Examples of social communication that the participant's attempt to understand are "lies, white lies, figure of speech, misunderstanding, double bluff, irony, persuasion, contrary emotions, forgetting, jealousy, intentions, empathy, and social blunders" (Kaland, 2002, p. 517).

Available from:

Nils Kaland

Hogskolen I Lillehammer

Serviceboks

2626 Lillehammer, Norway

E-mail: nils@kaland.net

MASC: A Movie for the Assessment of Social Cognition

Description:

The MASC is described as a new tool for the assessment of mind-reading abilities in individuals with a diagnosis of Asperger's syndrome, or, more specifically, a "video-based test for the evaluation of subtle mindreading difficulties (which) involves watching a short film and answering questions referring to the actors' mental states….According to a Receiver Operating Characteristic (ROC) analysis performed on the mindreading tests the MASC was found as discriminating the diagnostic groups most accurately" (Dziobek et al., 2006, p. 623). "The MASC requires study subjects to watch a 15 minute movie about four characters getting together for a dinner party. The video is paused 46 times and questions concerning the characters' feelings, thoughts, and intentions are asked" (p. 626).

According to the authors, "the results confirmed a selective impairment of social inferring in the affected group. IQ, executive function, memory, attention, and visual processing were not different among the study groups. The MASC proved to be sensitive in detecting mind-reading difficulties in the AS group (Dziobek et al., 2006, p. 631). "Very able AS individuals were found to have selective impairments in social cognition. Out of four measures of social understanding used, the newly developed video-test the MSC had the greatest sensitivity in differentiating AS individuals from control subjects" (p. 634).

Reading the Mind in the Voice

Description:

An adult-level test that extends the Reading the Mind in the Eyes test into the auditory domain and can be used with adults with IQ in the normal range of intelligence. Forty segments of speech, taken from dramatic series programs aired by the BBC are played on audio tapes. Participant listeners are then asked to choose which one of two possible answers best describes the speaker's mental state (intention) after each item (Rutherford, Baron-

Cohen, & Wheelwright, 2002). A revised version has been tested with modifications that include the removal of seven items that were deemed inappropriate, and exclusion of another eight items following validation by a sample of 15 typically developing adults. The final task included 25 items with 4 possible answers for each of them. The test items were then "cleaned" via computer in order to minimize background noise and interference and field tested in an effort to enhance its overall effectiveness (Golan, Baron-Cohen, & Hill, 2006; Golan et al., submitted for publication).

Chapter 24

Parents and Caregivers

<u>Research Gems: Leading Reasons for Parental Concerns</u>
(Chawarska et al, 2007, p. 63)

- delays in speech and language development
- abnormal social responsivity level
- medical problems
- nonspecific difficulties related to sleeping, eating and attention
- unusual rate of progress (reaching milestones)
- apparent slowing of development
- loss of previously acquired skills
- regression (loss of words, vocalizations, nonverbal communication skills, social dyadic interaction skills, imitation, or pretend play)
- unusual interests
- stereotyped behaviors

<u>Introduction</u>: The Essential Role of Parents and Caregivers

When parents, or caregivers, are first confronted with a child who shows some of the signs or symptoms of autism, Asperger's, or a non-verbal learning disability their thoughts and emotions typically run through a number of cycles. The mind, confused and racing typically searches for information that has been heard, read, or maybe even already discussed in an informal, "what if" manner with other friends, family members or acquaintances. Television documentaries and popular movies about autism typically come to mind. Cover articles about autism and Asperger's, which have been flooding the market over the past few years, may also resurface in one's mind. Books on autism, the mind recalls, seem to be everywhere so the information is there, but, where does one start? What is fact vs. fiction? Autism vs. Asperger's? And what about this NLD, why haven't I heard of this before? The more popular movies, such as "Rainman," may come to mind. Is that what autism is? My child is certainly not like that! Memories about the "old" autism, family stories, and antiquated notions about the disorder may also rush in to further cloud the mind and fuel the imagination. If diagnosed, will my child end up in an institution? In a sheltered setting? Will he ever marry? Have children? Be able to attend regular school? Have friends? Get a job? Be happy…?

Leading Reasons for Parental Concerns

Emotion—anxiety, fear, worry—serve to further cloud the mind and create a mental chaos that can easily spin out of control. Anger, frustration, denial, depression are all likely reactions to suspecting, and later hearing, that one's child does, in fact, "have" autism—even if it is "high functioning," Asperger's syndrome, or non-verbal learning disorder or disability. The words in themselves, "disorder," "syndrome," "disability," do not exactly help to alleviate the mind or quell the emotions. Other attempts at "milder," less anxiety evoking words, such as "challenge," or "condition," are not much help. After all, who really embraces "challenges" within this context?

The thought that your child's life will be "a challenge," is not one that parents will welcome. Knowing that one's son or daughter has a "condition," especially one that has received so much press and media exposure over the past few years will also raise cause for alarm.

Concerns about how one's child "got" this, are typically not far behind the confusion, denial, anxiety, anger, depression and fear that first strike. "Was it something I did, or did not do? Was it the vaccinations? Was it something I ate, or drank? Is it something in our home that caused this? When exactly did it start? Was it in the womb? At the hospital? At home?

The answers to most of these questions, unfortunately, will likely never be answered. In effect, upon suspecting that one's child may, in fact, have some form of autism spectrum disorder, or non-verbal learning disorder, parents need to summon every aspect of their support system in order to gather the strength, courage and patience that it will take to go through the process of properly evaluating and diagnosing the child. Only by following the proper course of screening, assessment, and receiving a recognized diagnosis from a qualified practitioner will the child be able to qualify for the benefits, supports and services in school, and later the community, that will make the qualitative difference in their lives. Recognizing that this process will be lengthy, trying, and often framed in numerous battles against various facets of a system just now attempting to understand and define these conditions will also be necessary before solutions can be realized.

In the middle of this mental and emotional maelstrom, then, it is helpful to understand some of the processes that may lie ahead. With that in mind, the following section is designed to assist parents and caregivers in understanding what may be expected when one seeks a formal evaluation.

What is an evaluation?

There are generally three different types of evaluations:
- Screening
- Standard Evaluation
- Comprehensive Evaluation

What is screening?

Since parents are usually the first to notice unusual or atypical behaviors in their child it is up to them to make the initial referral to a qualified practitioner for the purpose of screening. Recognizing that most parents are not qualified to distinguish among variations in developmental milestones, and the possibility of mild symptoms that may in fact be "red flags" signifying the possibility of autism, the American Academy of Pediatrics recommends that all children be screened for the possibility of autism spectrum disorders as early as 18 months, with a follow up at 24 -30 months of age. Although there is research indicating that autism can be diagnosed as early as 12-14 months, a more standard age of diagnosis is typically between 18-24 months, with some cases, or milder forms of autism, diagnosed later. Asperger's syndrome, on the other hand, is often not diagnosed until the child enters the "social milieu," which occurs at around the kindergarten, pre-school, or even first grade stages. Children with NLD are often not diagnosed until around the age of ten, but may not receive a formal diagnosis until somewhere between the ages of 12-14, or the middle to junior high school periods. Professionals experienced with children presenting with Asperger's or NLD, however, can often diagnose them much earlier.

Screenings are typically brief and designed to address specific questions that pertain to particular concerns one may have. In terms of AS/HFA & NLD there are screening tools that have been designed for parents/caregivers, teachers, and mental health and other professionals. A number of screening tools for both laypersons and professionals are available throughout this book. More formally, screenings are aimed at identifying the possibility of a disorder early during the process of evaluation. The earlier a condition is identified the sooner interventions can be decided upon and treatment plans arranged to help maximize a child's potential for improvement. In some cases, unfortunately, screenings may lead to overdiagnosis or misdiagnosis which may lead the parent in the wrong direction regarding potential services. Missing a diagnosis, on the other hand, may give parents a false sense of security and result in valuable time being lost with regard to seeking and implementing treatment services.

For these reasons, once parents or caregivers feel that a child is exhibiting symptoms which may warrant professional intervention every effort must be made to assure that the initial screening be conducted by a qualified, or team of qualified, clinical practitioners who are both experienced in diagnosing the condition in question, and qualified by the state with all of the proper licensing and certification requirements. In general, formal screenings may take from one to two hours and require face to face testing with a child, including a diagnostic interview. These procedures are almost always completed in one session.

Before the Assessment: Suggestions & Recommendations

Tests that were performed and a description of the assessment
Diagnosis of the child's disability or a description of the child's disability
Description of the unique needs of the child
Description of how the child's disability may affect his/her education
Recommended Goals and Objectives for the child
Description of the recommended placement (classroom environment, teaching methodologies, personnel
    qualifications, teacher/staff to student ratio, provision of a trained aide)
Teaching methods that should be used
Services that should be provided (times per week, maximum group size, provider qualifications)
Consequences if the program or services are not provided

(adapted from "Sherman & Ziegler, Autism – Your child's Legal Rights to a Special Education," at http://aboutautismlaw.com/full_article.html#14)

What are "standard" and "comprehensive" evaluations?

Standard evaluations will typically cover one or more areas of concern in depth, examining a number of concern areas and answering questions posed by the presenting symptoms. Tests in various areas (psychological, educational) may be performed and may stretch into 2-4 sessions.

Comprehensive evaluations are meant to address all presenting questions much more extensively. Extensive and more detailed—and costly—testing will be performed to assure that every possible underlying concern has been covered. Various professionals, working together in mutual concert, will consider the necessity of psychological, medical, biological, genetic, neuropsychological, and environmental testing possibilities. Procedures may extend into 3-6 meetings with the various examiners.

After the Diagnosis: Ten Steps to Take

Use the professional guidance you have been given

Get organized – use a filing system for all records

Inform yourself – read books, surf the web, attend workshops

Evaluate treatment possibilities

Assemble your treatment team

Learn your child's rights, and take steps to secure them

Understand your insurance plan—what it does and does not cover

Network with other parents—join local and national groups

Take steps to nurture your entire family, including your partner and children

Nurture yourself – eat right, exercise, tap your support system

(Reference: http://www.firstsigns.org/articles/waltz_10 things.htm)

Who is qualified to conduct screenings and evaluations for autistic, AS and NLD populations?

In order to assure that a child will receive proper services following the process of formal assessment efforts should be made to assure that the school, insurance company, and others in question will recognize the examiner's credentials. Since this will not only differ from state to state—but also, in different states, and regarding different diagnostic labels—from county to county, district to district, and at times even school to school within the same district, parents are strongly advised to secure signed, formal documents from the parties who will be providing services (schools, insurance companies, mental health clinics, social work facilities, speech and language or occupational practitioners) attesting that they will recognize and accept the assessment and diagnostic impressions arrived at by a particular professional. In other words, if a school will only recognize a diagnosis from their in-house, school psychologist parents should not go to the expense of hiring expensive, outside experts whose opinion will not be recognized. If a district will not accept the qualifications of a particular practitioner, assurance should be made that the properly qualified professional conducts the evaluation and arrives at a diagnostic impression.

A description of various mental health professionals who are qualified to conduct formal assessments, and arrive at diagnostic impressions is listed below:

Professional Title	Degree	Licensing
Clinical or Counseling Psychologist	Ph.D. or Psy.D.	Psychologist
School Psychologist	Ed.D.	LEP
Counselor or Psychotherapist	Ph.D.	MFT/LPC
Psychiatrist	M.D./D.O.	Psychiatrist
Clinical Social Worker	Ph.D./MSW	LCSW
Family Physician, General Practitioner	M.D./D.O	Medical Doctor Doctor of Osteopathy

What is an assessment?

Assessments, or evaluations performed for the purpose of gaining insight into presenting conditions and leading to hypotheses about psychological, behavioral or emotional problems are typically performed by psychologists. Assessments, involving any number of formal testing measures, professional interviews, a review of existing records, clinical observations, and physical examinations are most often geared at conceptualizing general impressions that will lead to establishing a set of treatment plans. Some of the tests that might be considered for an assessment include intelligence (or IQ), achievement, personality, educational and neuropsychological tests.

Intelligence, cognitive, or IQ tests, are designed to measure a person's cognitive (or intellectual) functioning and abilities. As well as measuring traits such as one's general knowledge, memory, processing, attention span, logical reasoning, visual and spatial perception, and motor abilities these tests will also yield two three types of scores: verbal, performance and full-scale which will be presented as IQs as well as in terms of strengths and weaknesses. Some popular intelligence tests include the Wechsler and Stanford Binet. Typically, ability tests will be presented in terms of standard scores, based on an average score of 100 and subtest scores, which are based on an average score of 10.

Motor Functioning assessments will evaluate the effectiveness of whole body, gross motor, and fine motor skills and will typically include tests of handwriting skills and motor proficiency, performed by Occupational Therapists.

Sensorymotor functioning assessments, also performed by Occupational Therapists, are vital to obtaining an overall, clear picture of persons with AS, HFA and/or NLD. Through various degrees of observation, tests, checklists the OT will evaluate responsivity to sensory information and degree of under, and/or over sensitivity to environmental triggers.

Speech-Language Pathologists will conduct assessments to include descriptions and interpretation of receptive and expressive language processing, verbal comprehension and reasoning, and general abilities in verbal and language domains. Pragmatic communication skills, social and interactive communication styles and abilities, and other patters of behavior related to overall verbal and nonverbal communication provide invaluable information regarding the strengths, deficits and overall potential of persons with AS, HFA and NLD.

Personality tests fall into two categories, objective and projective, and are designed to describe patterns of thoughts, feelings and behaviors. Objective personality tests, such as the MMPI, revolve around simple, double choice (yes-no, true-false) answers or rating scales. Projective tests, such as the Rorschach or the Thematic Apperception Test, are designed to generate open-ended answers that are theoretically aimed at revealing unconscious processes. The latter are typically not recommended for AS/HFA/NLD populations.

Neuropsychological tests revolve around numerous tasks designed to measure psychological functions that are related to various brain structures or pathways. Although geared to assess impairment after an injury or illness related to neurocognitive functioning they are typically helpful when assessing persons with autism and AS, and particularly effective for proper assessment of persons with NLD.

Clinical observations are integral to the diagnosis of persons with AS/HFA and NLD and are preferably performed by trained, experienced clinicians. Used in conjunction with formal, standard measures as described above clinical observations should be undertaken at various settings and rely on both structured and unstructured formats. By observing children, or adults, in various natural settings, such as at home, school, work, or even out in the community or other social settings, experienced clinicians can gather vital information from a person's general appearance, social behavior patterns, mood and affect, perception, general orientation, insight, ecological awareness, sensory triggers, patterns of perseveration or rituals, and communication styles.

In addition to the above, assessment of the following areas of functioning will contribute further vital data to formulating diagnostic impressions as well as comprehensive treatment plans:

- Visual-Spatial, Visual perceptual, and Visual-Motor assessments
- Memory Functioning
- Social-Emotional Functioning
- Educational Functioning
- Attention and Concentration
- Learning Style
- Executive Functions

How does one receive a diagnosis?

Having completed a comprehensive assessment, the clinician is now ready to assimilate the acquired, collective information and refer to one of the two primary diagnostic manuals in order to assign a diagnosis. The two manuals are the DSM-IV-TR (Diagnostic and Statistical Manual of Mental Disorders), and the ICD-10 (International Statistical Classification of Diseases and Related Health Problems).

The DSM-IV-TR most recently revised in the year 2000, is the manual most commonly used by practitioners, and required by insurance companies in the United States. The manual relies on a medical model and lists psychological problems, such as autism and Asperger's, as well as others like depression, anxiety, obsessive compulsive disorder and others, in terms of discrete illnesses which are defined by a minimum set of predetermined, explicitly specified criteria based on clinical consensus which take into account presenting symptoms, duration and intensity, onset of behaviors and others. Although other models have been proposed for arriving at different diagnostic impressions, such as "dimensional models" which would offer greater flexibility and clinical utility outside of the medical, or "illness" model, scientific attempts at deciding upon alternative systems are still in the stages of exploration. Unlike clinicians in the U.S., U.K. practitioners use a "formulation" approach, consisting of a mapping of difficulties presented by individual patients, that considers predisposing, precipitating, and ongoing factors.

According to the DSM-IV-TR, a diagnosis of autism will be made if a person, prior to age three, exhibits a total of six (or more) items from criteria in three sections, social interaction, communication, and restricted repetitive and stereotyped patterns of behavior, interests, and activities. More specifically, at least two impairments need to be significant in the area of social interaction, one in communication, and one in the third section.

Social interaction (section one) impairments in autism may include problems with:

- multiple nonverbal behaviors, such as eye-to-eye gaze, facial expression, body postures, and gestures to regulate social interaction
- failure to develop peer relationships appropriate to developmental level
- a lack of spontaneous seeking to share enjoyment, interests, or achievements with other people
- a lack of social or emotional reciprocity

Communication (section two) impairments in autism may include:
- a delay in, or total lack of, the development of spoken language
- in individuals with adequate speech, marked impairment in the ability to initiate or sustain a conversation with others
- stereotyped and repetitive use of language or idiosyncratic language
- lack of varied, spontaneous make-believe play or social imitative play appropriate to developmental level

Problems with restricted repetitive and stereotyped patterns of behavior, interests, and activities (section three) in autism may include:
- an encompassing preoccupation with one or more stereotyped and restricted patterns of interest that is abnormal either in intensity or focus
- an apparently inflexible adherence to specific, nonfunctional routines or rituals
- stereotyped and repetitive motor mannerisms (e.g., hand or finger flapping or twisting, or complex whole body movements)
- a persistent preoccupation with parts of objects

Although a diagnosis of "high-functioning" autism is not a formal category in the DSM-IV-TR, that label is typically given to children, or adults, who have a full-scale IQ of 70 or higher.

Although, currently, a diagnosis of Asperger's (disorder), according to either the DSM-IV-TR or the ICD-10, is not significantly different from that of autism there are presently number of different schools of thoughts which ascertain, alternatively, that the two categories are either (a) essentially indistinguishable, (b) different enough to be separated from under the same diagnostic umbrella, or (c) in need of further speculation. (please refer to Chapter 7, "AS vs. HFA" for a thorough discussion on this topic).

To receive a diagnosis of Asperger, the DSM-IV-TR divides the necessary criteria into the following:

Impairment in social interaction in at least two of the areas below:
- marked impairment in the use of multiple nonverbal behaviors
- failure to develop peer relationships appropriate to developmental level
- a lack of spontaneous seeking to share enjoyment, interests, or achievements with other people, and
- a lack of social or emotional reciprocity

Demonstration of restricted repetitive and stereotyped patterns of behavior, interests, and activities, must be manifested by at least one of the following:

- preoccupation with stereo-typed and restricted patterns of interest that is abnormal either in intensity or focus
- inflexible adherence to specific, nonfunctional routines or rituals ◆
- stereotyped and repetitive motor mannerisms
- persistent preoccupation with parts of objects

The problems presented by the above need to be deemed responsible for clinically significant impairment in social, occupational, or other important areas of functioning.

Additionally, unlike with autism, a diagnosis of Asperger (disorder) necessitates no clinically significant general delay in language (e.g., single words used by age 2 years, communicative phrase used by age 3 years) and no clinically significant delay in cognitive development or in the development of age-appropriate self-help skills, adaptive behavior (other than in social interaction), and curiosity about the environment in childhood

As indicated above, non-verbal learning disorder, or disability, is not at this point in time listed in either the DSM-IV-TR, or the ICD-10. As such, when a child's presenting symptoms warrant this label parents should assure that the professional conducting the evaluation recognizes the need for a related diagnostic label that will recognize the seriousness of this condition.

"After the Diagnosis: Moving Forward with Confidence"

Make sure your child gets a complete multidisciplinary evaluation

Find out about his/her strengths and weaknesses and how he/she learns

Check the credentials of all healthcare providers

Share everything you try with your providers

Speech, Occupational, Sensory-integration, and physical therapies are integral components of comprehensive assessment and treatment regimens

Medication for specific symptoms, such as OCD, anxiety, rage—are often helpful. At present, there are no medications for AS, HFA or NLD

Always begin with the lowest dose possible, and make increases gradually

Biological interventions – to address metabolic or immune-system problems—should be discussed with a licensed dietitian and your family physician Supplemental vitamins and mineral treatments help some children.

Be careful with "new therapies," autism is a complex condition involving both genetics and environment, and affecting multiple body systems. Treatment plans need to address that complexity.

Comprehensive treatment should start as early as possible to help maximize each child's potential

(Reference: http://www.firstsigns.org/articles/waltz_10 things.htm)

<u>Why does my child need a label</u>?

Although there are many arguments against diagnostic labels the reality of our current state of affairs, regarding the manner in which our present systems operate, dictates that—at least for the time being, and another system becomes fully operational—labels be assigned. As such, some of the arguments regarding the advantages of labels include:

- To help professionals to clearly communicate with each another
- To operationalize and facilitate billing and record keeping services
- To help decide upon courses of treatment through pre-determined standards
- To help predict the course of disorders by common, identifiable characteristics
- To facilitate objective discussion of diagnostic impressions
- To fulfill general scientific standards according to established criteria
- To standardize a common language that can help bridge various professions
- To assist with increasing reliability and validity of both diagnosis and categorization

---

<u>Services to Which Your Child May Be Entitled</u>

Speech-language pathology and audiology
Psychological
Physical and occupational therapy
Recreation, including therapeutic recreation
Early identification and assessment of disabilities
Counseling, including rehabilitation counseling
Orientation and mobility services
Medical services for diagnostic or evaluation purposes
School health services
Social work services in schools
Parent counseling and training
Transportation

(adapted from "Sherman & Ziegler, Autism – Your child's Legal Rights to a Special Education," at http:// aboutautismlaw.com/full_article.html#14)

The following section consists of a number of scales, rating forms and checklists designed for parents and/ or teachers that may be used to collect information that can then be shared with professional clinicians. The instruments listed are among the most commonly used based on their appropriateness to the conditions for which they have been designed. Additionally, they have been found to be both valid and reliable, as well as consistent and accurate, in quantifying what they purport to measure.

Scales and Checklists Designed for Parents and Caregivers

The First Year Inventory – Version 2.0 (FYI-2.0)

Version 2.0 is a modification of The First Year Inventory, described as a questionnaire designed to assess behaviors in 12-month-olds that suggest risk for an eventual diagnosis of autism.

Intended ages: 12-month-old infants
Testing time: Varies
Administration: Individual

Intended to be administered by: Parents and caregivers

Purpose: To screen for the risk of autism in infants age 12 months

Consists of: Sixty-three questions: 46 with response alternatives (never, seldom, sometimes, and often); and 14 with 3 or 4 ad hoc multiple choice answers. One parental response relates sounds produced by the infant from a list of consonants, while two open-ended questions relate to parental concerns and unusual physical or medical characteristics.

Eight Separate Constructs under Two Domains:
- Social Communication Domain
- Social Orienting and Receptive Communication
- Social Affective Engagement
- Imitation
- Expressive Communication
- Sensory-Regulatory Domain
- Sensory Processing
- Regulatory Patterns
- Reactivity
- Repetitive Behavior

Other information: The First Year Inventory authors have introduced a form of the version 2.0 test (The First Year Inventory-Retrospective Version –FYI-R) which, rewritten in the past tense, can be utilized by parents to share information about their children in retrospect beyond the age of 12 months.

Ages and Stages Questionnaires: Social-Emotional (ASQ: SE)

Intended ages: 6 – 60 months
Testing time: 10–15 minutes to administer and 1–3 minutes to score per questionnaire
Administration: Individual

Intended to be administered by: Parents/caregivers

Purpose: Described as a practical, simple to administer tool designed to focus on a child's social and emotional behaviors. It is completed by parents or caregivers, photocopy-able, and culturally sensitive.

Consists of: A set of 8 color-coded questionnaires enabling caregivers to assess a child's social-emotional development at 6 12-month intervals beginning with 6 months, and progressing through months 12, 18, 24, 30, 36, 48, and 60. Questionnaires consist of 22-36 questions each.

The questionnaires address 7 crucial behavioral areas including:
- self-regulation
- compliance
- communication
- adaptive functioning
- autonomy
- affect
- interaction with people

Other information: Described as "clear and comprehensive" the questionnaires are sensitive to children's environmental and cultural and social-emotional diversity. The User's Guide contains case examples, creative activities and lists of social-emotional behaviors that can be used for sharing information, writing case reports, or referral for further assessment. The ASQ: SE is available in both English and Spanish.

Available from Brookes Publishing: custserv@brookespublishing.com; (800) 638-3775; http://www. brookespublishing.com/tools/asqse/index.htm. (site accessed 8/15/2007)

RECOMMENDED
Children's Social Behavior Questionnaire (CSBQ)

Intended ages: 4 through 18
Testing time: varies
Administration: Individual

Intended to be administered by: Parents/caregivers
Purpose: A questionnaire designed for parents or caregivers of children with pervasive developmental disorders (PDD). The items describe a broad range of features that are typical of PDD, particularly in its milder forms. Helps to classify children as exhibiting general psychopathology, withdrawn behaviors, having a negative correlation with social insight problems and a positive correlation with anxiety and rigidity, and a strong relationship with stereotypical behaviors and anxious/rigid behaviors.

Consists of: Ninety-six items, 66 divided into 5 sections: Acting Out, Social Contact Problems, Anxious/Rigid, and Stereotypical Behaviors. The items are designed to reflect a broad range of features that are typical of PDD, particularly in its milder presentations.

Other information: Based on a sample of children diagnosed with PDD-NOS, high-functioning autism, ADHD, MR, a clinical control, and neurotypical control groups. The CSBQ authors indicate this instrument has validity in distinguishing between children with autism and those with PDD-NOS.

Research Gems: "CDBQ –Short-Form Version"

"The goal of this study was to refine the subscales of the CSBQ and reduce the length of the instrument, while maintaining good psychometric properties. The findings of the study indicate that the revised instrument is both reliable and valid. The procedures described in this paper led to a more concise CSBQ reducing the number of items from 96 to 49....Compared to the 96-item version, the current revised CSBQ gained in specificity for PDD, as problem items that tended to be more indicative of problem domains other than PDD (ADHD, worries) were removed." (Hartman et al., 2005, pp. 338-339)

"A report of the assessment should be given to the paint in writing, to avoid misunderstandings that might arise with spoken communication"
(Berney, 2004, p. 349)

RECOMMENDED
Ages and Stages Questionnaires: A Parent Completed, Child Monitoring System – Second Edition

Intended ages: Ages 40–60 months
Testing time: 10–15 minutes
Administration: Individual

Intended to be completed by: Parent/caregiver
Purpose: Quick, early screening of infants and young children with developmental delays.

Consists of: Thirty-item, 19 color-coded reproducible questionnaires that are administered from the age of 4 through 60 months at designated intervals covering 5 key developmental areas:
-   communication
-   gross motor
-   fine motor
-   problem solving
-   personal-social

Other information: Available in English, as well as Spanish, French, and Korean.

A sample, 7-page, 48-month (4 year) questionnaire is available from Brookes Publishing via free download at: www.brookespublishing.com/store/books/bricker-asq/. The complete kit is available at: www.brookespublishing.com.

RECOMMENDED
The Child Development Review System (CDRS)
The Child Development Inventory (CDI)

Intended ages:
- CDI: 15 months – 6 years.
- CDR-Parent Questionnaire – Toddlers and preschoolers
- Infant Development Inventory: up to 18 months of age
- Child Development Inventory – Toddlers and preschoolers
- Child Development Chart: Infants, toddlers, and preschoolers
- Teacher's Observation Guide (TOG): Infants, toddlers, and preschoolers

Testing time: 30–50 minutes

Administration: Individual

Intended to be completed by: Parents/caregivers with observational assistance from a health care professional

Purpose: The Child Development Inventory (which replaces the original Minnesota Child Development Inventory) is designed to provide detailed information about a child's current development, symptoms, and adjustment based on a parent or caregiver's report.

The Developmental scales measure:
- social
- self-help
- gross motor
- fine motor
- expressive language
- language comprehension
- letters
- number
- general development

The CDR-Parent Questionnaire is a brief, comprehensive questionnaire designed to collect information about a child's health, development, and adjustment, as well as the parent's functioning. It includes six questions for parents, a comprehensive problems checklist, and a Child Development Chart covering from birth to five years of age.

The Child Development Chart consists of two charts, An Infant Development Chart, covering the first 21 months, and another covering the first five years. It is used for screening as well as a parent education handout.

The Infant Development Inventory is a brief questionnaire that asks parents to describe their infant by helping them track five developmental skill areas:
- social
- self-help
- gross motor

- fine motor
- language

The Child Development Inventory is used to obtain a detailed report of the child's current skills and potential problem areas. Also helpful in answering questions regarding a child's school readiness. The Inventory Profile provides information regarding the child's present development, including strengths and delays, while the Problems Checklist addresses parental concerns regarding health, vision, hearing, development, and behavior.

The Teacher's Observation Guide contributes to a teacher's ability to observe young children, appreciate their abilities, and set up an educational plan. It describes how to involve parents in a child's overall assessment plan and helps to examine an infant's development in the areas social, self-help, motor, language, letter and number skills, and behavior areas.

Consists of: Various separate measures:

- CDR-Parent Questionnaire (for Screening) (CDR-PQ)
- Infant Development Inventory (IDI)
- Child Development Inventory (a parent questionnaire for assessment) (CDI)
- Child Development Chart (a child observation tool for Screening) (CDC)
- Teacher's Observation Guide (TOG) (a child observation tool for assessment)

More information can be obtained through Pearson Publishing at 800-627-7271; agsinfo@pearson.com.

Research Gems: Regression in Autism

"The profile of regression that emerged included loss of skills between 18 and 21 months, on average, with language-only regression less common than loss of other, nonlanguage skills only or of full regression (loss of language and other skills). The onset of regression typically was gradual in nonlanguage areas and split between gradual and sudden loss for language skills….Parents tended to attribute loss to medical factors such as immunizations. Many of the children regained some of the lost skills when they were 3.5-5 years of age, with therapeutic and instructional interventions given credit for the regain." (Goldberg et al., 2003, p. 607)

MacArthur Communicative Development Inventories (CDIs), Second Edition

Intended ages: children ages 8–37 months
Testing time: 20–40 minutes for each form
Administration: Individual

Intended to be administered by: Parents/caregivers

Purpose: To help assess and focus on a child's emerging language and communication skills, current behaviors, and salient emergent behaviors that can be tracked for clear documentation.

Consists of: A "words and gestures" section designed to assist in documenting a (8- to18-month-old) child's understanding of hundreds of early vocabulary items separated into semantic categories (animal names, household items, action words). A second section is used to record the child's communicative and symbolic gestures as these are tried or completed.

A separate, "words and sentences" form (for ages 16-30 months) is where a child's production and use of words are divided into semantic categories. The second part is used to analyze the early phases of grammar, understanding of word forms, and the complexity of the child's multi-word utterances.

A new extension (CDI-III) is aimed at older children (30-37 months) in the form of a short, single-sheet tool designed to measure expressive vocabulary and grammar, word combinations, and various aspects of comprehension, semantics, and syntax.

Other information: Helps parents/caregivers and health professionals to track a child's day-to-day knowledge with regard to the above areas and address legislative issues that require parental input in child evaluations. The CDI also comes in a Spanish adaptation form.

The complete kit is available at Brookes Publishing: www.brookespublishing.com.

Research Gems: AS – Not "Different," but Simply an "Extreme Variant"

"The sex differences in close relationships revealed by the FQ in the general population may help us understand conditions like autism or AS not as qualitatively different from anything else we are familiar with but, instead, simply as an extreme of the normal quantitative variation we in any sample." (Baron-Cohen & Wheelwright, 2001, p. 514)

Communication and Symbolic Behavior Scales Developmental Profile Infant-Toddler Checklist (CSBS DP)

Intended ages: 6.0 months to 24 months of age.
Testing times:

- Infant-Toddler Checklist – 5–10 minutes
- Caregiver Questionnaire – 15–25 minutes
- Behavior Sample – 30 minutes

Administration: Individual

Intended to be completed by: Parent/caregiver (along with brief observation of the child by a trained healthcare or childcare service provider)

Purpose: To help determine the communicative competence (use of gaze, gestures, sounds, words, understanding, and play) of children with a functional communication age between 6 months and 24 months (chronological age from about 6 months to 6 years).

Designed for:
- Screening to identify children at risk for developmental delay or disability.
- Evaluation to determine if a child is delayed in social communication, expressive speech/language, and symbolic functioning
- Evaluation to document changes over time in a child's behavior

Consists of:

Seven language predictors are measured in young children:
- Emotion and eye gaze
- Communication
- Gestures
- Sounds
- Words
- Understanding
- Object use

Each area is measured with the three main components:
- a 1-page Infant-Toddler Checklist
- a 4-page follow-up Caregiver Questionnaire
- a Behavior Sample, taken while the child interacts with a parent present

A free download of the Infant-Toddler Checklist is available at: (site accessed 8/5/2007) http://www.brookespublishing.com/store/books/wetherby-csbsdp/checklist.htm.

The complete kit is available from Brookes Publishing: www.brookespublishing.com.

RECOMMENDED
The Achenbach System of Empirically Based Assessment (ASEBA)

Child Behavior Checklist (CBCL/1.5-5), and Caregiver-Teacher Report Form (C-TRF), Language Development Survey (LDS)

Intended ages: Children ages 1.5 through 5 years
Testing time: ASEBA preschool form and LDS: 10 minutes; total CBCL: 20 minutes

Administration: No professional training is required

Intended to be administered by: CBCL is completed by parents and caregivers; C-TRF is designed for daycare providers and preschool teachers.
Purpose: To assess behavioral and emotional problems in young children and identify children with deviant problem scores who may benefit from referral to a health-care professional. Can be used to help identify children with behavior difficulties, extending from the borderline through clinical range that can help screen for Pervasive Developmental Disorders

Consists of: CBCL: Internalizing (Emotionally Reactive, Anxious/Depressed, Somatic Complaints, Withdrawn, Sleep Problems) and Externalizing (Attention Problems and Aggressive Behavior) scales. Central features consist of assessment of behavioral and emotional problems; profiles of scores on statistically derived, empirically based syndromes; profiles of scores on DSM-oriented scales; age- and gender-based norms; multiple informant ratings; and scores on Internalizing, Externalizing, and Total Problems scales.

Other information: An empirically based instrument that helps to evaluate children in special education, child development, and mental health settings and evaluate the appropriateness of interventions and outcomes.

Nine DSM categories were collapsed into five scales:

- Affective Problems (Major Depressive and Dysthymic Disorders)
- Anxiety Problems (Generalized Anxiety and Separation Anxiety Disorders, and Specific Phobia)
- Attention Deficit/Hyperactivity Problems (Hyperactive-Impulsive and Inattentive types)
- Pervasive Developmental Problems (13-item Pervasive Developmental Disorders Scale, including Asperger's Disorder)
- CBCL/1.5-5 versus C-TRF.

Behavior Assessment System for Children, Second Edition (BASC-2)

Intended ages:
- Teacher Rating Scales (TRS): ages 2–5, 6–11, 12–21
- Parent Rating Scales (PRS): ages 2–5, 6–11, 12–21
- Parenting Relationship Questionnaire (PRQ): parents/caregivers
- Self-Report of Personality (SRP): ages 8–11, 12–21, 18–25
- Self-Report of Personality Interview (SRP-I): ages 6–7

Testing time:
- Teacher Rating Scales: 10–20 minutes
- Parent Rating Scales: 10–20 minutes
- Parenting Relationship Questionnaire: 10–15 minutes
- Self-Report of Personality: 30 minutes
- Self-Report of Personality Interview: 20 minutes

Administration: Individual

Intended to be administered by: Parents/caregivers, teachers, self-administered

Purpose: To help obtain a comprehensive assessment of behavior and emotions in children, adolescents, and college students.

Consists of: Teacher, parent and self-report scales that look at multi-dimensional issues related to adaptive and maladaptive behaviors in school settings ranging from the preschool through college levels. Scales include measures for activities of daily living, adaptability, aggression, attention problems, atypicality, depression, functional communication, hyperactivity, learning problems, social skills, withdrawal, school attitudes, interpersonal relations, locus of control, self-esteem, sensation seeking, somatization, developmental social disorders, emotional self-control, executive functioning, negative emotionality, anger control, ego strength, mania, test anxiety, and many others.

Other information: Designed to provide a balanced evaluation by drawing from three vantage points—teacher, self, and parent/caregiver—that look at adaptive and maladaptive behavior patterns and measures areas relevant to both IDEA and DSM-IV classification systems. The test forms help to assess not only personality issues, behavioral problems, and emotional disturbances but also to identify positive attributes that can be accessed throughout the treatment process. Test items are also provided on audio CD form for parents and students who may have reading difficulties.

The Behavioral Style Questionnaire (BSQ)

Intended ages: 3 – 7 years
Testing time: 5 – 10 minutes
Administration: Individual

Intended to be administered by: Parents

Purpose: To examine the relation of temperament to problem behaviors in children ages 3 – 7.

Consists of: A 100-item parental report measure designed to yield scores on nine dimensions of temperament:
- Activity Level
- Rhythmicity
- Approach
- Adaptability
- Intensity
- Mood
- Persistence
- Distractibility
- Threshold of response

The items are verbalized as statements about a child's behavior and the parent rates how often the child behaves in the manner described using a score ranging from "almost never" to "almost always."

Sensory Processing Disorder screening tools designed for parents and teachers:

Infant/Toddler Symptom Checklist – ages 7-30 months
DeGangi, Poisson, Sickel & Wiener (1995)
Available from Therapy Skill Builders, San Antonio, TX; 800-763-2306

Screening checklists for birth-3, preschool, school-age, and adult:
Occupational Therapy Association

Sensory History Questionnaire for Parents of Preschool Children – ages: 3-5

The Checklist for Autism in Toddlers (CHAT)

Includes a parent report and items that assess pretend play skills, gaze, and protodeclarative pointing. This scale is designed for use by health-care professionals looking to identify 18-month-old infants who might be at risk for autism.

Research Gems: The CHAT

"The Checklist for Autism in Toddlers (CHAT), the Modified Checklist for Autism in Toddlers (M-CHAT), and the Infant/Toddler Checklist of Communication and Language Development (CHECKLIST). These instruments may be used in the primary caregiver's office as an initial attempt to identify children who should be further examined for autism and other social-communication disorders." (Blackwell, 2002, p. 390).

Available at: http://nas.org.uk/nas/jsp/polopoly.jsp?d=128%a=2226

Contact:
The National Autistic Society
nas@nas.org.uk

Sally Wheelwright
Autism Research Centre
Cambridge University
Douglas House
18b Trumpinton Road
Cambridge CB2 2AH, UK
sjw18@cam.ac.uk

Checklist for Autism in Toddlers: A Screening Tool

A brief screening device, composed of nine questions for parents, and five observations for the clinician, designed to be administered by general practitioners or health-care professionals to 18-month-olds. The absence of pretend play, gaze monitoring, and protodeclarative pointing are suggested predictors of children who later received a diagnosis of autism at age 3.5 with an 83.3% accuracy rate. The CHAT is most effective when used as a two-stage measure with two administrations one month apart (Kope et al., 2001, p.268).

The Modified Checklist for Autism in Toddlers (M-CHAT)

An extended parent report version of the CHAT, the M-Chat includes a number of the CHAT items in addition to observational items and some autism specific symptoms not included in the latter. The M-CHAT is also designed for screening children aged 24 months, rather than 18 months of age.

Research Gems: M-CHAT

"The current study found that, after controlling for language level, 4 of the 23 M-CHAT items significantly differentiated the children with ASD and the children with DD/DLD (developmental delay/developmental language disorder)....All of the items that differentiated the children with ASD and the children with DD/DLD were also found to differentiate typically developing children from children with ASD." (Ventola et al., 2007, p. 435)

Available at: http://www.northshorelij.com/body.cfm?id=2869; (site accessed 7/22/2007)
North Shore – Long Island Jewish Health System and at:
    http://www.gsu.edu/~wwwpsy/faculty/robins.htm
    Diana Robins
    Department of Psychology
    University of Connecticut
    drobins@gs.edu

Chapter 25

Other Recommended Measures

Assessment Instruments Designed for Clinical Issues Typically Associated with AS, HFA, and NLD

"Many, if not most, social concepts are abstract, and may only be understood by someone on the autism spectrum by translating the concept into concrete examples of behaviours that would occur. Grandin (1996) reported using this strategy to understand concepts like honesty. She collected pictures and video examples of what honesty would look like in real life, and stored these in her mind as a way to understand the concept. She was able to understand abstract social concepts only when the concept was made concrete and visual. She could not understand the abstract concepts without translating them into images." (Paxton & Estay, 2007, p. 51)

Abstract Reasoning

Raven's Progressive Matrices

Intended ages:
- children aged 5 to 11 years (The Coloured Progressive Matrices – CPM)
- ages 6–16 (Standard Progressive Matrices – SMP)
- ages 12 and up (The Advanced Progressive Matrices – APM)

Testing time: 15–30 minutes (CPM), 45 minutes (SPM), 40–60 minutes (APM)

Administration: Individual or small groups

Intended to be administered by: Trained professionals

Purpose: To measure educible ability, a component of Spearman's "g," related to the ability to educe (e.g., extract, obtain, bring forth) relationships.

Consists of: Test forms for three ability levels designed to measure educible ability—the capacity to make sense of complex situations, draw meaning out of confusion, and perceive and think clearly. Also helps to detect "sub-optimal performance" or "faking bad."

Matrices:

The Coloured Progressive Matrices (CPM) – designed for children aged 5-11, mentally impaired adolescents, and the elderly.

Standard Progressive Matrices (SPM) – includes five untimed sets of 12 problems each. A "Plus" version is aimed at older adolescents and young adults who score near the ceiling on the original SPM.

The Advanced Progressive Matrices (APM) – designed for people of above-average intellectual ability, aged 12 and up. Includes two sets of matrices.

Other information: Parallel versions of each of the above are available that contain items and score distributions that match those of the original versions. "Difficult" level test in the Advanced Progressive Matrices extends the scores of the top 20% of the population and includes gifted educational applications. The "Average" level test reflects the general population, while the "Easy" level test spreads the scores of the bottom 20% of the general population for children, adolescents, mentally and physically impaired persons, and the elderly.

Research Gems: Misleading Personality Disorder Markers

"When a child displays language disorder, poor pragmatic behaviors (such as unrelated or circumscribed utterances) he may be erroneously considered to have Schizotypal Personality Disorder, or Schizophrenia. This is particularly likely when circumscribed interests and preoccupations are prominent." (Volkmar et al., 2005, p. 179)

Personality Characteristics

Personality Inventory for Children, Second Edition (PIC-2)

Intended ages: Ages 5 – 19
Testing time: 40 minutes
Administration: Individual

Intended for: Trained professionals
Purpose: An objective, multidimensional test of child and adolescent behavior and emotional and cognitive status designed to measure psychopathology and emotional/behavioral problems in children and adolescents. Constructs measured include hyperactivity, conduct problems, social skills, violent behaviors, eating behaviors, and substance abuse.

Consists of: A 275-item profile designed to assess a full range of developmental, cognitive, adjustment, and interpersonal issues, with subscales that provide clinical detail and an optional critical items list divided into nine content categories, including measures for:

- Cognitive Impairment
- Impulsivity and Distractibility
- Delinquency
- Family Dysfunction
- Reality Distortion
- Somatic Concern
- Psychological Discomfort
- Social Withdrawal
- Social Skills Deficits

Other information: The PIC-2 also contains a 15-minute, 96-item Behavioral Summary designed for screening, researching, or monitoring behavior change, and provides a Total Score as well as those for three composites: Externalization, Internalization, and Social Adjustment with a focus on brief intervention and treatment planning.

Research Gems: MMPI-2 with HFA and Asperger Populations

A 2005 study by Ozonoff and colleagues, described as the "first study to study personality and psychopathology in adults diagnosed with an ASD who function in the average range of intelligence or better" (Ozonoff et al., 2005, p. 90), found a number of results that could be considered in clinical and research settings as potential markers for persons with high functioning autism and Asperger's syndrome. One essential finding showed that a group of adults with ASD had higher scores than comparison group of college students matched on age, gender, and intelligence on several MMPI-2 scales, reflecting social isolation, interpersonal difficulties, depressed mood, and coping deficits. Large group differences and elevations in 25% of the ASD group on Clinical Scale 2 (D) indicated an association with symptoms of depression symptoms as well as suggesting that unhappiness and dysphoria may be common across the behavioral phenotype of high-functioning autism and AS in adulthood.

The Minnesota Multiphasic Personality Inventory-Second Edition
(MMPI-2- RF)

Intended ages: 18 years and older
Testing time: 60-90 minutes
Administration: Individual

Intended for: Trained professionals

Purpose: To assist with the diagnosis of mental disorders and designing the most appropriate intervention and treatment strategies according to each person's clinical profile. The test is designed to assess primary symptoms of social and personal adjustment; assist with the classification, treatment and management decisions for various vocations; establish solid empirical foundations to assist with clinical expert testimony; provide insight for marriage and family interventions; and support advanced education and vocational counseling recommendations.

<u>Consists of</u>: 338 items divided across 50 scales each of which are linked to current models of psychopathology and personality. The MMPI-2-RF scales include:

- 8 Validity Scales
- 3 Higher-Order Scales
- 9 Restructured Clinical Scales
- 3 Somatic Scales
- 11 Internalizing Scales
- 4 Externalizing Scales
- 5 Interpersonal Scales
- 2 Interest Scales
- 5 PSY-5 (Personality Psychopathology-Five) Scales specifically adapted for the MMPI-2-RF

<u>Other information</u>: The MMPI-2 is available in 14 languages, including Chinese, Hmong, Korean, Spanish (two versions), Croatian, Czech, Dutch/Flemish, French, Greek, German, Hebrew, Italian, Norwegian, and Swedish. Translations are available through the University of Minnesota Press Web site at: www.upress.umn.edu/tests/translations, or by phoning (612) 627-1964.

Scores showing substantial rates of elevation over those of the control group on Clinical Scale O (Si), Content scale SOD, Supplementary scale R, and PSY-5 scale INTR suggested a direct association with a constellation of behaviors that includes discomfort in social situations, social reservation and introversion, shyness, and social anxiety, all often described as typical across HFA and AS populations. The authors also indicate that "the low positive emotionality that is captured by the INTR and RC2 scales may also be consistent with the difficulty processing and talking about emotions that is a prominent feature of adults with ASD" (Ozonoff et al., 2005, p. 91).

Other scores reflecting associations of clinical descriptions of adults with Asperger's syndrome and HFA, as well as and DSM-IV-TR criteria, were rigidity, inflexibility, and resistance to change, all of which have been associated with high scores on Scale O. Anxiety, described as a correlate of Scale O elevations, was also consistent with the high rate of comorbid anxiety disorders typically seen in populations with ASD. The (Ozonoff et al., 2005) study also reported medium-size group differences from the control sample and elevations in 30-40% of the ASD group on Scale 8 (Sc). According to the authors, "many of the correlates of high scores on this scale fall in the realm of psychosis, including delusions, hallucinations, and extreme cognitive disorientation….This is consistent with the low scores, few elevations, and similarity to controls on the Bizarre Mentation (BIZ) and Aberrant Experiences (RC8) scales. Scale 8 also measures social alienation and general maladjustment" (Ozonoff et al., 2005, p. 91). The authors conclude that the MMPI-2 appears to be both a valid and a valuable tool for use with ASD populations.

<u>Research Gems: PDD or Personality Disorder?</u>

"It is unknown whether characteristic features of PDD are displayed through childhood and adolescence in persons with Avoidant, Schizoid, or Schizotypal Personality Disorder. Tantam suggests that differences do exist, insofar as elevated scores on measures of abnormal non-verbal expression were correlated with early developmental disturbances, whereas schizoid features were not. Tantam reports that features of developmental delays and abnormal nonverbal expression clustered together, but schizotypal features did not correlate with developmental abnormalities." (Volkmar et al., 2005, p. 179)

Coolidge Personality and Neuropsychological Inventory for Children (CPNI). (Contact: fcoolidg@uccs.edu)

<u>Intended ages</u>: 5 – 17 years of age
<u>Testing time</u>: 30 – 45 minutes
<u>Administration</u>: Individual

<u>Intended for</u>: Parents, caregivers, or someone intimately familiar with the child's behavior in a variety of settings

<u>Purpose</u>: To assess personality disorders. Based on the Axis II criteria for personality disorders listed in the Diagnostic and Statistical Manual of Mental Disorders. Also intended to screen for other clinical conditions including depression, anxiety, gender identify disorder, and eating disorders.

<u>Consists of</u>:
A 200-item pencil and paper test, the first 198 of which are designed to be answered on a 4-point Likert scale ranging from "Strongly False, More False than True, More True than False, to Strongly True." Items 199 and 200 require "True or False" answers. A total of 50 scales: 49 scales (see below) and 1 validity scale.

- A broad neuropsychological scale
- A mild neurocognitive disorder scale
- A postconcussional disorder scale
- An executive functions of the frontal lobe scale

<u>Other information</u>:
- 13 of the scales measure DSM-IV Axis I syndromes
- 10 of the scales measure Axis II personality disorder syndrome
- 4 of the scales measure syndromes from the DSM-IV Appendix

"The CPNI has a three-fold purpose: (a) to assess the 12 personality disorders according to the criteria on Axis II and Appendix B of the Diagnostic and Statistical Manual of Mental Disorders; (b) to assess neuropsychological dysfunction, including Attention-Deficit/Hyperactivity Disorder, Mild Neurocognitive Disorder, executive function deficits, and other related symptoms, and (c) to measure some Axis I diagnoses including Separation Anxiety Disorder, Oppositional Defiant Disorder, depression, and general anxiety, as well as other clinical syndromes. The scale reliabilities and test-retest reliabilities were moderate to high, and construct validity was good." (Coolidge et al., 2002, p. 550)

<u>Research Gems: Adaptive Functioning in Autism</u>

"Adaptive functioning refers to an individual's effectiveness in 'meeting the standards expected for his or her age by his or her cultural group.'…Children with autism demonstrate not only deficits in cognitive functioning, but also deficits in adaptive functioning….A review of available research indicates that children with autism demonstrate adaptive functioning deficits that exceed their cognitive deficits, and that adaptive social skills are specifically impaired." (Gabriels & Hill, 2002, p. 54)

Adaptive Behaviors

RECOMMENDED
Adaptive Behavior Assessment System – Second Edition (ABAS-II)

<u>Intended ages</u>: 0 – 89 years.
<u>Testing time</u>: 15 – 20 minutes
<u>Administration</u>: Individual

<u>Intended to be administered by</u>: Trained professionals

<u>Purpose</u>: To help assess individuals with autism, ADHD, learning difficulties, mental retardation, Alzheimer's disease, and other impairments. Measures behaviors relevant to determining eligibility under the Individuals with Disabilities Education Act (IDEA), DSM-IV-TR, Supplemental Security Income (SSI), and Disability Insurance (DI). The test is designed to help determine a person's response to daily demands, develop treatment and training goals, determine eligibility for services and Social Security benefits, and assess capability of adults to live independently.

<u>Consists of</u>: Five forms:
- Parent/Primary Caregiver Form: Birth – 5
- Parent Form: 5 – 21
- Teacher/Daycare Provider Form: 2 – 5
- Teacher Form: 5 – 21
- Adult Form: 16 – 89

Evaluates three general areas of adaptive behavior: conceptual, social and practical and links to the Wecshler Scales to evaluate relationships between adaptive skills and cognitive functioning as well as gathering information from relevant sources including parents, teachers, caregivers, and/or adult clients.

<u>Other information</u>: DSM-IV-TR Areas assessed include: communication, community use, functional academics, home living, health and safety, leisure, self-care, self-direction, social, work, and young children's motor skills. Incorporates American Association of Mental Retardation (AAMR) guidelines by providing composite norms for the three general areas of adaptive behavior specified in their 2002 definition of mental retardation.

<u>Also recommended</u>:
Vineland Adaptive Behavior Scales, Scales of Independent Behavior – Revised (SIB-R)

Research Gems: Autistic Logic in Problem Solving

"Autistic logic is the base for autistic problem solving. This is why many of the attempts to solve problems that are brought to the awareness of counselors and clinicians are strange. As with anyone, the attribution of meaning to a situation will affect behaviour, although the meaning that someone on the autism spectrum may attribute to a situation may not seem apparent and may not be expressed. Often we cannot make sense of the ASD person's behaviours, and many people not on the autism spectrum will attribute inaccurate meaning to the behaviours." (Paxton & Estay, 2007, p. 72)

Problem-Solving Abilities

Porteus Maze

<u>Intended ages</u>: 3 – 12; 14, and adults
<u>Testing time</u>: 25 minutes
<u>Administration</u>: Individual

<u>Intended to be administered by</u>: Trained professionals

<u>Purpose</u>: To measure information used to assess a person's ability to plan and change problem-solving approaches.

<u>Consists of</u>: A cognitive measure component that yields various applications including:
- Verbally impaired programs
- Anthropological research
- Studies of the effects of drugs and neurosurgery

<u>Other information</u>: Described as being a culture-free test based on extensive research with various populations.

Research Gems: Stereotypic Behaviors

"Many authors have hypothesized that impaired sensory processing contributes to some of the atypical behaviours used to diagnose AS. These behaviours include restricted patterns of interest, inflexible adherence to routines or rituals, stereotypic movement patterns, and preoccupation with objects. Temple Grandin reports that many of her stereotypic behaviours were strategies she developed to cope with her hyper-reactivity to auditory and tactile input." (Stoddart, 2005, p. 199)

Repetitive and Stereotypic Behaviors

The Repetitive Behavior Scale-Revised (RBS-R)

<u>Intended ages</u>: 3 – 48 years of age
<u>Testing time</u>: 10–15 minutes
<u>Administration</u>: Individual

<u>Intended for</u>: Parents/caregivers and others informed persons

<u>Purpose</u>: To accurately assess and help to distinguish among the variety of repetitive behaviors seen in autism spectrum disorder populations.

<u>Consists of</u>: An informant-based rating scale designed to capture the breadth of repetitive behavior characteristics in persons with autism spectrum disorders. The RBS-R items are conceptually grouped into five subscales:

- Stereotypy subscale
- Self-Injurious subscale
- Compulsive subscale
- Ritualistic/Sameness subscale
- Restricted subscale

Other information: "Our five-factor solution is likely to be more stable and reproducible than the original six-subscale approach, although this needs to be confirmed by future research. The psychometric characteristics of the five-subscale scoring method of the RBS-R appear to be sound, particularly in outpatient settings. Therefore, researchers and clinicians using the RBS-R may wish to use our amended scoring procedures, which are available from both authors as pdf files. It is also available from the Web at http://psych-med.osu.edu." (Lam & Aman, 2007, p. 864)

Research Gems: Empathy = The Glue of the Social World

"Empathy is without question an important ability. It allows us to tune into how someone else is feeling, or what they might be thinking. Empathy allows us to understand the intentions of others, predict their behavior, and experience an emotion triggered by their emotion. In short, empathy allows us to interact effectively in the social world. It is also the 'glue' of the social world, drawing us to help others and stopping us from hurting others." (Baron-Cohen & Wheelwright, 2004, p. 163)

Empathy

The Empathy Quotient (EQ)

Intended ages: Adults
Testing time: Varies
Administration: Individual

Intended for: Self-report

Purpose: To measure varying degrees of empathy among adults of normal intelligence.

Consists of: Forty "empathy" items and 20 "filler/control" items, yielding scores ranging from 0 to 80 (maximum). The filler items are designed to distract the participant from attempts to focus on empathy. The EQ is based on a forced choice format and is designed for self-administration with no need for interpretation beyond the actual final score indicating degree of subjective empathy.

The EQ as a Screening Tool

"The finding the EQ is inversely correlated with the AQ is one indicator of the validity of the EQ, in that two of the domains of the AQ measure social sensitivity and sensitive communication, both of which require empathy.

The fact that more than 80% of adults who have a diagnosis of AS or HFA score above 32 on the AQ and below 30 on the EQ may indicated their potential for use as screening instruments within clinic settings." (Baron-Cohen & Wheelwright, 2004, p. 169)

Other information: Preliminary studies with the EQ support the notion that women score consistently higher than men across empathy-related variables in the general (neurotypical) population. The EQ also supports the notion of an empathy deficit across persons with Asperger's syndrome and high-functioning autism.

Research Gems: The EQ as a Theory of Mind Test

"As a group, the patients with HFA/AS scored significantly lower on the EQ than controls matched for age and gender who were drawn from a general population. This provides some support for the view of HFA/AS as an empathy disorder. Many of the EQ items tap what could also be described as a need for a "theory of mind," which previous studies have found to be impaired in autism. The EQ thus confirms an empathizing deficit in HFA/AS, as measured by self-report and using items referring to every day understanding of minds." (Baron-Cohen & Wheelwright, 2004, 34:, p. 169)

Research Gems: Facial Processing

"Both AD (autistic disorder) and AS show deficits in neutral face perception in the context of person identify tasks. Recognition of individual faces is an integral part of interpersonal interactions and successful functioning within a social group. Face perception is normally a holistic process, reliant on the configuration of major features….Results suggest that individuals with AD may be performing perceptual processes on faces as if they were objects, perhaps because of their early deficits in 'affiliative drive' and the consequent failure to develop configural processing capabilities characteristics of 'face experts'." (Klin, Volkman, & Sparrow, 2000, pp. 185-186)

Reading Faces / Emotions

Facial Expressions of Emotion: Stimuli and Tests (FEEST)

Intended ages: Adults
Testing time: 25 – 30 minutes.
Administration: Individual

Intended to be administered by: Trained professionals
Purpose: To assess recognition of facial expressions of emotion.

Consists of: Stimuli consisting of six basic emotions from the Ekman and Friesen series:

- Happiness
- Surprise
- Fear
- Sadness
- Disgust
- Anger

and neutral faces

The test images vary in intensity to allow clinicians and researchers to create tasks that can be graded in difficulty, ranging from subtle to intensely expressed emotions.

Other information: The FEEST includes control data and supplementary stimuli for creating new tests.

Central Coherence

Central Coherence refers to a person's ability to pick up on the gist, bottom line, or primary theme of a given situation. A person with weak central coherence (WCC), for instance, is one who can be thought of as seeing "the trees for the forest." Perceived as a "weakness," the presence of WCC in an individual can be thought of as limiting one's access to the big picture, which can be particularly limiting when related to communication and social interactions in both personal and professional pursuits. On the other hand, perceived as a perceptual-cognitive style adept at focusing on details, a WCC can be seen as a strength, or a valuable cognitive ability. Nurtured and pursued as a strength, the ability to avoid attention to the big picture, and focus on small details, can prove invaluable to a number of professions such as accounting, architecture, engineering, graphic design, surveying, research, laboratory and detective work, computer related pursuits, and a vast number of blue collar, technical and professional vocations. A large amount of contemporary research points to WCC as being at the core of many of the deficits, and strengths, of persons with autism and AS.

Research Gems: "Weak Central Coherence as a Strength"

"The notion of weak coherence as a processing bias, rather than deficit, lends itself to a continuum approach, in which weak coherence is seen as one end of a normal distribution of cognitive style, and people with ASD, and perhaps their relatives, are placed at the extreme end of this continuum. The opposite cognitive style, strong coherence, might be characterized as a tendency to process gist and global form at the expense of attention and memory for detail and surface form." (Happè & Frith, 2006, p. 15)

In an overview of current research, Happè and Frith summarize a large number of experimental group studies in which the notion of central coherence has been examined across individuals with autism spectrum disorders. A number of the primary tests, and subtest tasks used to examine weak coherence in their research overview are listed below arranged according to Visuo-spatial (EFT, Block Design, Hierarchical Figures, Visual Illusion, Drawings, Motion, Faces, and various) and Auditory (Pitch and Music, Homograph reading, and various) References. (For a review please refer to Happè & Frith, 2006, pp. 7-12.)

Central Coherence: Visuo-Spatial Reference

Embedded Figures Test (EFT)
> EFT
> Children's Embedded Figures Task (CEFT)
> Block Design
> DAS BD (+ Belief Tasks)
> Preschool EFT (children)
> Pattern Construction (DAS)

Block Design
> Wechsler Block Design

Hiearchical Figures
> Navon Hiearchical Figures task
> Palmer mental synthesis task
> Disembedding

Visual Illusion
> Judge Illusions in 2D & 3D forms
> Rey Figure drawing

Drawing
> Copying drawings

Motion Coherence
> Motion coherence threshold task
> Form coherence threshold task
> Flicker contrast sensitivity
> Global dot motion (GDM) task
> CEFT

Faces
> Upright face identify/emotion matching
> Inversion effect task
> Composite effect task
> Thatcher illusion
> Mooney faces
> Face and house photos
> Matching high-pass filter (local) or low pass-filter (global) faces

Various
> Forced-choice RT task
> Postural reactivity to visually perceived motion
> Dot counting in canonical vs. distributed arrays
> Visual search task
> Perceptual learning task

Object Integration test
Scenic test
Modified Hooper Visual Organization test
Rule-based category learning
Prototype task
Visual search task
Visual priming Memory for unrelated pictures
Biconditional configuration discrimination
Feature vs. configuration patterning

Research Gems: Weak Coherence

"While the person with weak coherence may be poor at seeing the bigger picture, the person with strong coherence may be a terrible proof reader." (Happè & Frith, 2006, p. 15)

Central Coherence: Auditory Reference

Pitch and Music
Memory for exact pitches
Same-different judgment of melodies
Discrimination and categorization of pure tones
Match pitch direction changes between 2 & 5-note auditory sequences
Pitch memory and labeling
Disembedding un/labeled tones from chords
Auditory filtering task

Homograph reading
Homograph reading
Stroop test
Gap tests
Bridging inference task
Ambiguous sentences test
Semantic priming task
Memory for un/related words

Various
Recall tests
False memory test
Global integration test
Global inferences test
Story comprehension and inference task

In general, the authors emphasize the relevance of perceptual process in ASD. Regarding perception in the auditory modality, they cite "demonstrations of stable memory for exact pitches, enhanced local processing of musical stimuli, reduced interference from melodic structure in music processing and a reduced McGurg effect (less influence from visual to auditory speech perception)." Relevant to perception in the visual modality, they cite "individuals with ASD show raised thresholds for perceiving coherent motion, and reduced susceptibility to visually induced motion. Superior visual search and superior discrimination learning of highly confusable patterns have also been reported. Active process of visual grouping may be affected, shown in reduced gestalt grouping, and reduced susceptibility to visual illusions" (Happè & Frith, 2006, p. 6).

Research Gems: The Theory of a Weak Central Coherence

"The theory of weak central coherence is yet another approach to explaining the purportedly unique cognitive processing style associated with people with autism. According to this theory, people with autism lack or are deficient in their ability to process information contextually: that is, they lack the ability to synthesize information in order to achieve 'higher-level meaning.' Consequently, people with autism tend to focus on parts through 'piecemeal processing' and have difficulty integrating information synthetically. At a neurological level, (it) suggests 'poor connectivity throughout the brain between more basic perceptual processes and top-down modulating processes, perhaps owing to failure of pruning'."

Memory

Research Gems: "Verbal Working Memory in HFA"

"The present study found no deficit in verbal working memory in high functioning children, adolescents and adults with autism using a well-established experimental test of verbal working memory and clinical test of verbal working memory....Rather the evidence suggests that impaired performance on these complex cognitive and language tasks reflect inherent impairments in these abilities as proposed by the central coherence and complex information processing-underconnectivity models." (Williams et al., 2005, p. 754)

Wechsler Memory Scale – Third Edition (WMS–III)

Intended ages: 16 – 89 years.
Testing time: 45–50 minutes (Primary Subtests)
Administration: Individual

Intended to be administered by: Trained professionals

Purpose: To obtain a comprehensive assessment of adult memory abilities.

Consists of: Eleven subtests (six primary and five optional). The Primary Indexes are organized into summary index scores:

- Auditory Immediate
- Visual Immediate
- Immediate Memory
- Auditory Delayed
- Visual Delayed
- Auditory Recognition Delayed
- General Memory
- Working Memory

Four supplemental Auditory Process Composites help evaluate clinically meaningful aspects of memory functioning:

- Single Trial Learning: To assess immediate memory capacity
- Learning Slope: To assess change over multiple learning trials
- Retention: To assess percent retention of material from immediate to delayed
- Retrieval: To assess discrepancy between recognition and recall

Other information: Used together with the WAIS-III the instruments can be used to examine the relationship between clients' memories and their intellectual functions. Group studies included populations with reading and math disabilities, attention deficit disorder, schizophrenia, and other clinical diagnoses.

N-back Letter Tasks – A Working Memory Measure

Description:
An experimental paradigm whereas a continuous stream of simple stimuli, such as letters (or other items) or instructions are viewed and a subject is asked to decide whether the current item matches the stimulus presented a designated number of stimuli back. Commonly used for functional neuroimaging studies of working memory, the subject may be asked to monitor the identity (e.g., a particular letter) or location (e.g., one of four corners) of a series of verbal or nonverbal stimuli and then indicate when the currently presented stimulus is the same as the one presented in previous trials. Research has suggested that working memory in persons with autism appears to be associated with behavior regulation, cognitive flexibility, abstract thinking, focusing and sustaining attention

Other Measures of Relevance

Yale Special Interest Interview (YSII)
(South, Klin, & Ozonoff, 1999)

Description:
The YSII is an unpublished (as of this date) semi-structured, parent-report interview that was designed specifically to collect information about circumscribed or "special" interest topics or topic areas. The instrument asks parents to report whether the child has exhibited any unusually strong interest in one or two topics or activities to the extent

that would be defined as much more so than other children of the same age. Follow-ups to the initial presentation of the interview directs itself to special topic interests that may have been established and expand on those by asking about the topic area's content, frequency, and duration of the special topic. If the child's interest is considered unusual within social context in which it is pursued, this is considered to be additional valuable information. The questions on the test are then referred back by the interviewer in order to decide whether it meets DSM-IV-TR clinical criteria as a circumscribed interest over the course of at least three months, as well as the level of impairment the interest may be having on the subject's individual, family, and social functioning.

Yale-Brown Obsessive-Compulsive Scale,
Children's Yale-Brown Obsessive-Compulsive Scale

Online form: (sites accessed 7/19/2007) http://www.brainphysics.com/ybocs.php http://209.85.165.104/search?q=cache:8UD7IuZFWk4J:www.cnsforum.com/streamfile.aspx%3Ffilename%3DYBOCS.pdf%26path%3Dpdf+Yale-Brown+Obsessive-Compulsive+Scale&hl=en&ct=clnk&cd=7&gl=us

Carey Temperament Scales
(McDevitt & Carey, 1978)

Description:

The instrument consists of a series of questionnaires designed to assess temperament in infancy and childhood through measurement of nine New York Longitudinal Study temperament characteristics:

- Activity Level
- Regularity
- Approach-withdrawal
- Adaptability
- Intensity
- Mood
- Persistence
- Distractibility
- Sensory Threshold

The five questionnaires in the five age-specific scale series, designed to organize and systematize information into a valuable behavioral profile include:

- The Early Infancy Temperament Questionnaire (EITQ): age 1– 4 months
- The Toddler Temperament Scale (TTS): age 1– 3 years
- The Behavioral Style Questionnaire (BSQ): age 3 – 7 years
- The Middle Childhood Temperament Questionnaire (MCTQ): age 8 – 12 years

Appendix A

Four-Step Assessment and Diagnosis Diagram: Step One

Adapted from Klin, A., & Volkmar, F. R. *Asperger's Syndrome: Guidelines for Assessment and Diagnosis*, Yale Child Study Center, New Haven, Connecticut. Published by the Learning Disabilities Association of America, June 1995.

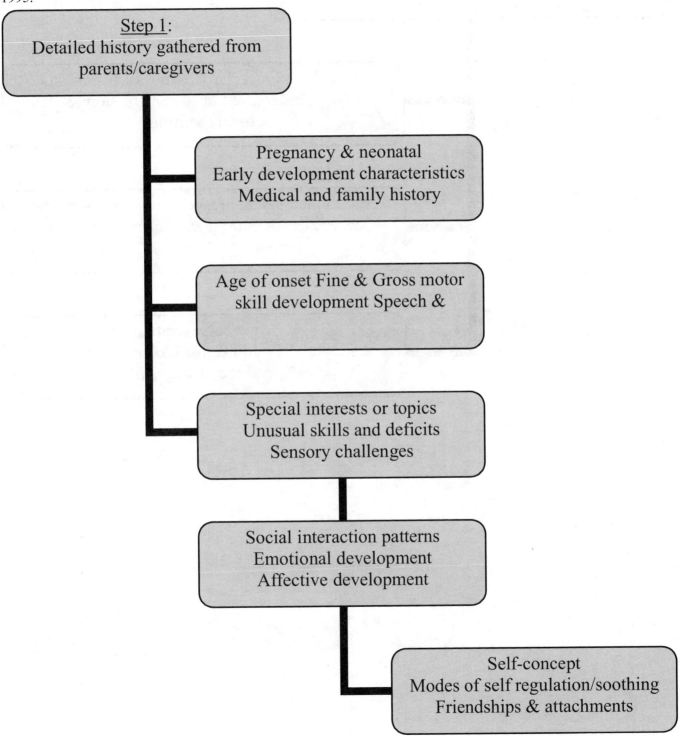

Step 1:
Detailed history gathered from parents/caregivers

Pregnancy & neonatal
Early development characteristics
Medical and family history

Age of onset Fine & Gross motor
skill development Speech &

Special interests or topics
Unusual skills and deficits
Sensory challenges

Social interaction patterns
Emotional development
Affective development

Self-concept
Modes of self regulation/soothing
Friendships & attachments

Four-Step Assessment and Diagnosis Diagram: Step Two

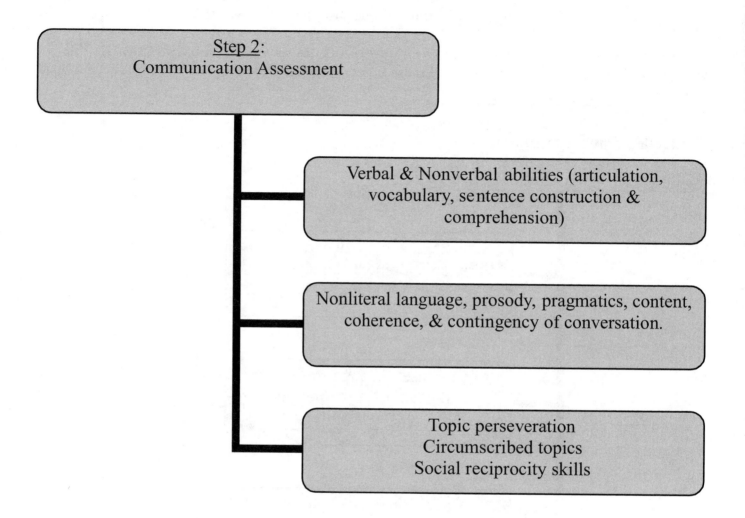

Step 2:
Communication Assessment

Verbal & Nonverbal abilities (articulation, vocabulary, sentence construction & comprehension)

Nonliteral language, prosody, pragmatics, content, coherence, & contingency of conversation.

Topic perseveration
Circumscribed topics
Social reciprocity skills

Four- Step Assessment and Diagnosis Diagram: Step Three

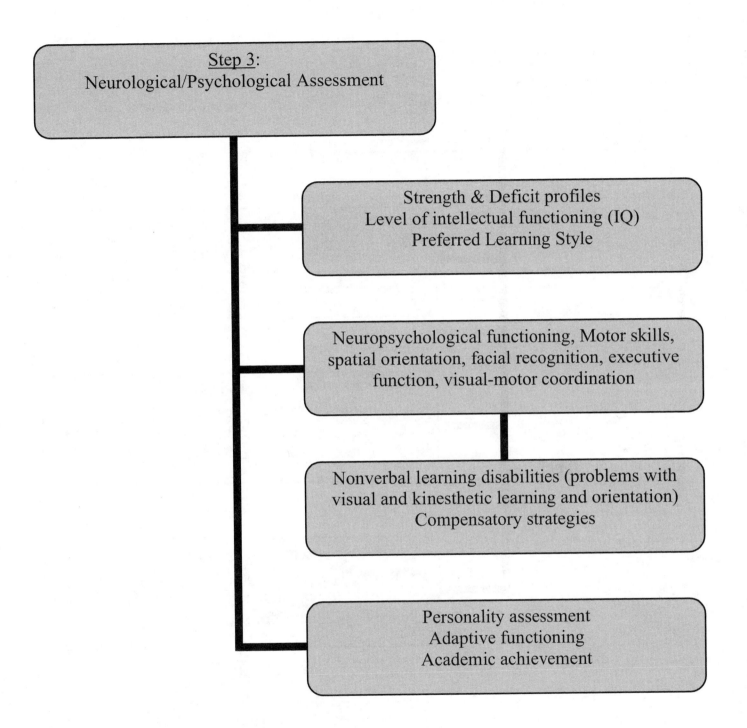

Four-Step Assessment and Diagnosis Diagram: Step Four

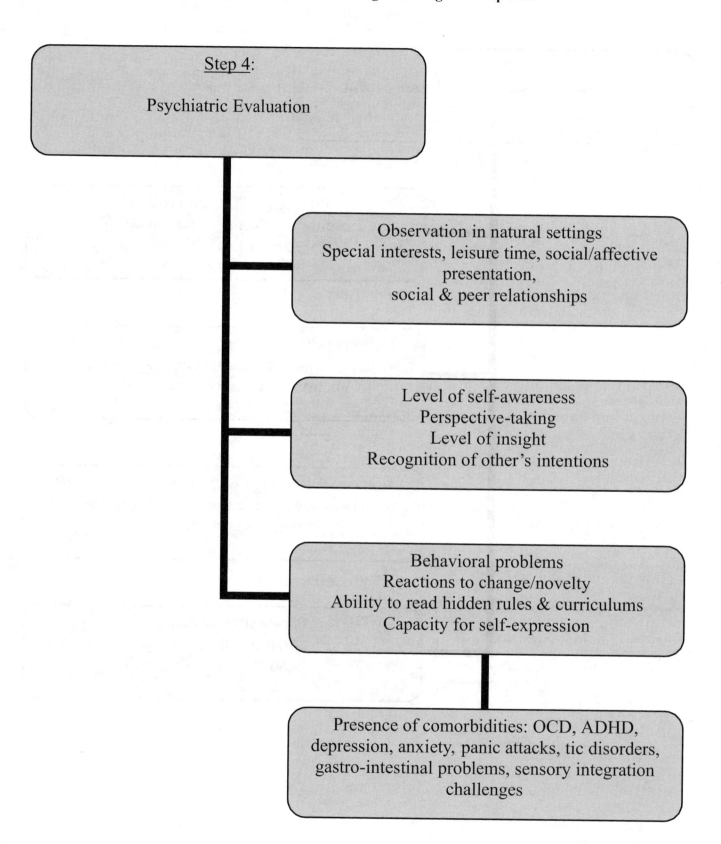

Step 4:

Psychiatric Evaluation

Observation in natural settings
Special interests, leisure time, social/affective presentation,
social & peer relationships

Level of self-awareness
Perspective-taking
Level of insight
Recognition of other's intentions

Behavioral problems
Reactions to change/novelty
Ability to read hidden rules & curriculums
Capacity for self-expression

Presence of comorbidities: OCD, ADHD, depression, anxiety, panic attacks, tic disorders, gastro-intestinal problems, sensory integration challenges

Appendix B

The following checklist draws from Byron Rourke's NLD deficits and strength characteristics as proposed by Rourke for Consideration as ICD Diagnostic Criteria for Research in NLD. AS comparison characteristics draw from research studies and anecdotal clinical information cited in chapter 5.
 (Note: NLD information adapted from Rourke, 2007, www.nld-bprourke.ca)

Characteristics Comparing/Differentiating NLD from AS
as detailed in Byron Rourke's System

Comparative Characteristics	NLD	AS
Bilateral deficits in tactile perception – left side	Common	Rare
Bilateral deficits in psychomotor coordination – left side	Common	Sometimes
Marked visual-spatial-organization impairment	Common	Rare
Difficulties dealing with novel situations	Common	Common
Difficulties dealing with complex situations	Common	Common
Difficulties with nonverbal problem-solving	Common	Rare
Difficulties with concept-formation	Common	Common
Difficulties with hypothesis-testing	Common	Common
Difficulties estimating time	Common	Common
Marked difficulties in mechanical arithmetic	Common	Rare
Marked difficulties in reading comprehension	Common	Sometimes
Marked difficulties with social perception	Common	Common
Marked difficulties with social judgment	Common	Common
Marked difficulties with social interactions	Common	Common
Social isolation and withdrawal	Common	Common

	NLD	AS
Delays in meeting developmental milestones	Common	Common
Delays in exploratory behavior	Common	Common
Impaired complex psychomotor skills	Common	Common
Preference for familiarity, avoidance of novelty	Common	Common
Preference for verbal vs. visual information	Common	Rare

Simple, repetitive motor activities a strength	Common	Common
Rote verbal memory a strength	Common	Common
Deficits with visual and tactile domains	Common	Rare
Auditory-verbal memory a strength	Common	Rare
Visual or tactile memory a deficit	Common	Rare
Early difficulties with oral-motor praxis	Common	Common
A pattern of being described as "hyperactive"	Common	Common
A pattern of being described as "inattentive"	Common	Common

Difficulties analyzing, organizing, & synthesizing information	Common	Depends on area
Difficulties with language prosody, content, and pragmatics. Poor psycholinguistic pragmatics	Common	Common
Strengths in single-word reading/recognition	Common	Common
Difficulties with handwriting/penmanship	Common	Common
Phonetic-related spelling errors	Common	Rare
Difficulties with social perception, judgment, and interaction	Common	Common
Difficulties with understanding and interpreting facial expressions and emotions	Common	Common
A pattern of moving from hyperactivity to either normally active or hypoactive in later years	Common	Common

Appendix C

Autism "Red Flags" Checklist©
John M. Ortiz, Ph.D.

Early childhood

	Rarely	Sometimes	Often
Lack of reciprocal social smiling			
Apparent hyper- and/or hypo-sensitivity to sensory triggers (tactile, visual, auditory, olfactory, gustatory)			
May appear to have speech or hearing disorder			
Problems with motor skills or coordination (praxis, body percept, vestibular, propioceptive, bilateral coordination, Lateralization)			
May not respond to his or her name when called			
Lack of gesturing or pointing by the age of one year			
Lack of babbling by age of 1 year			
Not using single words to communicate by 18 months			
Apparent regression of social or communication skills			

General
Code: Rarely (R) Sometimes (S) Often (O)

	(R)	(S)	(O)
Lack of interest or responding to people			
May appear inattentive or absent in social settings			
Difficulties forming social relationships with peers			
Inappropriate vocalizations			

Vocalizations non-context related			
Delays in social/emotional reciprocity			
Lack of awareness of others			
Lack of spontaneity			
Self-stimulation when stressed or anxious			
Pragmatic language delays			
Hyperactive or withdrawal behaviors			
Speech oddities			
- (echolalia, pronoun reversal, rhyming)			
Speech impediments			
- (stuttering, cluttering, stammering)			
Adherence to "nonfunctional" rituals & routines			
Inappropriate sensory play			
Extreme variation in cognitive abilities			
Blunted, flat, or constricted affect			
Appears bossy, inflexible, or conduct disordered			
Preoccupation with objects or special interest topics			
Comes across as "off-task" or "in her own world"			

Problems with nonverbal communication			
- (slang, metaphors, analogies)			
Lack of social engagement or reciprocal play with peers			

Appendix D

Positive Characteristics of AS/HFA and NLD Checklist©
John M. Ortiz, Ph.D.

The following list of adjectives and positive qualities, all of which are typically descriptive of persons with autism spectrum disorders, can be used by parents, caregivers, and others involved in the care of the child when sharing information for educational or clinical purposes.

My child could be described as:

	Almost Always	Often	Sometimes	Rarely
"An original"				
Artistic				
Charming				
Computer savvy				
Conscientious				
Dependable				
Determined				
Ethical				
Faithful				
Gifted (in areas)				
Honest				
Humorous				
Impartial				
Inimitable				
Inventive				
Laser-focused				
Law-abiding				
Loyal				
Mechanically inclined				
Meticulous				

Moral				
Musical				
Open & Earnest				
Precise				
Principled				
Punctual				
Reliable				
Sensitive				
Sincere				
Naturally Smart				
Steadfast				
Strong-minded				
Technologically gifted				
Trustworthy				
Unbiased				
Unique				
Unprejudiced				
Verbally gifted				

Specific Problem Behaviors

My child displays behaviors that could be described as:

	Almost Always	Often	Sometimes	Rarely
Ritualistic				
Obsessive				
Perseverative				
Compulsive				
Oppositional				
Disruptive				
Destructive				
Bossy or controlling				
Argumentative				
Defiant or combative				

Appendix E

Executive Function Challenges: Checklist©
John M. Ortiz, Ph.D.

My child could be described as having:

	Rarely	Sometimes	Often
AREA I: Organization			
Difficulties with novel situations & learning			
Slow processing speed			
Rigid thinking			
Concrete interpretation			
Perfectionism			

Focuses on the wrong detail			
Difficulty with "if-then" thinking			
AREA II: Integration			
Poor frustration tolerance: gives up easily			
Work production limited: is overwhelmed by a heavy load			
Has difficulty creating written documents			
Rigid & perfectionistic about work			
Easily overwhelmed: emotional shutdown often occurs			
AREA III: Production			
Fails to comprehend the main idea			
May see all details as equally important			
Has poor ability understanding metaphors & analogies			
Has difficulty reading between the lines			
Relies on pattern learning and misses concept			
Prefers step-by-step, sequential learning, often losing the whole concept			

Appendix F

List of publishers for assessment instruments listed throughout this book.
Assessment instruments can be purchased either directly through the publishers or located, and purchased, over the internet.

Brookes Publishing Company
P.O. Box 10624
Baltimore, MD 21285
800-638-3775

California School of Professional Psychology-Los Angeles
1000 South Freemont Avenue
Alhambra, CA 91803
818-284-2777

American Guidance Service
4201 Woodland Road
Circle Pines, MN 55014
800-328-2560

Behavioral Developmental Initiatives
14636 North 55th Street
Scottsdale, AS 85254
800-405-2313

Achenbach System of Empirically Based Assessment
Room 6436
One South Prospect Street
Burlington, VT 05401
800-656-8313

Multi-Health Systems, Inc.
908 Niagara Falls Boulevard
North Tonawanda, NY 14120
800-456-3003

Kaplan Companies
PO Box 609
Lewisville, NC 27023
800-334-2014

Scholastic Testing Services
480 Meyer Road
Bensenville, IL 60106
630-766-7150

Sopris West
4093 Specialty Place
Longmont, CO 80504
303-651-2829

Psychological Assessment Resources, Inc.
PO Box 998
Odessa, FL 33556
800-331-8378

Therapy Skill Builders
3830 East Bellevue
Tucson, AZ 85716
800-872-1726

PRO-ED
8700 Shoal Creek Boulevard
Austin, TX 78757

References

Ad Hoc Committee on Autism Spectrum Disorders (2006). Roles and Responsibilities of Speech-Language Pathologists in Diagnosis, Assessment, and Treatment of Autism Spectrum Disorders Across the Life Span. American Speech-Language-Hearing Association, 1-3, Available at: http://www.asha.org/docs/html/PS2006-00105.html

Ad Hoc Committee on Autism Spectrum Disorders. (2006) Guidelines for speech-sanguage pathologists in diagnosis, assessment, and treatment of autism spectrum disorders across the life span. American Speech-Language-Hearing Association, 1 – 69, Available from www.asha.org/policy.

Adachi, T., Hirabayashi, S., Shiota, M., Suzuki, S., Wakamiya, E., Kitayama, S., Kono, M. Maeoka, Y., & Koeda, T. (2006). Study of situational recognition of attention deficit/hyperactivity disorders, Asperger's disorder and high-functionint autism with the Metaphor and Sarcasm Scenario Test (MSST). No to Hattatsu, 38, 177-181.

Adams, C. (2002). Practitioner review: The assessment of language pragmatics. Journal of Child Psychology and Psychiatry, 43, 973-987.

Adams, C., Cooke, R., Crutchley, A., Heskety, A., & Reeves, D. (2001). Assessment of Comprehension and Expression 6-11. Windsor, U.K.: NFER-Nelson.

Ad Hoc Committee on Autism Spectrum Disorders (2006). Principles for Speech-Language Pathologists in Diagnosis, Assessment, and Treatment of Autism Spectrum Disorders Across the Life Span. American Speech-Language-Hearing Association, Technical Report. http://www.asha.org/members/deskref-journal/deskref/default

Akshoomoff, N., Farid, K., Courchesne, E., & Haas, R. (2007). Abnormalities on the neurological examination and EEG in young children with pervasive developmental disorders. Journal of Autism and Developmental Disorders, 37, 887-893.

Allison, C., Williams, J., Scott, F., Stott, C., Bolton, P., Baron-Cohen, S., & Brayne, C. (2007). The Childhood Asperger Syndrome Test (CAST): Test-retest reliability in a high scoring sample. Autism, 11, 173-185.

Almasy, L., & Blangero, J. (2001). Endophenotypes as quantitative risk factoers for psychiatric disease: Rationale and study design. American Journal of Medical Genetics, 105, 42-44.

Atwood, T. (1998). Asperger's syndrome: A guide for parents and professionals. London, UK: Jessica Kingsley Publishing.

Ayres, A. J. (2005). Sensory integration and the child: 25th anniversary edition. Los Angeles, CA: Western Psychological Services.

Baron-Cohen, S. & Wheelwright, S. (2003). The Friendship Questionnaire: An investigation of adults with Asperger syndrome of high-functioning autism, and normal sex differences. Journal of Autism and Developmental Disorders, 33, 509-517.

Baron-Cohen, S. (2004). The cognitive neuroscience of autism. Journal of Neurology, Neurosurgery and Psychiatry, 75, 945-948.

Baron-Cohen, S. & Wheelwright, S. (2004). The Empathy Quotient: An investigation of adults with Asperger syndrome or high functioning autism, and normal sex differences. Journal of Autism and Developmental Disorders, 34, 163-175.

Baron-Cohen, S. & Wheelwright, S., Skinner, R., Martin, J., & Clubley, E. (2001). The Autism-Spectrum Quotient (AQ): Evidence from Asperger syndrome/high-functioning autism, males and females, scientists and mathematicians. Journal of Autism and Developmental Disorders, 31, 5-17.

Baron-Cohen, S. (2003). The truth about the male & female brain: The essential difference. New York, N.Y.: Basic Books.

Baron-Cohen, S., & Wheelwright, S., Skinner, R., Martin, J., & Clubley, E. (2001). The Autism-Spectrum Quotient (AQ): Evidence from Asperger syndrome/high-functioning autism, males and females, scientists and mathematicians. Journal of Autism and Developmental Disorders, 31, 5-17.

Baron-Cohen, S., Allen, J., & Gillberg, C. (1992). Can autism be detected at 18 months? The needle, the haystack, and the CHAT. British Journal of Psychiatry, 161, 839-843.

Baron-Cohen, S., Harrison, J., Goldstein, L., & Wyke, M. (1993). Coloured speech perception: Is synaesthesia what happens when modularity breaks down: Perception, 22, 419-426.

Baron-Cohen, S., Hoekstra, R.A., Knickmeyer, R. & Wheelwright, S. (2006). The Autism-Spectrum Quotient (AQ)—Adolescent Version. Journal of Autism and Developmental Disorders, 36, 343-350.

Baron-Cohen, S., Scott, F., Wheelwright, S., Johnson, W., Bisarya, D. Desai., A., & Ahluwalia J. (2006). Can Asperger syndrome be diagnosed at 26 months old? A genetic high-risk single-case study. Journal of Child Neurology, 21, 351-356.

Baron-Cohen, S., Wheelwright, S. Hill, J., Raste, Y., & Plumb, I. (2001). The "Reading the Mind in the Eyes" test revised version: A study with normal adults, and adults with Asperger syndrome or high-functioning autism. The Journal of Child Psychology and Psychiatry and Allied Disciplines, 42, 241-252.

Baron-Cohen, S., Wheelwright, S., Cox, A., Baird, G., Charman, T., Swettenham, J., Drew, A., & Doehring, P. (2000). Early identification of autism by the Checklist for Autism in Toddlers (CHAT). Journal of the Royal Society of Medicine, 93, 521-525.

Baron-Cohen, S., O'Riordan, M., Stone, V., Jones, R., & Plaisted, K. (1999). Recognition of faux pas by normally developing children and children with Asperger syndrome or high-functioning autism. Journal of Autism and Developmental Disorders, 29, 407-418.

Barrett, S., Prior, M., & Manjiviona, J. (2004). Children on the borderlands of autism. Autism, 8, 61-87.

Bellini, S. & Hopf, A. (2007). The development of the Autism Social Skill Profile: A preliminary analysis of psychometric properties. Focus on Autism and Other Developmental Disabilities, 22, 80-87.

Berney, T. (2004). Asperger syndrome from childhood into adulthood. <u>Advances in Psychiatric Treatment, 10</u>, 341-351.

Beversdorf, D. Q., Anderson, J. M., Manning, S. E., Anderson, S. L., Nordgren, R. E., Felopulor, G. J., & Bauman, M. L. (2001). Brief report: Macrographia in high-functioning adults with autism spectrum disorder. <u>Journal of Autism and Developmental Disorders, 31</u>, 97-101.

Biel, L. & Peske, N. (2005). <u>Rasing a sensory smart child: The definitive handbook for helping your child with sensory integration issues.</u> New York, N.Y.: Penguin Books.

Billdstedt, E., Gillberg, C., & Gillberg, C. (2005). Autism after adolescence: Population-based 13- 22-year follow-up study of 120 individuals with autism diagnosed in childhood. <u>Journal of Autism and Developmental Disorders, 35</u>, 351-360.

Bishop, D. (1998). Development of the Children's communication Checklist (CCC): A method for assessing qualitative aspects of communicative impairment in children. <u>Journal of Child Psychology and Child Psychiatry, 39</u>, 879-891.

Bishop, D. (2003). <u>Children's Communication Checklist (CCC-2)</u>. London: The Psychological Corporation.

Bishop, D.V.M. (1998). Development of the Children's Communication Checklist (CCC): A method for assessing qualitative aspects of communicative impairment in children. <u>Journal of Child Psychology and Psychiatry, 39</u>, 879-891.

Bishop, D.V.M., & Baird, G. (2001). Parent and teacher report of pragmatic aspects of communication: Use of the Children's Communication Checklist in a clinical setting. <u>Developmental Medicine & Child Neurology, 43</u>, 809-818.

Blacher, J., Kraemer, B., & Schalow, M. (2003). Asperger syndrome and high functioning autism: Research concerns and emerging foci. <u>Current Opinion in Psychiatry 16</u>, 535-542.

Blackwell, P. B. (2002). Screening young children for autism and other social-communication disorders. <u>Journal of Kentucky Medical Association, 100</u>, 390-394.

Blakemore-Brown, L. (2002). *Reweaving the autistic tapestry:* <u>Autism, Asperger Syndrome and ADHD.</u> London, UK: Jessica Kingsley Publishing.

Bogdashina, O. (2003). <u>Sensory perceptual issues in autism and Asperger syndrome: Different sensory experiences, different perceptual worlds.</u> London, UK: Jessica Kingsley Publishing.

Bolte, S. & Poustka, F. (2004). Diagnostic observation scale for autistic disorders: Initial results of reliability and validity. <u>Z Kinder Jugendpsychiatrie Psychoter, 32</u>, 45-50.

Bragdon, A. D., & Gamon, D. (2000). <u>Brains that work a little bit differently: Recent discoveries about common brain diversities.</u> West Yarmouth, MA: Brainwaves Books.

Brasic, J. R. & Morgan, R. H. (2005). Pervasive developmental disorder: Asperger syndrome. *eMedicine*, June 6, http://www.emedicine.com?PED/topic147.htm

British Columbia Medical Association. Child development. Head to Toe, Winter 1997:2

Brock, S. E. The identification of autism spectrum disorders: A primer for the school psychologist. California State University, Sacramento January 21, 2004.

Bujas-Petkovic, Z. (1993). Asperger's syndrome—a separate nosologic entity or part of the spectrum of autism. Lijecnicki Vjesnik, 115, 60-62.

Carter, A. S., Black, D. O., Tewani, S., Connolly, C. E., Kadlec, M.B., & Tager-Flusberg, H. (2007). Sex differences in toddlers with autism spectrum disorders. Journal of Autism and Developmental Disorders, 37, 6-97.

Cesaroni, L, & Garber, M. (1991). Exploring the experiences of autism through first-hand accounts. Journal of Autism and Developmental Disorders, 21, p. 3.

Chawarska, K., Paul, R., Klin, A., Hannigen, S., Dichtel, L.E., & Volkmar, F. (2007). Parental recognition of developmental problems in toddlers with autism spectrum disorders. Journal of Autism and Developmental Disorders, 37, 2-72.

Clifford, S., Young, R., & Williamson, P. (2007). Assessing the early characteristics of autistic disorder using video analysis. Journal of Autism and Developmental Disorders, 37, 301-313.

Cohen, J. (1988). *Statistical* Power Analysis for the Behavioral Sciences, 2nd edition. Lawrence Erlbaum Associates, New Jersey.

Coolidge, F. L., Thede, L. L., Stewart, S. E., Segal, D. L. (2002). The Coolidge Personality and Neuropsychological Inventory for Children (CPNI): Preliminary Psychiatric Characteristics. Behavior Modification, 26, 550-566.

Craig, J., & Baron-Cohen, S. (1999). Creativity and imagination in autism and Asperger syndrome. Journal of Autism and Developmental Disorders, 29, 319-326.

Cytowic, R. E. (1989). Synaesthesia: A union of the senses. New York, NY: Springer Verlag.

Cytowic, R. E. (1995). Synaesthesia: Phenomenology and neuropsychology. A review of current knowledge. PSYCH 2, 10.
    http://psyche.cs.monash.edu.au

Dawson, G., Estes, A., Munson, J., Schellenberg, G., Bernier, R., & Abbott, R. (2007). Quantitative assessment of autism symptom-related traits in probands and parents: Broader phenotype autism symptom scale. Journal of Autism and Developmental Disorders, 37, 523-546.

De Bruin, E. I., Verheij, F. & Ferdinand, R. F. (2006). WISC-R subtest but no overall VIQ-PIQ difference in Dutch children with PDD-NOS. Journal of Abnormal Child Psychology, 34, 263-271.

de Bruin, E. I., Verheij, F., & Ferdinand, R. F. (2006). WISC-R subtest but no overall VIQ-PIQ difference in Dutch children with PDD-NOS. Journal of Abnormal Child Psychology, 34, 263-271.

Delmolino, L.M. (2006). Brief report: Use of DQ for estimating cognitive ability in young children with autism. Journal of Autism and Developmental Disorders, 36, 959-963.

DeLong G. R., & Dwyer, J. T. (1988). Correlation of family history with specific autistic subgroups: Asperger's syndrome and bipolar affective disease. Journal of Autism and Developmental Disorders, 18, 593-600.

Dietz, C., Swinkels, S., van Daalen, E, van Engeland, H., & Buitelaar, J.K. (2006). Screening for autistic spectrum disorders in children aged 14-15 months. II: Population screening with the Early Screening of Autistic Traits Questionnaire (ESAT). Design and general findings. Journal of Autism and Developmental Disorders, 36, 713-722.

DiMatties, M. E. (2004) LDOnline, http://www.ldonline.org/article/5612?theme, 1-5.

Dingfelder, S. F. (2004). A dilemma of definition: Refined understanding of disorders within the autism spectrum may aid research and treatment, some researchers claim. Monitor on Psychology, 11, p. 48.

Drummond, C. R., Ahmand, S. A., & Rourke, B. P. (2005). Rules for the classification of younger children with Nonverbal Learning Disabilities and Basic Phonological Processing disabilities. Archives of Clinical Neuropsychology, 20, 171-182.

Dyck, M. J., & Ferguson, K., & Schochet, I. M. (2001). Do autism spectrum disorders differ from each other and from non-spectrum disorders on emotion recognition tests? European Child and Adolescent Psychiatry, 10, 105-116.

Dziobek, I., Fleck, S., Kalbe, E., Rogers, K., Hassenstab, J., Brand, M., Kessler, J., Woike, J. K., Wolf, O.T., & Convit, A. (2006). Introducing MASC: A movie for the assessment of social cognition. Journal of Autism and Developmental Disorders, 36, 623-636.

Eaves, L. C., Wingert, H. D., Ho, H. H., Mickelson, E. C. (2006). Screening for autism spectrum disorders with the social communication questionnaire. Journal of Developmental and Behavioral Pediatrics 27, 95-103.

Ehlers, S., Nydèn, A., Gillberg, C., Sandberg, A. D., Dahlgren, S-O., Hjelmquist, E., & Odèn, A. (1997). Asperger syndrome, autism and attention disorders: A comparative study of the cognitive profiles of 120 children. The Journal of Child Psychology and Psychiatry, 38, 207-217.

Eisenmajer, R., Prior, M., Leekam, S., Wing, L., Gould J., Welham, M., & Ong, B. (1996). Comparison of clinical symptoms in autism and Asperger's disorder. Journal of the American Academy of Childhood Adolescence and Psychiatry, 35, 1523-1531.

Ellis, H. D. & Gunter, H. L. (1999). Asperger syndrome: A simple matter of white matter? Trends in Cognitive Science, 3, 192-200.

Fast, Y. (2004). Employment for individuals with Asperger syndrome or non-verbal learning disability: stories and strategies. London, UK: Jessica Kingsley Publishing.

Filipek, P., Accardo, P., Baranek, G., Cook, E., Dawson, G., & Gordon, B., et al. (1999). The screening and diagnosis of autistic spectrum disorders. Journal of Autism and Developmental Disorders, 29, 439-484.

Fine, J. Bartolucci, G., Binsberg, G., & Szatmari, P. (1991). The use of intonation to communicate in pervasive developmental disorders. Journal of Child Psychology and Psychiatry, 32, 771-782.

Fitzgerald, M. & Corvin, A. (2001). Diagnosis and differential diagnosis of Asperger syndrome. Advances in Psychiatric Treatment, 7, 310-318.

Frazier, J. A., Doyle, R., Chiu, S., & Coyle, J. T. (2002). Treating a child with Asperger's disorder and comorbid bipolar disorder. American Journal of Psychiatry, 159, 13-21.

Freeman, B. J., Lucas, J. C., Forness, S. R., & Ritvo, E. R. (1985). Cognitive processing of high-functioning autistic children: Comparing the K-ABC and the WISC-R. Journal of Psychoeducational Assessment, 4, 357-362.

Freitag, C. M., Kleser, C., Schneider, M., & von Bontard, A. (2007). Quantitative assessment of neuromotor function in adolescents with high functioning autism and Asperger syndrome. Journal of Autism and Developmental Disorders, 37, 948-959.

Gabriels, R. L. & Hill, D. E. (2002). Autism—from research to individualized practice. London, UK: Jessica Kingsley Publishing.

Gagnon, L., Mottron, L., Bherer, L., & Joanette, Y. (2004). Quantification judgment in high functioning autism: Superior or different? Journal of Autism and Developmental Disorders, 34, 679-689.

Georgiades, S., Szatmari, P., Swaigenbaum, L., Duku, E., Bryson, S., Roberts, W. Goldberg, J., & Mahoney, W. (2007). Structure of the autism symptom phenotype: A proposed multidimensional model. Journal of the American Academy of Childhood Adolescence and Psychiatry, 46:, 188-196.

Geurts, H. M., Vertè, S., Oosterlaan, J., Roeyers, H., Hartman, C. A., Mulder, E. J., van Berckelaer-Onnes, I. A., Sergeant, J.A. (2004). Can the Children's Communication Checklist differentiate between children with autism, children with ADHD, and normal controls? Journal of Child Psychology and Psychiatry, 45, 437-1453.

Ghaziuddin, M., Leininger, L, & Tsai, L. (1995). Brief report: Though disorder in Asperger Syndrome: Comparison with high-functioning autism. Journal of Autism and Developmental Disorders, 25, 3, 311-317.

Ghaziuddin, M., & Butler, E. (1998). Clumsiness in autism and Asperger syndrome: A further report. Journal of Intellectual Disability Research, 42, 43-48.

Ghaziuddin, M & Gerstein, L. (1996). Pedantic speaking style differentiates Asperger syndrome from high-functioning autism. Journal of Autism and Developmental Disorders, 26, 6, 585-595.

Ghaziuddin, M., & Mountain-Kimchi, K. (2004). Defining the intellectual profile of Asperger syndrome: Comparison with high-functioning autism. Journal of Autism and Developmental Disorders, 34, 279-284.

Gilchrist, A., Green, J., Cox, A., Burton, D., Rutter, M., & Lecouteur, A. (2001). Development and current functioning in adolescents with Asperger's syndrome: A comparative study. Journal of Child Psychology and Psychiatry and Allied Disciplines, 42, 227-240.

Gilchrist, A., Green, J., Cox, A., Burton, D., Rutter, M., Couteur, A. L. (2001). Development and current functioning in adolescents with Asperger Syndrome: A comparative study. The Journal of Child Psychology and Psychiatry and Allied Disciplines, 42, 227-240.

Golan, O., Baron-Cohen, S., & Hill, J. (2006). The Cambridge Mindreading (CAM Face-Voice Battery: Testing complex emotion recognition in adults with and without Asperger syndrome. Journal of Autism and Developmental Disorders, 36, 169-183.

Golan, O., Baron-Cohen, S., Rutherford, M.D., & Hill, J. J. (Submitted for publication). The Reading the Mind in the Voice test-Revised: A study of complex emotion recognition in adults with and without Autism Spectrum Conditions.

Goldgerg, E. 2001. The executive brain: Frontal lobes and the civilized mind. New York, NY: Oxford University Press.

Goldberg, W. A., Osann, K., Filipek, P. A., Laulhere, T., Jarvis, K., Modahl, C., Flodman, P., & Spence, M. A. (2003). Language and other regression: Assessment and timing. Journal of Autism and Developmental Disorders, 33, 607-616.

Goldgerg, E. (2001). The executive brain: Frontal lobes and the civilized mind. New York, NY: Oxford University Press.

Happè, F., & Frith, U. (2006). The Weak Coherence account: Detail-focused cognitive style in autism spectrum disorders. The Journal of Autism and Developmental Disorders, 36, 5-25.

Happè, F.G.E. (1994). An advanced test of theory of mind: Understanding of story characters' thought and feelings by able autistic, mentally handicapped and normal children and adults. Journal of Autism and Developmental Disorders, 24, 129-154.

Hartman, C.A., Luteijn, E., Serra, M., & Minderaa, R. (2005). Refinement of the Children's Social Behavior Questionnaire (CSBQ): An instrument that describes the diverse problems seen in milder forms of PDD. Journal of Autism and Developmental Disorders, 35, 325-342.

Heavey, L., Phillips, W., Baron-Cohen, S., & Rutter, M. (2000). The Awkward Moments Test: A naturalistic measure of social understanding in autism. Journal of Autism and Developmental Disorders, 30, 225-236.

Heller, S. (2003). Too loud too bright, too fast too tight: What to do if you are sensory defensive in an overstimulating world. New York, NY: HarperCollins Publishers.

Hooper, S. R., Poon, K. K., Marcus, L., & Fine, C. (2006). Neuropsychological characteristics of school-age children with high-functioning autism: Performance on the Nepsy. Child Neuropsychology, 12, 299-305.

Howlin, P. (1998). Children with autism and Asperger syndrome: A guide for practitioners and carers. John Wiley and Sons: West Sussex, England: John Wiley and Sons.

Howlin, P. (2003). Outcome in high-functioning adults with autism with and without early language delays: Implications for the differentiation between autism and Asperger syndrome. Journal of Autism and Developmental Disorders, 33, 3-13.

Hubbard, K., & Trauner, D. A. (2007). Intonation and emotion in autistic spectrum disorders. Journal of Psycholinguistic Research, 36, 159-173.

Jepson, B. (2005). Autism: The evolution of a disease. Paper presented at the National Autism Association conference. Thoughtful House Center for Children, 1-24, http://www.thoughtfullhouse.org/0405-conf-bjepson.htm

Juranke, J., Filipek, P. A., Berehi, G. R., Modahl, C., Osann, K., & Spence, A. (2006). Association between amygdale volume and anxiety level: Magnetic resonance imaging (MRI) study in autistic children. Journal of Child Neurology, 21, 1051-1058.

Kaland, N., Moller-Nielsen, A, Callesen, K., Mortensen, E. L., Gottlieb, D., & Smith, L. (2002). A new 'advanced' test of theory of mind: Evidence from children and adolescents with Asperger syndrome. Journal of Child Psychology and Psychiatry, 43, 517-528.

Kampe, K., K., W., Frith, C. E., and Frith, U. 2003. "Hey John": Signals conveying communicative intention toward the self activate brain regions associated with "mentalizing," regardless of modality. The Journal of Neuroscience 23:5258-5263.

Kamphaus, R.W., Petoskey, M.D., & Rowe, E.W. (2000). Current trends in psychological testing of children. Professional Psychology: Research and Practice, 31, 155-164.

Kampe, K., K., W., Frith, C. E., & Frith, U. (2003). "Hey John": Signals conveying communicative intention toward the self activate brain regions associated with "mentalizing," regardless of modality. The Journal of Neuroscience, 23, 5258-5263.

Kaufman, A. S. (1972). A short form of the Wechsler Preschool and Primary Scale of Intelligence. Journal of Consulting and Clinical Psychology, 39, 361-369.

Kaufman, A. S. (1976). A four-test short form of the WISC-R. Contemporary Educational Psychology, 1, 180-196.

Kaufman, A. S., Kaufman, J. C., Palgopal, R., & McLean, J.E. (1996). Comparison of three WISC-III short forms: Weighing psychometric, clinical, and practical factors. Journal of Clinical Child Psychology, 25, 97-105.

Keller, W. D., Tillery, K. L., & McFadden, S. L. (2006). Auditory processing disorder in children diagnosed with nonverbal learning disability. American Journal of Audiology, 15, 108-113.

Kerbeshian, J., Burd, L. & Fisher, W. (1990). Asperger's syndrome: To be or not to be? British Journal of Psychiatry, 156, 721-725.

Khalsa, S. S. (1996). Group exercises for enhancing social skills and self-esteem. Sarasota, FL: Professional Resource Press.

Klin, A., Volkmar, F. R., & Sparrow, S. S. (2000). Asperger syndrome. London, UK: The Guilford Press.

Klin, A., & Volkmar, F. R. 1995. Asperger's Syndrome: Guidelines for Assessment and Diagnosis, Yale Child Study Center, New Haven, CT/ Published by the Learning Disabilities Association of America, June 1995.

Klin, A., Volkmar, F. R., Sparrow, S. S., Cicchetti, D. V., & Rourke, B. P. (1995). Validity and neuropsychological characterization of Asperger syndrome: Convergence with Nonverbal Learning Disabilities syndrome. The Journal of Child Psychology and Psychiatry, 36, 1127-1140.

Kope, T. M., Eaves, L. C., & Ho, H. H. (2001). Screening for autism and pervasive developmental disorders in very young children. BC Medical Journal, 43, 266-271.

Kope, T. M., Eaves, L. C., & Ho, H. H. (2001). Screening for autism and pervasive developmental disorders in very young children. British Columbia Medical Journal, 43, 5, 266-271.

Kotulak, R. (1997). Learning how to use the brain. Paper presented at the "Brain Development in Young Children: New Frontiers for Research, Policy and Practice" Conference in Chicago, on June 13, 1996. New Horizons for Learning. http://www.nldontheweb.org/kotulak.,htm.

Koyama, T., Tachimori, H., Osada, H., Takeda, T., & Kurita, H. (2007). Cognitive and symptom profiles in Asperger's syndrome and high-functioning autism. Psychiatry and Clinical Neurosciences, 61, 99-104.

Kranowitz, C. S. (1998). The out-of-sync child: Recognizing and coping with sensory integration dysfunction. New York, NY: The Berkley Publishing Group.

Kurita, H. (1997). A comparative study of Asperger syndrome with high-functioning atypical autism. Psychiatry and Clinical Neurosciences, 51, 67-70.

Lam, K. S. L., & Aman, M. G. (2007). The Repetitive Behavior Scale—Revised: Independent validation in individuals with autism spectrum disorders. Journal of Autism and Developmental Disorders, 37, 855-866.

LDOnline: Visual and Auditory Processing Disorders, National Center for Learning Disabilities, 1999, 1-7, http://www.ldonline.org/article/6390?theme.

Lecavalier, L. (2005). An evaluation of the Gilliam Autism Rating Scale. Journal of Autism and Developmental Disorders, 35, 795-805.

Leekam, S. R., Nieto, C., Libby, S. J., Wing, L., & Gould, J. (2007). Describing the sensory abnormalities of children and adults with autism. Journal of Autism and Developmental Disorders, 37, 894-910.

Lemley, G. (1999). Do you see what they see? Discover, 20, p. 12.

Levine, M. D.). Childhood neurodevelopmental dysfunction and learning disorders. Childhood neurodevelopmental dysfunction and learning disorders, 12, Harvard Mental Health Letter, 12, 07/01/July 1, 1995.

Little, L. (2001). The misunderstood child: The child with a nonverbal learning disorder. Journal for the Society of Pediatric Nurses, 4, 113-122.

Lord, C., Risi, S., Lanbrecht, L., Cook, E. H., Leventhal, B.L. (2000). The Autism Diagnostic Observation Schedule-Generic: A Standard Measure of Social and Communication Deficits Associated with the Spectrum of Autism. Journal of Autism and Developmental Disorders, 30, 205-223.

Lotspeich, L. J., Kown, H., Schumann, C. M., Fryer, S. L., Goodlin-Jones, B. L., Buonocore, M. H, Lammers, C. R., Amaral, D. G., Reiss, A. L. (2004). Investigation of neuroanatomical differences between autism and Asperger syndrome. Archives of General Psychiatry, 61, 291-298.

Lovecky, D. V. (2004). Different minds: Gifted children with AD/HD, Asperger Syndrome, and other learning deficits. New York, NY: Jessica Kingsley Publishers: NY, New York.

Luria, A. R. (1987). The mind of a mnemonist. Cambridge, MA: Harvard University Press.

Lynn, A. Balzer-Martin, Ph.D., O.T.R,. in Kranowitz, C. S., (1998). The Out-of-Sync Child: Recognizing and coping with sensory integration dysfunction., New York, NY: Skylight Press.

Lyons, V., & Fitzgerald, M. (2004). Humor in autism and Asperger syndrome. Journal of Autism and Developmental Disorders, 34, 521-528.

Macintosh, K., & Dissanajake, C. (2006). A comparative study of the spontaneous social interactions of children with high-functioning autism and children with Asperger's disorder. Autism, 10, 199-220.

Mandell, D. S., Maytali, M. N., & Zubritsky, C. D. (2005). Factors associated with age of diagnosis among children with autism spectrum disorders. Pediatrics, 116, 1480-1486.

Manjiviona, J. & Pryor, M. (1999). Neuropsychological profiles of children with Asperger syndrome and autism. Autism, 3, 327-256.

Matese, M., Matson, J. L., & Sevin, J. (1994). Comparison of psychotic and autistic children using behavioral observation. Journal of Autism and Developmental Disorders, 24, 83-94.

Mayes, S.D., & Calhoun, S.L. (1999). Symptoms of autism in young children and correspondence with the DSM. Infants and Young Children, 12, 90-97.

Mazefsky, C.A., & Oswald, D.P. (2006). The discriminative ability and diagnostic utility of the ADOS-G, ADI-R, and GARS for children in a clinical setting. Autism: The International Journal of Research and Practice, 10, 533-549.

McConachie, H., Le Couteur, A., & Honey, E. (2005). Can a diagnosis of Asperger syndrome be made in very young children with suspected autism spectrum disorder? Journal of Autism and Developmental Disorders, 35, 167-175.

McDevitt, S.C., & Carey, W. B. (1996). Manual for the behavioral style questionnaire. Scottsdale, AZ: Behavioral-Developmental Initiatives.

McDevitt, S.C., & Carey, W. B. (1978). The measurement of temperament in 3-7 year old children. Journal of Child Psychology and Psychiatry and Allied Disciplines, 19, 245-253.

Mikami, K., & Matsumoto, H., (2007). Differentiation between childhood autism and Asperger's syndrome. Nippon Rinsho, 65, 487-491.

Minshew, N. J., Turner, C. A., & Goldstein, G. (2005). The application of short forms of the Wechsler Intelligence scales in adults and children with high functioning autism. Journal of Autism and Developmental Disorders, 35, 45-52.

Minshew, N.J. (2005). Ask the Editor. Journal of Autism and Developmental Disorders, 35, 877-879.

Minshew, N.J., Turner, C.A., & Goldstein, G. (2005). The application of short forms of the Wechsler Intelligence Scales in adults and children with high functioning autism. The Journal of Autism and Developmental Disorders, 35, 45-52.

Nation, K., Clarke, P., Wright, B., & Williams, C. (2006). Patterns of reading ability in children with autism spectrum disorder. Journal of Autism and Developmental Disorders, 36, 911-919.

Norbury, F., & Bishop, D. V. M. (2002). Inferential processing and story recall in children with communication problems: A comparison of specific language impairment, pragmatic language impairment and high-functioning autism. Internal Journal of Language Communication Disorders, 37, 227-251.

O'Neill, J. L. (1999). Through the eye of aliens: A book about autistic people. London, UK: Jessica Kingsley Publishing.

Ortiz, J. M. (2006). The Gifts of Asperger. Dillsburg, PA: The Asperger's Syndrome Institute.

Ortiz, J. M. (1997). The Tao of Music: Sound Psychology. York Beach, ME: Red Wheel/Weiser.

Ozonoff, S. Rogers, S. J., & Pennington, B. F. (1991). Asperger's syndrome: Evidence of an empirical distinction from high-functioning autism. Journal of Child Psychology and Psychiatry, 32, 1107-1122.

Ozonoff, S., Garcia, N., Clark, E., & Lainhart, J. E. (2005). MMPI-2 Personality profiles of high-functioning adults with autism spectrum disorders. Assessment, 12, 86-95.

Ozonoff, S., South, M., & Miller J. N. (2000). DSM-IV-defined Asperger syndrome: Cognitive, behavioral and early history differentiation from high-functioning autism. Autism, 4, 29-46.

Palmer, R. F., Blanchard, S., Jean, C. R., & Mandell, D. S. (2005). School district resources and identification of children with autistic disorder. American Journal of Public Health, 95, 125-130.

Palombo, J. (2006). Nonverbal Learning disabilities: A clinical perspective. New York, N.Y.: W.W. Norton and Company.

Paxton, K., & Estay, I. A. (2007). Counselling people on the autism spectrum: A practical manual. London, UK: Jessica Kingsley Publishing.

Pelletier, P. M., Ahman, S. A., & Rourke, B. P. (2001). Classification rules for basic phonological processing disabilities and nonverbal learning disabilities: formulation and external validity. Child Neuropsychology 7:84-98.

Perry, A., Condillac, R. A., Freeman, N. L., Dunn-Geier, J., & Belair, J. (2005). Multi-site study of the Childhood Autism Rating Scale (CARS) in five clinical groups of young children. Journal of Autism and Developmental Disorders, 35, 625-634.

Pfeiffer, B., Kinnealey, M., Reed C., & Herzberg, G. (2005). Sensory modulation and affective disorders in children and adolescents with Asperger's disorder. American Journal of Occupational Therapy, 59, 335-345.

Pine, E., Luby, J., Abbacchi, A., & Constantino, J. M. (2006). Quantitative assessment of autistic symptomatology in preschoolers. Autism: The International Journal of Research and Practice, 10, 344-352.

Poirier, N., & Forget, J. (1998). Diagnostic criteria of autism and Asperger's syndrome: Similarities and differences. Santè mentale au Quèbec, 23, 130-148.

Prelock, P. A. (2006). Understanding and assessing the communication of children with ASD. In P.A. Prelock (Ed.) Autism Spectrum Disorders: Issues in Assessment and Intervention, Austin, TX: Pro-Ed.

Prior, M., Reitzel, J-A., & Szatmari, P. (2003). Cognitive and academic problems, in Margaret Prior's Learning and Behavior Problems in Asperger Syndrome. The Guilford Press: NY, New York.

Rescorla, L. A. (2005). Assessment of young children using the Achenbach system of empirically based assessment (ASEBA). Mental Retardation and Developmental Disabilities Research Review, 11, 226-237.

Rescorla, L.A. (2005). Assessment of young children using the Achenbach system of empirically based assessment (ASEBA). Mental Retardation and Developmental Disabilities Research Review, 11, 226-237.

Richler, J., Bishop, S., Kleinke, J. R., & Lord, C. (2007). Restricted and repetitive behaviors in young children with autism spectrum disorders. Journal of Autism and Developmental Disorders, 37, 73-85.

Rinehart, N. J., Bradshaw, J. L., Brereton, A. V., & Tonge, B. J. (2003). A clinical and neurobehavioural review of high-functioning autism and Asperger's disorder. The Australian and New Zealand Journal of Psychiatry, 36, 762-770.

Rinehart, N. J., Bradshaw, J. L., Moss, S. A., Brereton, A. V., & Tonge, B. J. (2001). A deficit in shifting attention present in high-functioning autism but not Asperger's disorder. Autism, 5, 67-80.

Rinehart, N. J., Bradshaw, J. L., Moss, S. A., Brereton, A. V., & Tonge, G. (2006). Pseudo-random number generation in children with high-functioning autism and Asperger's disorder. Autism, 10, 70-85.

Robertson, L. C., & Sagiv, N. (2005). Synesthesia: Perspectives from cognitive neuroscience. New York, NY: Oxford University Press.

Roeyers, H., Buysse, A., Ponnet, K., & Pichal, B. (2001). Advancing advanced mind-reading tests: Empathic accuracy in adults with a pervasive developmental disorder. The Journal of Child Psychology and Psychiatry and Allied Disciplines, 42, 271-278.

Rutherford, M.D., Baron-Cohen, S., & Wheelwright, S. (2002). Reading the mind in the voice: A study with normal adults and adults with Asperger syndrome and high functioning autism. Journal of Autism and Developmental Disorders, 32, 189-194.

Roman, M. A. (1998). The syndrome of nonverbal learning disabilities: Clinical description and applied aspects. Current Issues in Education, 1. 1-21.

Ropar, D., & Mitchell, P. (2001). Susceptibility to illusions and performance on visuospatial tasks in individuals with autism. The Journal of Child Psychology and Psychiatry and Allied Disciplines, 42, 539-549.

Rourke, B. P., Ahmad, S. A., Collins, D. W., Hayman-Abello, B. A., Hayman-Abello, S. E., & Warriner, E. M. (2002). Child clinical/pediatric neuropsychology: Some recent advances. Annual Revue of Psychology, 53, 309-339.

Rourke, B. P. (1995). Syndrome of nonverbal learning disabilities. New York, NY: The Guilford Press.

Rutter, M., Lecouteur, A., & Lord, C. (2003). Autism diagnostic interview-revised. Los Angeles, CA: Western Psychological Services.

Sattler, J. M. (1988). Assessment of children. (3rd ed.). San Diego, CA: Sattler.

Schopler, E., Mesibov, G. B., & Kunce, L. J. (1992). Asperger syndrome or high-functioning autism? (current issues in autism). Springer NY, New York.

Scott, F. J., Baron-Cohen, S., Bolton, P., & Brayne, C. (2002). The CAST (Childhood Asperger Syndrome Test): Preliminary development of a UK screen for mainstream primary-school age children. Autism, 6, 9-31.

Search, E., Burd, L., Kerbeshian, J., Stenehjem, A., & Franceschini, L. A. (2000). Asperger's syndrome, X-linked mental retardation (MRX23), and chronic vocal tic disorder. Journal of Child Neurology, 15, 699-702.

Siegel, D. J., Minshew, N. J., & Goldstein, G. (1996). Wechsler IQ profiles in diagnosis of high-functioning autism. Journal of Autism and Developmental Disorders, 26, 389-406.

Siegel, D. J., Minshew, N. J., & Goldstein, G., (1996). Wechsler IQ profiles in diagnosis of high-functioning autism. Journal of Autism and Developmental Disorders, 26, 389-406.

Siegel, G. (1996). World of the autistic child: Understanding and treating autistic spectrum disorders. New York: Oxford University Press.

Skuse, D. H., Mandy, W. P. L., & Scourfield, J. (2005). Measuring autistic traits: Heritability, reliability and validity of the Social and Communication Disorders Checklist. British Journal of Psychiatry, 187, 568-572.

Smith, J. (2007). Unexpected difficulties. This way of life. http://www.thiswayoflife.org/unexpected.html.

South, M., Ozonoff, S., & McMahon, W. M. (2005). Repetitive behavior profiles in Asperger syndrome and high-functioning autism. Journal of Autism and Developmental Disorders, 35, 145-158.

South, M., Klin, A., & Ozonoff, S. (1999). The Yale Special Interest Interview. Unpublished measure.

Squires, J., Bricker, D., & Thombly, E., with assistance from Yockelson, S., Davis, M. S., & Kim, Y. (2002). Ages & stages questionnaires: Social emotional (ASQ: SE). A parent-completed, child-monitoring system for social-emotional behaviors. Baltimore, MD: Brookes Publishing Co.

Stein, M. T. (2004). When Asperger's syndrome and a nonverbal learning disability look alike. Pediatrics, 114, 1458-1463.

Stewart, K. (2002). Helping a child with nonverbal learning disorder or Asperger syndrome. Oakland: New Harbinger Publications.

Stewart, M. E., Barnard, L., Pearson, J., Hasan, R., & O'Brien, G. (2006). Presentation of depression in autism and Asperger syndrome. Autism, 10, 103-116.

Stoddart, K. P. (2005). Children, youth and adults with Asperger syndrome: Integrating multiple perspectives. London, UK: Jessica Kingsley Publishing.

Stone, W. L. Coonrod, E. E., Turner, L. M., & Pozdol, S. (2004). Psychometric properties of the STAT for early autism screening. Journal of Autism and Developmental Disorders, 34, 691-701.

Stroop, J. R. (1935). Studies of interference in serial verbal reactions. Journal of Experimental Psychology, 18, 643-662.

Sullivan, M., Finelli, J., Marvin, A., Garrett-Mayer, E., Bauman, M., & Landa, R. (2007). Response to joint attention in toddlers at risk for autism spectrum disorder: A prospective study. Journal of Autism and Developmental Disorders, 37, 37-48.

Swinkels, S. H. N., Dietz, C., van Daalen, E., Kerkhog, I. H. G. M., van Engeland, H., & Buitelaaar, J. K. (2006). Screening for autistic spectrum in children aged 14 to 15 months, I: The development of the early screening of autistic traits questionnaire (ESAT). Journal of Autism and Developmental Disorders, 36, 723-732.

Szatmari, P. (1991). Aspeger's syndrome: Diagnosis, treatment and outcome. Psychiatric Clinics of North America, 14, 81-93.

Szatmari, P., Archer, L., Fisman, S., Streiner, D. L., & Wilson, F. (1995). Asperger's syndrome and autism: Differences in behavior, cognition, and adaptive functioning. Journal of the American Academy of Childhood Adolescence and Psychiatry, 34:, 1662-1671.

Szatmari, P., Bartolucci, G., & Bremner, R. (1989). Asperger's syndrome and autism: Comparison of early history and outcome. Developmental Medicine and Child Neurology, 31, 709-720.

Szatmari, P., Bryson, S. E., Streiner, D. L., Wilson, F., Archer, L., & Ryerse, C. (2000). Children with Asperger's syndrome had higher socialization scores and fewer autistic symptoms than children with autism. American Journal of Psychiatry, 157, 1980-1987.

Szatmari, P., Tuff, L., Finlayson, M. A. J., & Bartolucci, G. (1990). Non-Significance of early speech delay in children with autism and normal intelligence and implications for DSM-IV and Asperger's disorder. Journal of the American Academy of Children and Adolescent Psychiatry, 29, 130-136.

Szatmari, P., Tuff, L., Finlayson, M. A., & Bartolucci, G. (1990). Asperger's syndrome and autism: Neurocognitive aspects. Journal of the American Academy of Childhood Adolescence and Psychiatry, 29, 130-136.

Tanguay, P. E., Robertson, J., & Derrick, A. (1998). A dimensional classification of autism spectrum disorder by social communication domains. Journal of the American Academy of Childhood Adolescence and Psychiatry, 37, 271-277.

Tani, P., Lindberg, N., Wend, T. N., Wend, L., Alanko, L., Appelberg, B., & Porkka-Heiskanen, T. (2003). Insomnia is a frequent finding in adults with Asperger syndrome. BMC Psychiatry, 3:12, http://www.ncbi.nlm.nih.gov/sites/entrez?cmd=Retrieve&db=PubMed&list_uids=14563215&dopt=Citation.

Tas, A., Yagiz, R., Tax, M., Esme, M., Uzun, C., & Karasalihoglu, A. R. (2007). Evaluation of hearing in children with autism by using TEOAE and ABR. Autism: The International Journal of Research and Practice, 11, 73-79.

Thompson, S. (1996). Nonverbal learning disorders: An Introduction LDOnlinehttp://www.ldonline.org/article/6114?theme.

Tomanik, S. S., Pearson, D. A., Loveland, K. A., Lane, D. M., & Shaw, J. B. (2007). Improving the reliability of autism diagnoses: Examining the utility of adaptive behavior. Journal of Autism and Developmental Disorders, 37, 921-928.

Tomchek, S. D., (2001). Assessment of individuals with an autism spectrum disorder utilizing a sensorimotor approach, in Huebner, R. A., ed., Autism: A sensorimotor approach to management. Austin, TX: PRO-ED, Inc., 103-138.

Tsatsanis, K. D., & Rourke, B. P. (1995). Conclusions and future directions, in Syndrome of Nonverbal Learning Disabilities., New York, NY: The Guilford Press

Vacca, J. J. (2007). Incorporating interests and structure to improve participation of a child with autism in a standardized assessment: A case study in analysis. Focus on Autism and Other Developmental Disabilities, 22, 51-59.

Ventola, P., Klienman, J., Pandey, J., Wilson, L., Esser, E., Boorstein, H., Dumont-Mathieu, T., Marshia, G., Barton, M., Hodgson, S., Green, J., Volkmar, F., Chawarska, K., Babitz, T., Robins, D., & Fein, D. (2007). Differentiating between autism spectrum disorders and other developmental disabilities in children who failed a screening instrument for ASD. The Journal of Autism and Developmental Disorders, 37, 425-436.

Ventola, P.E., Kleinman, J., Pandey, J., Barton, M., Allen, S., Green., J., Robins, D., & Fein, D. (2006). Agreement among four diagnostic instruments for autism spectrum disorders in toddlers. Journal of Autism and Developmental Disorders, 36, 839-847.

Ventola, P. E., Kleinman, J., Pandey, J., Barton, M., Allen, S., Green., J., Robins, D., & Fein, D. (2006). Agreement among four diagnostic instruments for autism spectrum disorders in toddlers. Journal of Autism and Developmental Disorders, 36, 839-847.

Vertè, S., Geurts, H. M., Roeyers, H., Rosseel, Y., Oosterlaan, J., & Sergeant, J. A. (2006). Can the children's communication checklist differentiate autism spectrum subtypes? Autism: International Journal of Research and Practice, 10, 266-287.

Volden, J. (2004). Nonverbal learning disability: A tutorial for speech-language pathologists. American Journal of Speech-Language Pathology, 13, 128-141.

Volkmar, F. R., Paul, E., Klin, A., & Cohen, D. (2005). Handbook of autism and pervasive developmental disorders.- 3rd ed. John Wiley and Sons: Hoboken, NJ.

Volkmar, F. R., Paul, R., Klin, A., & Cohen, D. (2005). Handbook of autism and pervasive developmental disorders: Diagnosis, development, neurobiology, and behavior, 3rd ed. – Volume 1. Hoboken, N.J.: John Wiley and Sons.

Volkmar, F. R., & Tsatsanis, K. D. (2005). Ask the Editor., Journal of Autism and Developmental Disorders, 35, 259-260.

Wakabayashi, A., Cohen-Baron, S., Wheelwright, S., & Tojo, Y. (2006). The Autism-Spectrum Quotient (AQ) in Japan: A cross-cultural comparison. Journal of Autism and Developmental Disorders, 36, 263-270.

Walker, D. R., Thompson, A., Zwaigenbaum, L., Goldberg, J., Bryson, S. E., Mahoney, W. J., Strawbridge, C. P., & Szatmari, P. (2004) Specifying PDD-NOS: A comparison of PDD-NOS, Asperger syndrome, and autism. Journal of the American Academy of Children and Adolescent Psychiatry, 43, 172-180.

Walker, D. R., Thompson, A., Zwaigenbaum, L., Goldberg, J., Bryson, S. E., Mahoney, W. J., Strawbridge, C. P. & Szatmari, P. (2004). Specifying PDD-NOS: A comparison of PDD-NOS, Asperger Syndrome, and autism. Journal of the American Academy of Childhood Adolescence and Psychiatry, 43, 172-180.

Watson, L. R., Baranek, G. T., Crais, E.R., Reznick, J. S., Dykstra, J., & Perryman, T. (2007). The First Year Inventory: Retrospective parent responses to a questionnaire designed to identify one-year-olds at risk for autism. Journal of Autism & Developmental Disorders, 37, 49-61.

Wechsler, D. (1999). The Wechsler abbreviated scale for intelligence. San Antonio, TX: The Psychological Corporation.

Wetherby, A. M., Allen, L., Cleary, J., Kublin, K., & Goldstein, H. (2002). Validity and reliability of the communication and symbolic behavior scales developmental profile with very young children. Journal of Speech, Language, and Hearing Research, 45, 1202-1218.

Wetherby, A., & Prizant, B. (2001). Communication and Symbolic Behavior Scales Developmental Profile-Preliminary Normed Edition. Baltimore, MD: Paul H. Brookes Publishing Co.

Wigg, E., & Secord, W. (1989). Test of language competence-expanded edition. San Antonio, TX: The Psychological Corporation, Harcourt Brace Jovanovich.

Wiggins, L. D., Bakeman, R., Adamson, L. B., & Robins, D. L. (2007). The utility of the social communication questionnaire in screening for autism in children referred for early intervention. Focus on Autism and Other Developmental Disabilities, 22, 33-38.

Williams, D. (1996). Autism: An inside-out approach. London, UK: Jessica Kingsley Publishing.

Williams, D. (1999). Like colour to the blind: Soul searching and soul finding. London, UK: Jessica Kingsley Publishing.

Williams, D. L., Goldstein, G., Carpenter, P. A., & Minshew, N. J. (2005). Verbal and spatial working memory in Autism. Journal of Autism and Developmental Disorders, 35, 747-756.

Williams, J., Scott, F., Stott, C., Allison, C., Bolton, P., Baron-Cohen, & Brayne, C. (2005). The CAST (Childhood Asperger Syndrome Test): Test accuracy. Autism, 9, 45-68.

Williams, J., & Brayne, C. (2006). Screening for autism spectrum disorders: What is the evidence? Autism, 10, 11-35.

Williams, J., Allison, C., Scott, F., Stott, C., Bolton, P., Baron-Cohen, S., & Brayne, C. (2006). The childhood Asperger syndrome test (CAST). Autism, 10, 415-427.

Wing, L., Leekam, S. R., Libby, S. J., Gould, J., & Larcombe, M. (2002). The diagnostic interview for social and communication disorders: Background, inter-rater reliability and clinical use. Journal of Child Psychology and Psychiatry, 43, 307-325.

Wing, L. (2001). The autistic spectrum: A parents' guide to understanding and helping your child. Berkeley, CA: Ulysses Press.

Woodbury-Smith, M., Klin, A., & Volkmar, F. (2005). Asperger's syndrome: A comparison of clinical diagnoses and those made according to the ICD-10 and DSM-IV. Journal of Autism and Developmental Disorders, 35, 235-240.

Woodbury-Smith, M. R., Robinson, J., Wheelwright, S., & Baron-Cohen, S. (2005). Screening adults for Asperger syndrome using the AQ: A preliminary study of its diagnostic validity in clinical practice. Journal of Autism and Developmental Disorders, 35, 331-335.

Zafeiriou, D. I., Ververi, A., & Vargiami, E. (2007). Childhood autism and associated comorbidities. Brain Development, 29, 257-272.

Zandt, F., Prior, M., & Kyrios, M. (2007). Repetitive behaviour in children with high functioning autism and obsessive compulsive disorder. Journal of Autism and Developmental Disorders, 37, 251-259.

Index

"The Myriad Gifts of Asperger Syndrome"

by John M. Ortiz, Ph.D.

(Formerly titled: "The Gifts of Asperger")

This book is designed with the goal of illustrating how, when provided with nurturing, supportive environments, persons with AS and HFA can realize their full potentials, live happy, productive lives, and make significant contributions to their families and communities while helping to enrich our world and collective consciousness.

Filled with positive, inspirational, and affirming stories the book features:

Forty inspirational stories of children and teens with Asperger which depict their gift-related talents including:

• Sensory-related acuities	Superb Memory
• Reading ability	Creative artist
• Sense of ethics and justice	Focused concentration
• Physical tolerance	Love of animals
• Exceptional verbosity	Quick mind for calculations
• Dedication to community	Loyalty to friends
• Outstanding ability for word-play	Academic aptitude in special areas
• Computer-related prowess	Spelling "b" champion

Twenty-one adult narratives involving occupational accomplishments feature accounts by:

* Graphic Artist	Archeologist	Engineer
* Environmentalist	Shipping Clerk	Librarian
* Physics Researcher	Agricultural Worker	Proofreader
* Landscape Architect	Forensic Science Analyst.	FX Artist
* Medical Transcriptionist	Meter Reader	Game Developer
* Surveyor	Stamp & Coin Collector	Military Engineer
* Comic store Manager	Paralegal/Legal Assistant	Statistician

Additional sections include:

• The Asperger Dimension	Notable Persons with Asperger Phenotypes
• "Vocational Fit"	"Marketable Strengths"
• "Vocational Choices"	"Typical Characteristics" and
• "Work-Related Strengths of Persons throughout the Asperger Spectrum	

Available: The Asperger's Syndrome Institute at www.asperger-institute.com

My Kitty Catsberger

by: John M. Ortiz, Ph.D.

Ever wonder which pets are the Aspies of the animal kingdom?

Why, the _cool_ ones of course!

My Kitty Catsberger is a colorful, rhyming, illustrated story that depicts how cats, much like Aspies, are cool, sensory enhanced, ultra-focused, sharp as tacks, highly specialized, self-motivated, and creatively playful beings who march to the tune of "I'll Do it My Way!"

My Kitty Catsberger is designed to teach children (of ALL ages) how "being an Aspie" is, indeed, a "cool-as-cats" opportunity in our world of Neuro-Diversity. Richly illustrated and vividly brought to life by Disney artist Don McGrath the book offers a creative insight into the wonderful similarities between the delightful quirks and eccentricities that are often shared by felines and their fellow human cousins.

Available: The Asperger's Syndrome Institute at www.asperger-institute.com

The Tao of Music: Sound Psychology
John M. Ortiz, Ph.D.

1998 Small Press Award *** Self Help/Psychology

Designed as an introduction to "Sound Psychology," *The Tao of Music: Sound Psychology* combines music and sound, basic psychological principles, and Eastern philosophy in a "reader friendly," practical guide form, making it accessible to both laypersons and health practitioners. Consisting of inspirational case stories, simple exercises and creative techniques this holistic resource provides hundreds of recommended "musical menus" to assist readers in "composing" their own complementary programs for healing, prevention and wellness.

Contents include:

Clinical Issues:
Depressed Moods   Chronic Pain   Self-Esteem   Stress
Anger   Sleeplessness   Control   Relaxation.

Personal Issues:
Memory Recall   Time Management   Grief and Loss
Growth & Change   Procrastination   Aging   Physical Exercise.

Social Issues:
Communication Skills   Companionship   Relationships
Motivation   Conscious Listening

Special Issues:
Centering   Creativity   HeAr and Now   Letting Go
Being vs. Trying to Be   Romantic Intimacy   Clearing the Mind.

Also: The Concepts of:

Rhythmic Synchronicity   Entrainment   Affirmations
Contextual Cueing Effects   Sound Making   Toning
Selecting music for every occasion, and more.

Available: The Asperger's Syndrome Institute at www.asperger-institute.com

The Soothing Pulse™ (on CD and audio tape)

From, John M. Ortiz, Ph.D. Author, *The Tao of Music: Sound Psychology*©

Ages: Adults & Teens

The Soothing Pulse:

Based on the technique of Pulse Entrainment™, *The Soothing Pulse* ™ is designed to synchronize, and then gradually slow down our intrinsic pulses and rhythms leading to a state of natural mind-body relaxation. The progressive relaxation sequence introduced in this quieting exercise accomplishes this by using a combination of Applied Psychomusicology techniques intended to help us achieve a state of deep, restful meditation. These include:

- A continuous, pulsating beat designed to synchronize--or entrain--the left and right brain hemispheres.

- Two interlacing drones. A bass drone (i.e., continuous, meditative sound) intended to ground us, and a light, melodic drone designed to quiet our thinking mind, helping to create a sense of peace and flow.

- A rhythmic, guided entrainment script that escorts the listener through a progressively deepening state of relaxation. The tempo begins at an up-beat, lively pace then gradually descends to a tranquil, soothing cadence.

- A series of thought stopping, meditative affirmations that emphasize restful breathing, flowing, and letting go.

Multimodal relaxation Designed for busy:

Adults & Teens   Educators   Mental Health   Professionals   Therapists
Parents & Caregivers   Speech Pathologists   Occupational & Physical Therapists

Effective for:

**Aspeger's Syndrome   *   Autism Spectrum Disorders   *
Attention Deficit Disorders   *   Regular sleeplessness
Nonverbal Learning Disorders   *   Sensory Integration Disorders**

*Relaxation * Yoga * Massage * Tai-Chi * Home Base * Meditation *
Down TimeStress Reduction * Reducing Hyperactivity * Sleep *
Rhythmic Pulsing for Speech & Reading * Biofeedback * Imagery*

Available: The Asperger's Syndrome Institute at www.asperger-institute.com

Turning Daydreams Into Dreams: A Bedtime Story©
By: John M. Ortiz, Ph.D.

A Relaxation CD for children <u>AGES 6 –12</u> from the author of *The Tao of Music: Sound Psychology*, and *Nurturing Your Child with Music*

"Soothing sound-tapestries help busy daydreams turn into restful dreams"

In this exercise, a tapestry of peaceful sound textures, calming ocean waves, & a quieting, balancing pulse serve as backdrop to a serene voice that gently guides your child through a soothing, bedtime journey that helps to turn busy daydreams into peaceful dreams. Borrowing from standard, progressive relaxation & meditation techniques the narration uses positive, reassuring affirmations to encourage restful breathing, comfort, & letting go while promoting deep, tranquil sleep.

Track One
Guided *Daydreams to Dreams* story
with Soothing Pulse™ music
for older children
(22 minutes)

Track Two
Soothing Pulse™ music
for older children
(22 minutes)

Multimodal relaxation Designed for busy:

Parent   *Educators*   *Mental Health Professionals*   *Therapists*
Caregivers   *Speech Pathologists*   *Occupational & Physical Therapists*

Effective for:

Aspeger's Syndrome   *   Autism Spectrum Disorders
Attention Deficit Disorders   *   Regular sleeplessness
Nonverbal Learning Disorders   *   Sensory Integration Disorders

Relaxation * Yoga * Massage * Tai-Chi * Home Base * Meditation
Down Time   *   Stress Reduction   *   Reducing Hyperactivity * Sleep *
Rhythmic Pulsing for Speech & Reading * Biofeedback * Imagery

Available: The Asperger's Syndrome Institute at www.asperger-institute.com

It's Sleepy Time!©
By: John M. Ortiz, Ph.D.

A Relaxation CD for children <u>AGES pre-natal through 8</u> from the author of *The Tao of Music: Sound Psychology*, and *Nurturing Your Child with Music*

"Simply listen, as scenes of swirling sounds sway your child into soothing sleep!"

Tossing and turning after a day of playing and learning? This calming exercise guides your child through a soothing journey of how the body falls asleep, from toes to head! A gentle combination of musical pulses, ocean waves, and sleep-inducing sound textures help to gradually escort your child to a deep, restful sleep. The Pulse Entrainment™ techniques used in this recording are based on years of clinical research findings and sound collages found effective for relaxing young children.

Track One	Track Two
Guided *Sleepy Time!* story with Soothing Pulse™ music for young children	Soothing Pulse™ music for young children (22 minutes)

<u>Multimodal relaxation Designed for busy</u>:

Parent   Educators   Mental Health Professionals   Therapists
Caregivers   Speech Pathologists   Occupational & Physical Therapists

<u>Effective for</u>:

Aspeger's Syndrome   *   Autism Spectrum Disorders
Attention Deficit Disorders   *   Regular sleeplessness
Nonverbal Learning Disorders   *   Sensory Integration Disorders

*Relaxation * Yoga * Massage * Tai-Chi * Home Base * Meditation*
*Down Time * Stress Reduction * Reducing Hyperactivity * Sleep*
*Rhythmic Pulsing for Speech & Reading * Biofeedback * Imagery*

Available: The Asperger's Syndrome Institute at www.asperger-institute.com